AN ANS MONOGRAPH

ISOTOPE SEPARATION

Stelio Villani

Joint Research Centre of the
European Communities
Brussels, Belgium

Published by
American Nuclear Society

FOREWORD

This book is published as one of a continuing series in the American Nuclear Society's program for providing to the nuclear community and related fields authoritative information in monograph form. Authors and titles are selected to bring to print the most useful material in the more active areas of nuclear science and technology development. Advancing the peaceful uses of nuclear energy is a general objective of this publishing endeavor, while advancement of the professional interests of ANS members is a primary purpose.

ANS-published books are directed largely to the interests of scientists and engineers concerned with nuclear energy applications. Often these volumes are of particular value in various areas of industrial management. And, usually they are of considerable help to teachers and students who seek readily accessible information in the specialized technical directions covered.

The American Nuclear Society regards these publishing activities and their contributions to the growing achievements in nuclear energy application as an essential obligation to the society membership and the nuclear field.

Norman H. Jacobson
Manager, ANS Publications

iii

PREFACE

This book originated in the course of lessons written in 1961 in collaboration with B. DeMichelis and published jointly by the Milan Politecnico and the Centro Informazioni Studi Esperienze (CISE).

Although the subdivision of the material is substantially unchanged, very little is left of the original text. Only Chap. 13, by DeMichelis, on magnetic separation remains practically the same. For the remainder, the text has either been completely redone or reworked in depth.

On the separation of ^{235}U, I have taken into consideration both the greater quantity of data available on gaseous diffusion and the developments of the last decade in centrifugation and in the separation-nozzle process. A new chapter has been devoted to the latter.

As for heavy water, the portion devoted to the processes of monothermic and dual-temperature chemical exchange has been considerably expanded.

I have kept in mind the primarily didactic purposes of this book and have purposely left many mathematical passages, and sometimes numerical passages as well, in extenso.

I thank all those who have helped in collecting data and illustrations, particularly Prof. Donald R. Olander of the University of California, for much helpful advice.

I express my appreciation to my daughter Giovanna for the cover design of this book.

The reader should be warned that separative work units, frequently referred to as SWU in American literature, are expressed simply as kg U or tons U in this book.

Stelio Villani
Joint Research Centre of the European Communities
on assignment to
Chalk River Nuclear Laboratories, Atomic Energy of Canada Limited

CONTENTS

1   Isotopic Makeup of the Elements   1
Stable and Radioactive Isotopes in Nature   1
Nuclear Stability   4
Regularity in the Isotopic Composition of Elements   7
Abundance of the Elements in Nature   8
Variations in Isotope Abundances in Nature   10
Uses for Separated Isotopes   15
References   16

2   Methods of Isotopic Analysis   18
Mass Spectrometry   18
Special Methods for Analyzing ^{235}U   21
Special Procedures for Deuterium Analysis   23
References   33

3   The Physical Principles of Isotope Separation   35
General Remarks   35
Distillation   37
Molecular Distillation   45
Exchange Reactions   49
Ion-Exchanging Resins   61
Chemical Exchange and Reaction Speed   63

Gaseous Diffusion 66
Mass Diffusion 71
Thermal Diffusion 75
Centrifugation 78
The Separation Nozzle 81
Electrolysis 84
Electromigration 86
Electromagnetic Separation 88
Photochemical Separation 91
Energy Consumption 92
References 95

4   The Theory of Cascades **98**
Continuous and Discontinuous Processes 98
Stages, Cascades, and Separating Elements 99
Cascade Schemes 100
Stage Equations 102
Equations for the Generic Symmetrical Cascade 105
Equations for the Ideal Symmetrical Cascade 111
Equations for the Square Cascade 116
Transport and Concentration Gradient:
  Separative Power 120
Yield 123
Value Function and Separative Work 128
Equilibrium Time 134
The Ideal Cascade as a Term for Comparison 139
Optimizing the Square Cascade 140
Optimizing Squared-Off Cascades 145
Optimizing the Stripping Section 149
Discontinuous Processes 151
References 154

5 UF_6 Diffusion Plants **155**
General Remarks 155
Barrier Efficiency 155
Stage Efficiency 160
Connection in Cascade 164
Stages with Two or More Diffusers in Series 165
Physicochemical and Chemical Properties of UF_6 . . . 168
Choice of Operating Conditions 172
Plant Construction Features 177
Production, Supply, and Extraction of UF_6 183
Technical and Operating Problems: Inspection 186
Calculations Relating to the Cascade 191

Production Plants 195
Economic Considerations 200
References 204

6   Centrifugation **207**
Types of Centrifuges 207
Rotor Materials 210
Beyerle and Groth's Countercurrent Centrifuges 214
Zippe Countercurrent Centrifuge 218
Theory of the Countercurrent Centrifuge 221
Experimental Findings 233
Economics of the Process 234
Example of an Ideal Cascade 237
Pilot and Demonstration Plants 239
References 241

7   Mass Diffusion **242**
Various Types of Separating Elements 242
Screen Performance 248
Process Operating Conditions 254
Cascades of Separating Elements 256
Countercurrent Columns 257
Applications 260
References 263

8   The Separation Nozzle **265**
Operating Conditions 265
The Separating Element 266
The Cascade 269
References 273

9   Water Distillation **274**
Elementary Effect 274
Plate Columns 277
Packed Columns 282
Column Dimensions 284
Typical Column Parameters 286
Energy Consumption 287
Operating Pressure 289
Columns in a Cascade 291
Process Economy 292
Plants 293
References 297

10 Hydrogen Distillation 299
   Properties of Liquid Hydrogen 299
   Hydrogen Fractionation 300
   Energy Consumption 302
   Hydrogen Purification 305
   Thermal Insulation 308
   Plants 309
   Economics of the Process 320
   References 321

11 Electrolytic Plants 322
   Electrolytic Plants for Preliminary Enrichment 322
   Electrolytic Plants for Thorough Enrichment 325
   Final Enrichment and Reconcentration 330
   References 333

12 Exchange-Reaction Plants 335
   Monothermal Processes: General Remarks 335
   Monothermal H_2O/H_2 Processes 336
   Monothermal NH_3/H_2 Processes 345
   Dual-Temperature Processes: General Remarks 348
   Dual-Temperature H_2O/H_2S Process 353
   H_2O/H_2S Process Plants 360
   Dual-Temperature H_2O/H_2 Processes 369
   Dual-Temperature NH_3/H_2 and Amine/H_2 Processes . . . 370
   References 373

13 Electromagnetic Separation 375
   Magnetic Field 375
   Causes of Aberration 377
   Ion Sources 384
   Isotope Collection 388
   Chemical Aspects of Separation 391
   Electromagnetic Separation Plants 392
   References 395

Appendix A Physical Constants and Data in Common Use . . . 397

Appendix B Natural Isotopic Concentrations 399

Appendix C Finite Difference Equations 409

Appendix D Table of Separation Potential V' 410

INDEX 414

ISOTOPIC MAKEUP OF THE ELEMENTS

STABLE AND RADIOACTIVE ISOTOPES IN NATURE

The fact that elements in nature are mostly made up of various isotopes, each of them present in more or less abundance, is due primarily to the stability level of the individual nuclides and to the process of formation of these nuclides, either in the prestellar stages of the universe or in the interior of the stars.

Stable isotopes are those whose half-lives are very long in relation to present geological time ($\sim 5 \times 10^9$ years). The unstable, or radioactive, isotopes, which are found in considerable quantities in nature, are those whose half-lives are longer, or at least not much shorter, than the span of geological time. Also, isotopes having much shorter half-lives occur naturally when generated in radioactive equilibrium processes. All isotopes of the elements from atomic number $(Z) = 84$ (polonium) on up are radioactive. In general, we can say that there are no stable isotopes with mass number $(A) > 209$, whereas, for numbers of lower mass, there is at least one Z for which there is a stable isotope, with the exceptions only of $A = 5$ and $A = 8$.

Lead $(Z = 82)$ has four stable isotopes: 204, 206, 207, and 208. Of these isotopes, the three heaviest are the end products of decay of the three natural radioactive series:

$$\text{Uranium–radium} \quad\quad {}^{238}\text{U} \rightarrow {}^{206}\text{Pb} + 8\text{He}^4$$

$$\text{Uranium–actinium} \quad\quad {}^{235}\text{U} \rightarrow {}^{207}\text{Pb} + 7\text{He}^4$$

$$\text{Thorium} \quad\quad {}^{232}\text{Th} \rightarrow {}^{208}\text{Pb} + 6\text{He}^4$$

1

whose ancestors decay with the following half-lives:

$$^{238}U \qquad 4.51 \times 10^9 \text{ years}$$

$$^{235}U \qquad 7.13 \times 10^8 \text{ years}$$

$$^{232}Th \qquad 1.41 \times 10^{10} \text{ years}$$

Bismuth (Z = 83) is found in nature with a single stable or quasi-stable isotope, 209; the others are radioactive nuclides belonging to the three natural radioactive series. Bismuth 209 is the end product of the decay of the artificial radioactive series of neptunium: $^{241}Pu \rightarrow ^{209}Bi + 8He^4$, whose first stages of decay are the following:

$$^{241}Pu \xrightarrow[\text{13.2 years}]{\beta} {}^{241}Am \xrightarrow[\text{458 years}]{\alpha} {}^{237}Np$$

The α-active ^{237}Np gives its name to this series because of a half-life higher than that of any other member: 2.14×10^6 years.

In addition to the heavy elements whose isotopes are members of the radioactive series, there are other elements in nature which have radioactive isotopes with long half-lives. Some of these elements are listed in Table 1.1.

In the stable zone of the periodic system of elements, the zone that goes up to Z = 83, there are two atomic numbers, Z = 43 and Z = 61, which were empty for a

Table 1.1

NATURAL RADIOACTIVE ELEMENTS WITH Z < 84

Element	Atomic No. (Z)	Mass No. (A)	Type of decay	Half-life, years	Abundance, %
K	19	40	β^-; K electron capture	1.28×10^9	0.0118
Rb	37	87	β^-	5×10^{11}	27.85
La	57	138	β^-; K electron capture	7×10^{10}	0.089
Sm	62	147	α	1.06×10^{11}	14.97
		148	α	1.2×10^{13}	11.24
		149	α	$\sim 4 \times 10^{14}$	13.83
Lu	71	176	β^-	3×10^{10}	2.59
Re	75	187	β^-	7×10^{10}	62.93
Pt	78	190	α	6×10^{11}	0.0127
		192	α	$\sim 10^{15}$	0.78

long time. In recent decades these elements, called, respectively, technetium (Tc) and promethium (Pm), have been produced artificially. Several isotopes of technetium, all of them radioactive, are now known, two of which, ^{97}Tc and ^{99}Tc, have relatively long half-lives: 2.6×10^6 years for ^{97}Tc and 2.12×10^5 years for ^{99}Tc. The latter can be obtained by neutron activation of molybdenum and subsequent beta decay, according to the following reactions:

$$^{98}Mo(n,\gamma)^{99}Mo \xrightarrow[67 \text{ hr}]{\beta^-} {}^{99}Tc$$

but it is also found among the fission products of uranium.

The relatively higher stability of the 97 and 99 isotopes of technetium by comparison with the others is in agreement with the theoretical predictions.

Several isotopes of promethium have been isolated, all of them radioactive. Among these, ^{145}Pm has the longest half-life, around 18 years, and it decays to ^{145}Nd by K electron capture. Also for this element the nonexistence of stable isotopes has been explained theoretically.

The half-lives of the isotopes of technetium and promethium, which are quite short in relation to geological time, explain the disappearance of these elements from the natural scene.

In the zone of relatively heavy elements, too, those with $Z > 83$, there long were empty spaces at atomic numbers 85 and 87. Several isotopes of these elements have recently been produced artificially, and they have been given the names astatine and francium, respectively. All these isotopes have very short half-lives, a few hours at most.

Of particular importance among the radioactive nuclides with short half-lives relative to geological time are ^{14}C and tritium (T), an isotope of hydrogen with a mass of 3.

Carbon-14, which is β^- active and has a half-life of 5730 years, is found in nature in weak concentrations. It is formed by the interaction of cosmic-radiation neutrons with the ^{14}N in the atmosphere, through a reaction (n,p). The concentration of ^{14}C in the atmosphere is constant and is determined by the radioactive equilibrium between the nuclei of ^{14}C transformed into ^{14}N and the new ^{14}C nuclei formed by neutron radiation of cosmic origin.

In the form of $^{14}CO_2$, the active isotope is assimilated into the biosphere. It is also transferred into such carbon compounds as carbonates and bicarbonates, which are found in chemical equilibrium with CO_2 in the atmosphere or taken from the atmosphere.

The specific activity of living matter due to ^{14}C is 15.3 dis/min per gram of carbon. Since the activity of a living organism starts to decline the moment its ^{14}C stops being replaced by biological metabolism, measuring its activity makes it possible to establish the date of its death. This method has been used to make archaeological datings of organic remains of past eras, ranging from around 500 to more than 50,000 years.

Tritium is also formed in the atmosphere in very minute quantities under the influence of the neutrons present in cosmic radiation, probably according to the reaction $^{14}N + n^1 \rightarrow {}^{12}C + {}^{3}T$. In keeping with the intensity of neutron radiation of cosmic origin and with the cross section of ^{14}N for this reaction (its yield is around 1% of that of the reaction which produces ^{14}C), the production of tritium on the earth's surface has been calculated as 0.14 atom sec^{-1} cm^{-2}. The half-life of tritium is 12.26 years. By calculating the radioactive equilibrium, we find that the total quantity of tritium on earth is 1.8 kg, less than 10 g of which is in the atmosphere. In natural waters, which it reaches by condensation of atmospheric vapors, tritium is present with a ratio of $T/H \cong 1$ to 6×10^{-18}, although it is more abundant ($T/H \cong 70 \times 10^{-18}$) in atmospheric humidity. This is apparently due to the relatively short half-life of tritium.

In water isolated from exchange with atmospheric humidity, the activity naturally declines according to the familiar law of radioactive decay. Measurements of activity can therefore be used to date waters, much as ^{14}C is used to date organic matter. The method was checked by W. F. Libby, who measured the activity of wines whose age was known, and obtained satisfactory results. The measurement of activity can be facilitated by electrolytically concentrating the tritium in the sample. Separation factors of approximately 13.4 to 14.7 are obtained. The enrichment thus achieved can be derived from the increase of deuterium concentration in the sample.

NUCLEAR STABILITY

Although it is not possible to deduce theoretically the abundance of the various nuclides present in nature nor the abundance of the individual isotopes of an element, it nevertheless is possible to provide qualitative explanations of many features of the isotopic composition of the elements on the basis of standards of nuclear stability. As we know, the energy of the nucleon bonds within the nucleus is strongly affected by the following factors:

1. The A/Z relation, which is equal or close to 2 in the light elements and gradually increases (from Z = 20 on, or after calcium, there are no stable isotopes with a number of neutrons N = Z) to compensate with a larger number of neutrons for the increase in Coulombian repulsions between the protons.

2. Parity of protons and neutrons, which, on the basis of Pauli's principle, determines the saturation of the nuclear energy levels, forming shells within the nucleus analogous to the orbital shells of electrons.

3. Coincidence of the number of neutrons or the number of protons or both with one of the so-called "magic numbers" (2, 8, 20, 28, 50, 82, and 126), which determine a particularly stable nuclear structure.

Taking the drop model for the nucleus, we can construct a semiempirical formula to determine the mass, M(A,Z) of a stable atom whose mass number is A and whose atomic number is Z. We obtain this by adding five corrective terms to the two terms relating to the protons and the neutrons:

$$M(A,Z) = 1.00813Z + 1.00898(A - Z) - a_1 A + a_2 A^{\frac{2}{3}}$$

$$+ a_3 \frac{(A/2 - Z)^2}{A} + 0.000627 \frac{Z^2}{A^{\frac{1}{3}}} + \delta(A,Z) \qquad (1.1)$$

The first corrective term, $-a_1 A$, introduces the "heat of condensation" due to the short range nuclear forces. The second corrective term modifies the first correction to allow for the "surface tension" that gives an effect proportional to the surface (remember that the radius of the nucleus, R, is given by $R = 1.5 \times A^{\frac{1}{3}} \times 10^{-13}$ cm). The term $a_3 (A/2 - Z)^2/A$ introduces a correction for the number of unpaired nucleons and is found by considering the energy states of the nucleus described as a cold Fermi–Dirac gas. The next to last term expresses the effect of Coulombian repulsion, and the last term allows for energy variations due to the pairing of the nucleons. With the symbols p and d to indicate even and odd, respectively, the possible situations are the following:

A	Z	N	$\delta(A,Z)$
p	p	p	$\delta(p,p) = -f(A)$
d	p	d	$\delta(p,d)$
d	d	p	$\delta(d,p)$ $\Big\} = 0$
p	d	d	$\delta(d,d) = +f(A)$

Among the isobars the p–p types of nuclei are therefore the most stable, followed by those of the p–d and d–p types at the same level, whereas the d–d nuclei are extremely unstable.

These facts have been proved in practice by the distribution of stable nuclides in the four above-mentioned categories, as shown in the following table:

A	Z	N	Number of stable nuclides
p	p	p	164
d	p	d	53
d	d	p	58
p	d	d	6

Exceptionally stable and very abundant among the nuclides of type p–p are those with mass numbers which are multiples of 4 (hence made up of complete shells), such as ^{4}He, ^{12}C, ^{16}O, ^{24}Mg, ^{28}Si, ^{40}Ca, and ^{56}Fe. Note that the elements oxygen, magnesium, silicon, calcium, and iron are among the eight commonest components of igneous rock.

Of the six nuclides in category d–d, ^{50}V is really only slightly active, changing into its adjacent isobars by β^- decay and K electron capture, with a half-life of 6×10^{15} years. The heaviest, $_{73}Ta^{180}$, is present in low concentration (0.0123%) along with the preponderant $_{73}Ta^{181}$.

The other four d–d nuclides are all light: ^2D, ^6Li, ^{10}B, and ^{14}N. Their stability may be explained by the presence of the proton–neutron pair, quite strongly bonded, either alone (^2D) or paired with a complete shell (one, two, and three shells, respectively, for ^6Li, ^{10}B, and ^{14}N).

The radioactivity of the three isotopes ^{40}K, ^{138}La, and ^{176}Lu shown in Table 1.1 can undoubtedly be attributed to the d–d structure of their nuclei.

It should also be pointed out that, given the greater stability of p–p nuclides, the absolute abundance of elements with even atomic numbers is greater than that of elements with uneven atomic numbers (the rule of abundance stated empirically by G. Oddo and W. D. Harkins).

From Eq. 1.1, after singling out the nature of the term $\delta(A,Z)$, we see that the progression of the isobaric masses with Z is parabolic.

We can find the coefficients a_1, a_2, and a_3 by considering only those nuclides with uneven A, for which $\delta(A,Z) = 0$. The stable nuclides will be those for which $\partial M/\partial Z = 0$.

Thus we have the equation

$$-0.00085 - 2a_3 \frac{(A/2 - Z)}{A} + 0.000627 \frac{2Z}{A^{\frac{1}{3}}} = 0 \tag{1.2}$$

which, with the values of A and Z of the known stable elements, gives $a_3 = 0.083$, clearly showing that the parabolic progression of Eq. 1.1 is governed by this term. Substituting the value we have found for a_3 in Eq. 1.2, we get the formula

$$A/Z = 1.98 + 0.015A^{\frac{1}{3}} \tag{1.3}$$

which quantitatively spells out the A/Z ratio and its growing progression with A by reason of Coulombian repulsion (the term $A^{\frac{1}{3}}$ derives precisely from the sixth addendum of Eq. 1.1).

Substituting in Eq. 1.1 the value found for a_3 and utilizing the values of mass of the known stable elements, we get for a_1 and a_2 the more plausible values $a_1 = 0.01507$ and $a_2 = 0.014$.

Now, applying the same procedure for the stable nuclides with even A numbers, we can determine the function $\pm f(A) = \pm 0.036A^{-\frac{3}{4}}$.

Whereas, with uneven A, Eq. 1.1 gives only a single parabola for the isobar masses, of which only one—that closest to the minimum—can be stable, we have, for every even value of A, two corresponding parabolas, as can be seen in Fig. 1.1. The figure, in which the broken line gives the values the masses would have were it not for the introduction of the corrective term $\pm f(A)$, provides the explanation of the instability

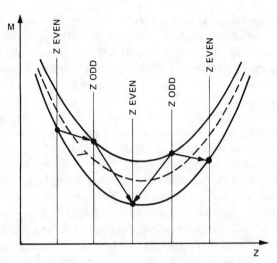

Fig. 1.1 Mass of even-A isobars (drawing not to scale).

of the d—d nuclides. Also, we can see that, for even A, there may be two stable isobars (sometimes even three), but that these isobars cannot belong to adjacent elements; i.e., their atomic number must differ by more than 1 (Mattauch's rule).

REGULARITY IN THE ISOTOPIC COMPOSITION OF ELEMENTS

The above-mentioned concepts on the stability of the nucleus afford qualitative explanation of several regularities in the distribution and abundance of stable nuclides. The following is a list of the more important regularities:

1. Elements with odd Z have only one stable isotope, or two at the most (naturally with odd A's). In this latter case, their mass numbers will differ by 2. Exceptions to this rule are a few light elements: helium, lithium, boron, and nitrogen. The stable isotopes of an element with odd Z have exclusively mass numbers of $A - 3, A - 1$, or $A + 1$, where A is the mass number of the heaviest isotope of the preceding element.

2. Elements with even Z have several isotopes. Among the light elements, only one with even Z, beryllium, has a single isotope (found as ^{9}Be), and two, helium and carbon, have two (^{3}He, ^{4}He, ^{12}C, and ^{13}C). The number of isotopes shows an average pattern of growth with Z, up to a maximum of 10 for Z = 50 (tin) and 9 for Z = 54 (xenon), after which it remains more or less constant at around 6 to 7 and drops sharply at the thresholds of the heavy radioactive elements. Thallium has only two stable isotopes, and lead has only four.

In elements with even Z, the isotopes tend to have even values of A, rising by steps of two units. The isotopes with odd A are: one in the zone between Z = 8 and Z = 40 (exception: Z = 22, with two isotopes); two and occasionally one from A = 42 on up, with the single exception of Z = 50 (tin) which has three, and Z = 58 (cerium) which has none. In any case, the lightest isotope and the heaviest isotope of each element with even Z both have even A. The isotopes with odd A have masses close to the average. And when there is more than one, they will differ in A numbers by two units. For three consecutive isotopes of an element (one with odd A and two with even A), the abundance of the isotope with odd A is always less than the sum of the abundance of its neighbors with even A. Furthermore, save for a few exceptions (Z = 4, Z = 54, and Z = 66), we find that the abundance of isotopes with even A runs between 70 and 100% of the total abundance.

3. For the light elements up to a certain Z, the light isotopes are generally more abundant; beyond that value of Z, the heavy isotopes are more abundant. For odd Z as the "inversion value," we might consider Z = 49, with the only exceptions being lithium (Z = 3) and boron (Z = 5) in the first zone and antimony (Z = 51) in the second zone. But for even Z, the inversion value is Z = 32, with the exceptions of helium and argon (Z = 18; most abundant isotope, ^{40}Ar) in the first zone. In the second zone the anomalies are zirconium (Z = 40; A = magic number 50) and neodymium (Z = 60; A = magic number 82). The anomaly in the isotopic composition of argon is really odd and can be explained, as we shall see, by the decay of ^{40}K through K electron capture.

4. The elements up to Z = 26 (iron) generally have one isotope that is far more abundant than the others, although this happens in only a few cases of higher Z. Often in this zone two or three isotopes will have fairly similar abundance levels. If an element has two stable isotopes with uneven A, there will be very little difference between their abundance levels. Also, it may be observed that in elements with even Z we find a quasi-periodic progression of abundance with mass number.

ABUNDANCE OF THE ELEMENTS IN NATURE

The rules of nuclear stability explain several features of the absolute abundance of the elements in nature. The cosmic abundance of the elements, shown in Fig. 1.2, has been studied both through analysis of the earth's crust and through statistical analysis of meteorites and spectrographic analysis of stellar matter. From analysis of meteorites, and particularly from the proportions of iron and stone which are their principal components, we have derived some indications as to the composition of the internal strata of Earth. Finally, it has been ascertained that the terrestrial abundance of the elements corresponds rather closely to their cosmic abundance, with the exception of hydrogen, helium, and a few other light elements. Probably this fact has something to do with the processes of nuclear fusion which occur during the evolution of stars.

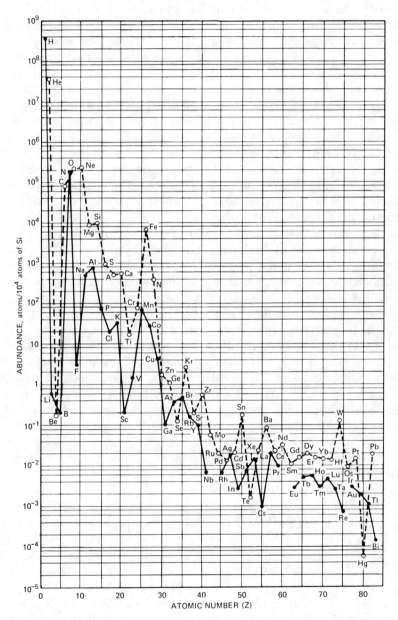

Fig. 1.2 Cosmic abundance of elements as a function of Z; ○, even Z; ●, odd Z. (From K. Rankama, *Isotope Geology*, p. 138, McGraw-Hill Book Company, Inc., New York, 1954.)

As shown in Fig. 1.2, abundance declines sharply with the rise in atomic number, up to values in the proximity of Z = 50 (in this interval there is a drop in abundance of a good 10 orders of magnitude), whereas for higher values of Z the drop is markedly less precipitous (three orders of magnitude at most). We can see the prevalence of elements with even Z over those with odd Z. More than 90% of Earth's mass and that of meteorites is made up of even-Z elements. A number of fluctuations in abundance can be explained with the rules for nuclear stability. Most remarkable is the iron–nickel peak: nickel's Z is the magic number 28, whereas the high abundance of iron can be explained on the basis of an initial abundance of the double-magic ^{56}Ni nuclide that is later decayed by two-beta radiation to ^{56}Fe, which is the most abundant (92%) isotope of iron.

Various attempts have been made to plot the theoretical curve of abundance, formulating several hypotheses as to the origin of the elements. These hypotheses can be separated into two general categories: (1) hypotheses based on conditions of equilibrium and (2) dynamic hypotheses.

According to the first category, in the primordial neutron–proton gas, the synthesis of these nucleons, at temperatures on the order of $10^9\,°$C, occurred according to the laws of statistical thermodynamics, leading to the formation of a mixture of assorted nuclei whose relative abundance was determined by the energy in their bonds and their respective neutron-capture cross sections.

Under the dynamic hypotheses, we assume, on the contrary, that the various nuclides were formed gradually from the simplest ones by a mechanism of successive neutron captures. The proportions of the various nuclides, however, would still be determined from bond energy and neutron-capture cross section. In this way many nuclides were formed with an excessive number of neutrons, and these were transformed by successive beta losses. The isotopes that gave off beta radiation and now exist in nature are, under these hypotheses, the longer half-lived remains of this category of nuclides.

VARIATIONS IN
ISOTOPE ABUNDANCE IN NATURE

The isotopic composition of the elements, determined, as mentioned before, by the level of stability in the various nuclei and by the conditions prevailing during cosmogony, may be considered only roughly constant on the universal scale. In fact, there are measurable variations in the isotopic composition of an element, both in relation to its origin and as the result of natural processes of fractionation.

For example, the isotopic composition of lead, three of whose four isotopes are radiogenic in origin, differs in the various uranium ores (uranium decay leads to ^{206}Pb) and in the ores of thorium (which forms ^{208}Pb). This difference is also reflected in the significant variations between the atomic weights of the substance according to its provenance.

The argon found in potassium minerals displays more of the 40 isotope than is found in atmospheric argon: the $^{40}Ar/^{36}Ar$ ratio is higher than normal even by a factor of 3 or more. This can be explained as the result of K-electron-capture decay of ^{40}K, which is also responsible for the abnormal abundance of ^{40}Ar in atmospheric argon. The argon present in the primordial terrestrial atmosphere was almost entirely lost in one of the early stages of Earth's evolution, and most of it was subsequently replaced by argon from radioactive decay. This would also explain the far greater abundance of argon than of the other rare gases on Earth, and the anomaly of its atomic weight which, in Mendeleev's periodic system, breaks the rule that the weight must grow as the atomic number. In this connection it should be noted that also the anomaly of the unusually low atomic weight of iodine can be explained by the discovery among the fission products of uranium of a 129 isotope giving off β^- radiation and having a half-life of 1.72×10^7 years. We believe that initially both the 127 and 129 isotopes were present in about the same amounts in nature, but the subsequent transformation of the heavier isotope into the adjacent ^{129}Xe isobar increased its abundance at the expense of iodine's.

Again, for the β^- decay of ^{87}Rb, which yields ^{87}Sr, there is considerable variation in the abundance of ^{87}Sr in minerals.

Isotopic analysis of lead (particularly by the measurement of the $^{206}Pb/^{207}Pb$ and $^{206}Pb/^{208}Pb$ ratios), argon, and strontium in minerals is an effective tool for geological dating.

There are also great variations in the isotopic composition of helium. In the atmosphere the $^3He/^4He$ ratio is 1.2×10^{-6}, whereas in natural gases it drops by an entire order of magnitude or more. Even lower is this ratio for helium in thorium and uranium ores, in which only ^4He is formed. On the other hand, $^3He/^4He$ ratios as high as 0.1 to 0.3 are found in certain ferrous meteorites. This has been explained by tritium formation due to interaction between nitrogen and cosmic neutron radiation and the subsequent β^- decay of the tritium thus formed.

In some classes of stars, spectrography has revealed a wide discrepancy between the stellar $^{12}C/^{13}C$ ratio and that found in terrestrial and meteorite materials: whereas the latter has a value of 90, the astrophysicists have found values running as low as 3 to 5. This is extremely important for the study of stellar evolution. The energy processes of the stars are explained in one of two ways: either by the "proton–proton chain"

$$p^1 + p^1 \to {}^2D + \beta^+$$
$$^2D + p^1 \to {}^3He \qquad (1.4)$$
$$^3He + p^1 \to {}^4He + \beta^+$$

in which four protons are transformed into one helium nucleus plus two positrons, liberating around 26 MeV of energy, or by the "carbon cycle" (suggested independently by Hans Bethe and Carl von Weizsäcker):

$$^{12}C + p^1 \rightarrow {}^{13}N \rightarrow {}^{13}C + \beta^+$$

$$^{13}C + p^1 \rightarrow {}^{14}N$$

$$^{14}N + p^1 \rightarrow {}^{15}O \rightarrow {}^{15}N + \beta^+ \qquad (1.5)$$

$$^{15}N + p^1 \rightarrow {}^{12}C + {}^4He$$

In this series of reactions, the carbon acts essentially as a catalyst for the synthesis of four protons. The result is once again formation of one helium nucleus plus two positrons, as in the proton–proton chain, with the liberation of the same amount of energy. The $^{12}C/^{13}C$ ratio in a star, given the presence of both these nuclides in the carbon cycle, will depend on the physical conditions prevailing in its interior.

Variations in isotopic composition, generally slighter than those connected with differing origins of substances, are found in nature as a consequence of various fractionation processes: crystallization, distillation, chemical exchange, centrifugation, etc. The variations in isotopic composition stemming from these phenomena are slight because in nature there are no countercurrent processes that, as will be shown later, multiply the effect of element separation.

For example, in atmospheric carbon dioxide the $^{12}C/^{13}C$ ratio is around 90, but it is higher (90.5 to 91.0) in carbon of vegetable and animal origin—perhaps because the light isotope is fixed more quickly—and it is generally lower (88 to 90) in the sedimentary-formation carbonates. This latter effect is due in good part to the exchange reaction

$$H^{12}CO_3^- + {}^{13}CO_2 \rightleftharpoons H^{13}CO_3^- + {}^{12}CO_2 \qquad (1.6)$$

which, at temperatures below $400°C$, tends to distribute most of the ^{13}C into the bicarbonate. This same reaction also leads to an enrichment of the carbonates in ^{18}O, and the values found for this enrichment agree with those for ^{13}C. In the $^{12}C/^{13}C$ ratio, therefore, we find deviations of a few percent (±3 at most) from the 90 figure. This fact often makes it possible to distinguish between carbon of organic provenance ($^{12}C/^{13}C > 90$) and carbon from magma ($^{12}C/^{13}C < 90$).

Of particular interest is the distribution of deuterium in natural waters and gases (such as methane), sought as raw materials for the production of heavy water.

As for water, the oceans are obviously the world's greatest reserve of deuterium. There is 300 times as much salt water on Earth as there is fresh water, which, for the whole world, amounts to around 4×10^{15} m^3.

It is believed then that, in the depths, the mass of sea water is substantially uniform as to isotopic composition. According to measurements taken in various laboratories, the deuterium content should be around 157 ppm mol D/H ±1 (see page 32 in Chap. 2).

Naturally the surface layers of the seas may be enriched by evaporation, given the fact that H_2O is more volatile than HDO. Analyses of tropical sea water have yielded values of around 160 ppm mol D/H. Some measurements of deuterium content in sea water are shown in Table 1.2.

Table 1.2

DEUTERIUM CONCENTRATION IN SAMPLES
OF SEA WATER

Locality	Concentrations ppm mol D/H	Ref.
Pacific Ocean (off Southern California)	149 ± 1	8
Pacific Ocean (48°28′ N, 124°36′ W)	155.2 ± 0.5	15
Atlantic Ocean (30°34′ N, 72°25′ W)	149 ± 1	8
Atlantic Ocean (off Halifax)	155.6 ± 0.5	15
Gulf of Mexico	151 ± 1	8

We know that most fresh water originates from precipitation of water evaporated from the sea. In 1 year some 4×10^{14} m³ of water evaporate from the seas, and about one-third of that amount condenses on land. The freshwater exchange cycle is thus fairly rapid. Nevertheless, the variations in deuterium concentration levels found in fresh surface waters are greater than those encountered in salt water. This may be attributed to the fractionation processes combined with the various phases of the hydrological cycles peculiar to each region. In this an important role is played by sundry meteorological factors (temperature, humidity, prevailing winds, etc.). Some values for deuterium content in fresh water are shown in Table 1.3. From this it is seen that the variations in deuterium concentration in fresh surface waters can be rather large, up to as much as 20 ppm mol D/H.

Systematic research into the deuterium content of natural waters was conducted in Canada in recent years. The findings, expressed in ppm mol D/H, are shown in Fig. 1.3. Some of the measurements refer to atmospheric precipitation. In the north central regions of Canada, an average value of 135 ppm D/H was found for precipitation, with a difference of 8 ppm between the (higher) summer average and the winter average. The surface waters also showed moderate seasonal fluctuations in concentrations.

Measurements of deuterium content in natural methane and petroleum taken in Canada yielded values of 110 to 134 ppm mol D/H for methane and 134 to 139 for petroleum.

Systematic samplings of deuterium content in natural springs are a keen point of interest to those in charge of choosing sites for new heavy-water plants. In this connection, a plant of this kind operated all through World War II at Trail, in British Columbia, where the deuterium content in water is particularly low (see Table 1.3), as it is in many other rivers of the Canadian western slope.

Of course, the processes of fractionation which cause these variations in the abundance of deuterium in natural waters also affect the abundance of oxygen

Table 1.3

ANALYSIS OF DEUTERIUM IN
FRESHWATER SAMPLES

Locality	Concentration, ppm mol D/H	Ref.
Milan, tap water	152 ± 4	12
Larderello (Tuscany), fumarole condensation	149 ± 6	12
New York, tap water, Columbia University	147 ± 1	8
Lake Ontario	147 ± 0.5	8
Lake Ontario	149.5 ± 0.5	15
Niagara River	147 ± 0.5	8
Niagara River	149 ± 0.5	15
Ottawa River, at Deep River	144.3 ± 0.3	15
Columbia River (B. C.)	139 ± 1	15
Columbia River, near Trail (B. C.)	135 ± 1	15
Porcupine River (Yukon)	131.5 ± 1	15
Fraser River, at Hope (B. C.)	136.1 ± 1	15

isotopes. We shall only say about this problem that the effects of separation of deuterium and ^{18}O (the ^{17}O isotope is negligible by reason of its rarity) are not generally comparable; in fact, the effects of opposite signs have sometimes been observed in the meteorological phenomena.

The measurements of the abundance of $^{235}U/^{238}U$ in natural uranium as performed in several laboratories[16,17] with uranium obtained from the various ores generally lie between 0.71 and 0.72 at.%. For example, a study[17] conducted in 1961 in the Capenhurst laboratories of the United Kingdom Atomic Energy Authority yielded this value: 0.7196 ± 0.0003 at.% or 0.7106 ± 0.0003 wt.%.

For a heavy element like uranium, we usually cannot expect any major variations in the abundance ratios of $^{235}U/^{238}U$ because the elementary effects of isotope separation decline as the atomic weight increases, and it is very rare to find effects in nature which multiply the elementary effect.

In exceptional and limited cases, however, we may find considerable variations in isotope composition, even in nature. These variations for uranium were discovered in 1972 in the Oklo deposit in Gabon.[18] Analyses yielded relative abundance levels, ranging from 0.64% to 0.44%, whereas in other sections of the deposit values as high as 0.74% were found, even higher than the natural level.

The phenomenon has been explained with the hypothesis of a nuclear chain reaction occurring spontaneously in a favorable environment (presence of water) around 1.7 billion years ago, when the concentration of ^{235}U was around 3%. This hypothesis finds some corroboration in the presence of several rare earths

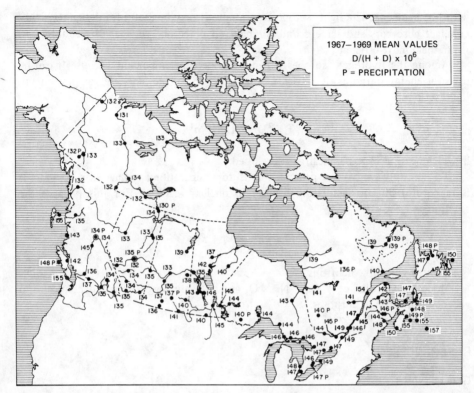

Fig. 1.3 Survey of deuterium content in natural waters on Canadian territory, performed by the Atomic Energy of Canada Ltd.

(neodymium, samarium, europium, and cerium), corresponding to fission products, in the uranium with the lowest concentration of ^{235}U.

USES FOR SEPARATED ISOTOPES

Today isotope separation is done on an industrial scale only for production of ^{235}U and heavy water.

Another element involved in isotope separation, on a scale that could be called semi-industrial, is boron. Of its two isotopes, ^{10}B and ^{11}B, the first (present in nature in concentrations of 19.78 mol %) is particularly interesting by reason of its broad capture cross section in the reaction

$$^{10}_{5}B + _{0}n^{1} \rightarrow {}^{7}_{3}Li + {}^{4}_{2}He$$

with hot neutrons. The light isotope separated out may be useful for designing highly compact absorbers and screens and for neutron detectors, such as BF_3 counters, to make them more efficient.

Among the hydrogen isotopes, tritium has become important because it can be used for energy purposes (it is used now as a trigger for thermonuclear explosions) in the reaction

$$_1^3T + {}_1^2D \rightarrow {}_2^4He + {}_0n^1$$

in which heat of 83×10^6 kcal/g is developed.

Tritium, however, is not produced by isotope separation (we have seen how rare it is in nature) but by irradiating lithium in nuclear reactors. For this purpose the reaction

$$_3^6Li + {}_0n^1 \rightarrow {}_1^3T + {}_2^4He$$

is exploited with slow neutrons.

Modest quantities of ^{13}C, ^{15}N, ^{18}O, and ^{34}S are needed for biochemical and geochemical research purposes.

REFERENCES

General Works

1. K. Rankama, *Isotope Geology,* p. 138, McGraw-Hill Book Company, Inc., New York, 1954.
2. A. I. Brodskij, *Himija Izotopov,* Akad. Nauk SSSR, Moscow, 1957.

Rules of Nuclear Stability and Systematics

3. E. Fermi, *Nuclear Physics,* University of Chicago Press, Chicago, 1950.
4. R. D. Evans, *The Atomic Nucleus,* McGraw-Hill Book Company, New York, 1955.

Abundance of the Elements in Nature

5. R. A. Alpher and R. C. Herman, *Rev. Mod. Phys.,* **22:** 153 (1950).
6. H. C. Urey, *Phys. Rev.,* **88:** 248 (1952).
7. V. V. Cherdyntsev, *Abundance of Chemical Elements,* University of Chicago Press, Chicago, 1961.

Variations in Isotope Abundance in Nature

a. Deuterium

8. I. Kirshenbaum, *Physical Properties and Analysis of Heavy Water,* McGraw-Hill Book Company, Inc., New York, 1951.
9. I. Friedman, Deuterium Content of Natural Waters and Other Substances, *Geochim. Cosmochim. Acta,* **4:** 89 (1953).
10. H. Craig and L. I. Gordon, *Stable Isotopes in Oceanographic Studies and Paleotemperatures,* E. Tangiorgi (Ed.), pp. 6-130, Consiglio Nazionale della Ricerche, Rome, 1965.

11. W. Dansgaard, The Isotopic Composition of Natural Waters, *Medd. Grøn.,* **165**(2): 120 (1961).
12. E. Cerrai et al., *Nuovo Cim.,* **9**: 511 (1952).
13. E. Halevy and B. R. Payne, Deuterium and Oxygen-18 in Natural Waters: Analyses Compared, *Science,* **156**: 669 (1967).
14. R. M. Brown, W. H. Stevens, and W. M. Thurston, Deuterium Content of Canadian Waters. I. A Collection of Data Available as of February 1967, Canadian Report AECL-2697, April 1967.
15. R. M. Brown, E. Robertson, and W. M. Thurston, Deuterium Content of Canadian Waters. II., Canadian Report AECL-3800, January 1971.

b. ^{235}U

16. R. F. Smith, R. E. Eby, and C. W. Turok, Variations in Isotopic Content of Natural Uranium, USAEC Report KY-373, June 1961.
17. B. R. Grundy and A. N. Hamer, Some Aspects of the Stoichiometry of $UO_{2.67}$ Relevant to the Preparation of Uranium Isotopic Standards and a Redetermination of the ^{235}U Content of Natural Uranium, *J. Inorg. Nucl. Chem.,* **23**: 148 (December 1961).
18. F. Perrin, Communication to the Academy of Sciences, Paris, September 25, 1972.

2 METHODS OF ISOTOPIC ANALYSIS

MASS SPECTROMETRY

One of the instruments most frequently used in isotopic analysis is the mass spectrometer. This instrument works on the basic principle that charged particles with equal energy but differing in mass are subjected to forces of different intensity as they cross magnetic fields. In general, the instrument consists of three fundamental components: (1) a source to produce a beam of ions of the substance to be analyzed, (2) a magnetic analyzer into which the beam is directed and by means of which it is broken down into its components, and (3) a display system to record the spectrum.

The band of ions produced by the source is initially accelerated by means of an electric field and then introduced into the analyzing magnetic field. The particular arrangement of the electric and magnetic fields in order to obtain maximum resolution at the collector is a problem in ion optics and may be solved in any of several ways. Often, in the spectrometers with higher resolution power, the ion beam is electrostatically bent in such a way that the velocity scattering of the electrostatic field precisely compensates for the velocity scattering due to the magnetic field. This behavior makes the operation of the spectrometer independent of any lack of homogeneity in the initial energy of a given (specific) ion beam. Sundry causes of aberration, which cut down the instrument's resolution power, can be eliminated by taking proper precautions. Among the causes are those due (1) to the angular opening of the beam, (2) to the effects of the·dispersed flow of the magnetic and electric fields, (3) to the effects of the space load (which are seldom discernible since the ion currents used in spectrometers are well below the limits of around 100 μA, at which such effects begin to be perceptible), (4) to the lack of homogeneity in the electric and magnetic fields, and (5) to the Rutherford scattering of the ions against the residual gas molecules in the apparatus. These shortcomings have been at least partially eliminated in the more advanced double-focus spectrometers, which use a combination of a radial electric field and a sectorial magnetic field in which the particles enter normally; with these instruments, which are peculiarly suited to accurate measurements of mass, resolution powers on the order of 100,000 can be obtained.

Special care is devoted to the construction of ion sources, and various types have been tested to obtain sources with a high ionization yield and low energy dispersal. Among the commonest are hot-anode sources that are extremely useful in analyzing elements with a low ionization potential; with a source of this kind, the material for analysis is applied directly to a filament. When this filament is heated in a vacuum, some of the material placed on it is evaporated in the form of ions, which are accelerated and directed through a suitable arrangement of slits. The ionization produced by the hot-anode source depends on the fact that the filament has a greater affinity for electrons than does the material applied to it. The level of ionization of the material evaporated from the filament is given by

$$n^+/n^0 = e^{F(W-I)/RT} \tag{2.1}$$

where n^+/n^0 = ratio between charged particles and neutral ones evaporated in the sample

F = Faraday constant

W = work function for the filament material

I = ionization potential of the material evaporated from the filament

R = constant of the gases

T = absolute temperature

The formula is strictly valid only for pure elements, but it can be applied with fair approximation to compounds as well. The formula shows that the ionization potential must be sufficiently low, whereas the work function of the filament must be high. From this point of view, the best material is platinum, whose work function comes to 6.2 V. However, the more commonly used material is tungsten ($W = 4.52$ V), which can be used at much higher temperatures.

Sometimes a variation of the above-mentioned hot-anode source is used, in which the sample is introduced in the form of a gas. This source is very handy to use whenever the material can be introduced in gaseous form, in that the problem of preparing the sample is greatly simplified.

A very widely used source is the electron-bombardment type. Ionization is produced here by bombarding the gaseous sample with electrons given off by a hot filament. The electrons are accelerated by a suitable potential of 70 to 100 V and are directed at their target through a magnetic field. The material to be examined must be introduced into the source in gaseous form, and therefore, if it is in the solid state, it must be evaporated in a crucible. This type of source is much used because of its great advantages of high stability and low energy dispersal.

Other fairly delicate problems in an isotope analysis are those of getting the sample for analysis into the source, particularly when it is introduced in gaseous form. The two requirements for ideal operation of a valve for introducing the gas into an electron-bombardment source are the following: (1) the composition of the gas mixture in the ionization region of the source must be identical with the composition of the sample, and (2) the concentration of the mixture and the flow of gas must not vary during the analysis. These conditions are satisfied by introducing the gas into the source in a molecular flow.

One of the problems to be resolved in isotope analysis is the need—a need felt very keenly in electromagnetic separation in which the quantities to be separated are usually quite small—to use the absolute minimum quantity necessary for analysis. This problem has been satisfactorily solved with instruments having measuring systems at the ion collector which make it possible to get the mass spectra using samples on the order of a microgram.

Various procedures have been used to detect the separated ion bands at the collector. The first methods used, which are now of no more than historical importance, are those based on ion-generated fluorescence on a suitable screen. Still in general use today is the method of detection and display on film strips. With very sensitive film, we can easily develop images produced by 10^9 ions of 10 keV energy hitting a surface of 1 mm^2.

In more widespread use, however, are systems for electrical recording of the currents by means of suitably designed circuits that can measure very low currents and directly record the mass spectrum. Special attention is given to getting rid of the secondary electrons freed by the impact of the ions on the collector, which could distort measurement of the currents. For this reason the collector proper is preceded by electrodes with a negative charge of several tens of volts with respect to the collector plate.

Mass spectrometry using the above-mentioned means has reached a high level of precision. Even so, errors can still occur to distort its findings.

We have already seen how a variation in isotope abundance can come about in the process of introducing the sample into the source. Such a variation can also come about during the ionization process, when there is a difference in the effectiveness of ionization between two isotopes. For example, in methane the effectiveness of ionization for CH_4 is different from that for CH_3D. Space-charge effects can also give rise to variations in the isotopic composition of the beams coming from the source. Even in the source itself, distortions may result from magnetic fields and from variation in the efficiency of the source as a consequence of a change in the ionizing potential during discharge. Various distortions of the spectrum recorded on the collector can be introduced by the electronic measuring equipment, specifically by the nonlinearity of the measuring resistances and electrometer amplifiers.

SPECIAL METHODS FOR ANALYZING ^{235}U

Although several procedures for isotopic analysis of uranium have been devised and used, a mass spectrometer coupled with some technique for isotope dilution has proved to be by far the most useful. Direct spectrometric measurement of enriched samples without any previous manipulation, simple though it may be, is no longer in use today because of the most disturbing memory effects that are encountered, primarily during analysis of uranium hexafluoride samples. The consequence of this memory effect is that two samples of different concentrations, analyzed in succession, are shown as less dissimilar in composition than they actually are. The dilution techniques now generally used reduce this memory effect to a minimum.

In general, dilution methods consist in isotopically diluting, for example, the enriched sample extracted from the top (product) of a gaseous diffusion plant to a concentration approximately similar to that of the impoverished sample extracted from the bottom (tail stream) of the same plant. By means of mass spectrometric measurement comparing the pair of samples, and with knowledge of the dilution ratios, it is possible to get directly to the separation factor the plant has achieved. Dilution is done with the desired uranium compound (hexafluoride for diffusion plants) extremely poor in ^{235}U, in such a way that the composition of resulting sample is so close to that of the impoverished tail as to make the memory effects completely negligible.

The reason for this spectrometer behavior is not very clear. Probably, at least in the case of uranium hexafluoride, it is due to a process of chemical exchange between the incoming hexafluoride and the nonvolatile uranium compounds found in the source, left over from previous analyses. Some of these reactions are of the type

$$UF_4 + UF_6 \rightleftharpoons 2UF_5 \tag{2.2}$$

with the nonvolatile residual tetrafluoride from earlier samples interacting with the incoming hexafluoride to form UF_5, upon which spectrometric analysis is most commonly performed. This reaction obviously distorts the measurement findings. Furthermore, the UF_5, which is unstable, can persist for a period of time in the source and hence affect the measurement of a sample introduced prior to the complete decay of the pentafluoride.

Other problems that cannot be overlooked from the technical point of view are raised by the introduction of hexafluoride into a mass spectrometer. The high corrosiveness of hexafluoride shortens the lives of certain components, particularly that of the ion source. When hexafluoride passes through the plant, there are generally reactions either with the spectrometer or with water, hydrocarbons, and other compounds adsorbed on plant surfaces. The effect can be grave in the source since the reaction products can be insulators and can thus change the operating properties of the source. Specifically the reaction products can cause fluctuations in the ion beam, with a resultant decline in the resolution power of the instrument and/or erratic amplifier output.

New types of sources have been specifically designed to be used with uranium hexafluoride. The basic concern is to prevent, insofar as possible, any contact between the gas and the material parts of the source, thus increasing the life of the individual parts of the apparatus and cutting down on reactions that give rise to memory effects. Designed for this purpose are sources into which the gas is introduced in the form of a narrow molecular beam that intersects the ionizing electron beam. Those molecules not ionized are immediately pumped away without time to interact with any surfaces, at least in the zone immediately around the source.

In installations where it is feasible to get the enriched sample in some other way than in the form of hexafluoride, it is preferred to opt for analyses of tetrachloride or uranyl nitrate, which can be processed through ordinary sources for solid materials.

The analytical procedures briefly described in the preceding paragraphs make it possible to get high precision, even in samples with very low levels of valuable isotope. With particularly careful dilution techniques, the ^{235}U content of hexafluoride samples with low concentrations of light isotope (0.038%) has been found with absolute precision ranging around ±0.00003%. For samples more heavily enriched in ^{235}U, the relative precision obtained is about 0.02%.

Sometimes activation-analysis methods are used. As is known, natural uranium is a mixture of three isotopes: ^{238}U (99.274%), ^{235}U (0.72%), and ^{234}U (0.0061%). The uranium sample to be analyzed is irradiated in a reactor, which produces the following reactions with slow neutrons:

$$^{238}U + {}_0n^1 \rightarrow {}^{239}U \rightarrow {}^{239}Np \rightarrow {}^{239}Pu$$

$$^{235}U + {}_0n^1 \rightarrow \text{fission products} \qquad (2.3)$$

$$^{234}U + {}_0n^1 \rightarrow {}^{235}U$$

In these reactions the production of ^{235}U from ^{234}U is negligible, partly because of the short irradiation periods. With this hypothesis, the ^{235}U content of a given sample can be assessed by directly counting the activity of a certain specific fission product that has been formed and comparing it with the corresponding activity of a standard sample of natural uranium that has been exposed to radiation for an identical period of time. In general, the fission product selected for counting is ^{140}Ba, which has a high fission yield (6.2%) and a handy half-life (12.8 days). It is also easily separable from the other fission products and is packaged for counting purposes in the form of barium sulfate. The measurement can be affected by the presence of ^{238}U fission by fast neutrons. The error engendered in this case has, however, proved to be negligible for samples in which the $^{235}U/^{238}U$ ratio is higher than 1/1000.

Usually with this method, accuracy is obtained to within a few percent.

For measuring ^{235}U concentrations with an equally modest degree of precision, we can also consider optical spectrometry, since the emission lines of ^{235}U are slightly shifted in relation to the ^{238}U lines. For example, for the 4244-Å line, there is a shift of 0.25 Å. This means that this shift can be perceived with an instrument whose resolution power is somewhere around 20,000.

A film-strip spectrograph of 3.4-m focal distance, with a flat grid (300 lines per millimeter) and a theoretical resolution power of about 28,500, was used by Capitini et al.[11] to make an isotope analysis of ^{235}U with accuracy ranging from 2.5 to 3% for concentrations close to natural and with about 1% accuracy for ^{235}U concentrations higher than 10%.

A fairly accurate determination of the absolute ^{235}U content in a sample can be obtained by comparing the sample with a standard sample of known concentration. The National Bureau of Standards (U.S.) has developed 18 standard samples of various ^{235}U concentrations. The extreme samples are, respectively,

$$0.01733 \text{ wt.\%} \pm 0.00005 \text{ (SRM U-0002)}$$

$$97.663 \text{ wt.\%} \pm 0.003 \text{ (SRM U-970)}$$

For a complete list of the uranium isotopic standards, see Ref. 12.

SPECIAL PROCEDURES FOR DEUTERIUM ANALYSIS

The mass spectrometer is particularly helpful in analyzing mixtures of hydrogen and deuterium and of water and heavy water. For hydrogen analysis a current of gas is sent into the source, while two separate collectors simultaneously gather the mass 2 and mass 3 ions, corresponding to the H_2 and HD molecules. The collectors generally operate on a zero resetting principle, which makes it possible to get a direct reading of the ratio between the numbers of ions of different masses. Note that some corrections have to be made because a small percentage of the mass 2 ions consists of monoatomic D^+ ions, and among the mass 3 ions there are some triatomic H_3^+ ions. The latter generally result from a collision between an H^+ ion and a neutral molecule. Naturally, in an isotope analysis we are interested only in the HD^+ ion contribution to the total of mass 3 ions. The correction may be made quite easily since the concentration of H_3^+ ions is proportional to the square of the pressure of the gas, whereas the concentration of HD^+ ions is simply proportional to the pressure. Consequently the number of mass 3 ions is given by the formula

$$I = ap + bp^2 \qquad (2.4)$$

Therefore, if we construct a diagram of I/p as a function of pressure and extrapolate the straight line to zero, we get the a constant in Eq. 2.4, and hence the contribution to the curve made by the HD^+ ions. Figure 2.1 shows the progression of the ratio between the 3 and 2 masses as a function of pressure. This ratio, which

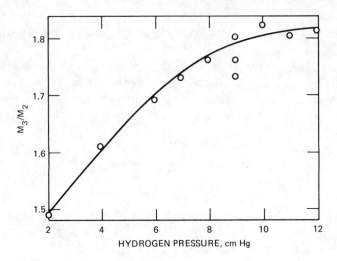

Fig. 2.1 Ratio between ion currents from mass 3 and mass 2 ions as a function of hydrogen pressure.

declines as the pressure, tends toward a limit value that represents the actual enrichment ratio.

These spectrometric measurements can achieve a high degree of precision. In ordinary analyses, errors of a few percentage points can be made on samples containing very low percentages of deuterium. In more precise analyses these errors can be reduced to a few points per thousand. In the case of analyses on samples very rich in deuterium, it is better to compare the concentrations of the mass 3 and mass 4 ions; the mass 4 ions are formed, in most instances, from D_2^+ ions, with an absolutely negligible percent of H_2D^+ ions; the mass 3 ions are formed almost exclusively of HD^+, and the possibility of their formation from H_3^+ ions is negligible.

Isotope analysis of mixtures of water and heavy water can be performed spectrometrically in several ways, according to the characteristics of the sample that is introduced into the source.

The analysis is sometimes made on the mixture of hydrogen and deuterium obtained by decay of the water sample under examination. Preparation of the hydrogen sample can be done electrolytically, although this method can lead to fairly serious error if the sample is not totally electrolyzed. In this case we get deuterium enrichment of the remaining electrolyte, and the sample of hydrogen to be used in the spectrometric analysis will no longer correspond in composition with the original material. For the above-mentioned reasons the preparation described is very seldom used.

Another method is to allow the water sample to decay on a filament of hot tungsten. This method has the advantage of requiring very small quantities of the material for analysis (about 10 mg) but does introduce several causes of error, such as isotopic exchange between the hydrogen formed and the residual water vapor, thanks to the catalytic effect of the tungsten oxide present and the memory effect due to the adsorption of hydrogen and vapor by the tungsten oxide in previous analyses.

This memory effect is generally typical of any analysis that makes use of hydrogen production by pouring water over metals at high temperature. Various metals are used, such as iron, zinc, magnesium, and uranium. Most frequently used are uranium and zinc. The latter has a less marked memory effect than tungsten and does not form oxides that encourage isotope exchange between hydrogen and steam. The operating temperature cannot go above $419°C$, which is the melting point of zinc.

Another method used is that of equilibration, in which a deuterium exchange takes place between the water sample to be analyzed and a sample of deuterium or hydrogen of known composition. The exchange reactions continue to occur on a platinum catalyst until equilibrium is achieved between the concentration levels. After equilibration the isotope concentration of the hydrogen sample is measured, and from this, since the initial concentration and the constants of equilibrium of the exchange processes that have taken place are known, the composition of the unknown water sample being analyzed is obtained. The sample of water for analysis must be chemically as pure as possible. Preliminary purification must be done in such a way as not to alter the concentration of the sample, which means that the chemical reagents used must not contain hydrogen or any compounds of hydrogen. One source of error, naturally, is uncertainty as to the values of the isotopic equilibrium constants.

Instead of producing hydrogen by treating water, we can obtain methane through suitable chemical reactions upon the water. Treating a sample of water with an excess of methyl magnesium iodide will give methane, which is formed according to the following reactions:

$$CH_3MgI + H_2O = CH_4 + Mg(OH)I$$

$$Mg(OH)I + CH_3MgI = CH_4 + MgO \cdot MgI_2$$

Generally this is how a mixture of methane and monodeuterated methane, CH_3D, is formed. With the use of the spectrometer, the isotopic composition of the methane thus produced is measured, and from that the composition of the water is obtained. Corrections are usually made to allow for the possible formation of the various kinds of isotopic molecules of methane.

The most direct method of analysis consists in putting the water, in the form of steam, into the ion source of the spectrometer. This method involves quantitative errors on the order of those obtained with hydrogen in the methods described above. The isotopic molecules that may be formed in the ion source are extremely varied and include all possible combinations of the two hydrogen isotopes and the three natural isotopes of oxygen, plus simpler molecules derived from the breaking of molecular bonds in water and more complex molecules formed by the collision of ions with neutral molecules. This means that manifold corrections must be made to the ratios between the measured ion currents. Errors in the deuterium concentration found in this way are due to discrimination effects in the ion source, to memory effects by adsorption of water vapor on the walls of the apparatus, and to the isotopic effect on the energy of the molecular bond.

Thurston[18,19] has developed an apparatus connected with a mass spectrometer for continuous analysis of deuterium in a flow of water or hydrogen. Various sampling probes are available for either case. The taking of samples of water or gas is done through a capillary. The water is evaporated and completely transformed into hydrogen as it passes over a strip of uranium at 600°C. The samples do not require preliminary purification, because the purification procedures are incorporated into the sample-taking system.

There is an automated version of the same apparatus for successive analyses of a large number of water samples ($\sim$10 cm^3), as shown in Fig. 2.2.

The time required for each analysis is 1 to 2 min, and the precision potential is 0.1 ppm D/H in the range of 0 to 600 ppm D/H.

At low concentrations of deuterium, the mass spectrometry systems give the greatest precision of all.

Analysis of water deuterium can be done by infrared spectrophotometry, with several possible variations in band frequencies and instrumentation.

Fig. 2.2 Thomson THN 202 spectrometer with an automatic sampling system and end printer (Atomic Energy of Canada Limited, Chalk River).

Particularly intense among the absorption bands is the 2500 cm^{-1} (3.980 μm) band, characteristic of the OD group, and the 3400 cm^{-1} (2.946 μm) band, characteristic of the OH group. As a consequence, the former is used for measurements in the area of low concentrations, up to a few percent of D/(H+D). In this case the deuterated molecules present, practically all of them of the HDO type, are greatly diluted in the mass of H_2O molecules.

The second band, however, is used for measurements at high deuterium concentrations, from about 99.5% and up. Thus we have a mixture of very diluted HDO molecules in a mass of D_2O. Figure 2.3 shows a typical spectrum.

The situation in the area of intermediate concentrations is more complicated. Here we have significant quantities of all three molecular species: H_2O, HDO, and D_2O. Neither of the bands considered is usable here, so intense is the absorption. For a situation of this kind, some have used the 1.445-μm band for H_2O (Ref. 21), the

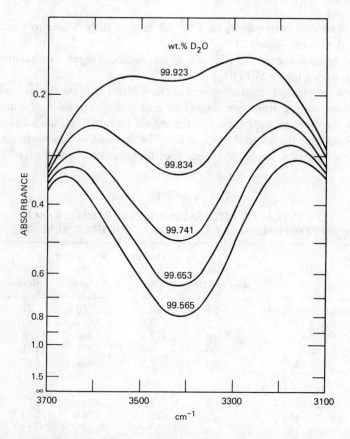

Fig. 2.3 Typical infrared absorption spectrum for high concentrations of deuterium (Atomic Energy of Canada Limited, Chalk River).

"transparency peaks" of D_2O at 1900 cm^{-1} (5.25 μm) and of H_2O at 2600 cm^{-1} (3.85 μm), or a combination of other absorption bands of the three molecular species.[23]

As a general consideration, we would remind readers that the absorption of a monochromatic beam by a substance present in N concentration in a cell of ℓ thickness is described by the Beer–Lambert law:

$$d = \ln (I_0/I) = \epsilon\ell \times N$$

where I_0 and I are, respectively, the intensities of the incident and emergent beams. Determination of the optical density d would allow an absolute measurement of N, provided we know the attenuation coefficient ϵ of the various molecular species. Although it is possible to measure ϵ of the pure substances H_2O and D_2O, it is impossible to find the ϵ for HDO, since this substance does not exist in the pure state.

Hence the measurements of deuterium concentrations in water can never be more than relative and therefore call for calibration of the apparatus with samples of known concentration.

Spectrophotometers frequently used for this kind of analysis are those with double beams, e.g., the Perkin–Elmer 21.

In a spectrophotometer the response of the outgoing signal to a variation ΔN is proportional to $\Delta(I/I_0) = (\Delta I/I)(I/I_0)$.

To obtain the greatest sensitivity, we must have high values for this product. As for the first factor, we see from Beer's law that $\Delta I/I$ is proportional to the thickness ℓ, which must therefore be kept high. For the second factor (I/I_0), the usual values are more or less within the interval ~0.3 to 0.9. The intervals of concentration and the corresponding precision levels for several spectrophotometers are given in Table 2.1.

Table 2.1

CONCENTRATION INTERVALS MEASURED WITH INFRARED
SPECTROPHOTOMETRY AND ACCURACY OF MEASUREMENTS

D/(H + D), %	Precision, ppm mol D/H	Thickness (ℓ), mm	Wavelength (λ), μm	Refs.
0.015 to 0.080	20	0.25	3.980	21
0 to 0.060	2	2.5	3.980	22
0 to 0.8	30	2.5	3.980	22
45 to 55	60	5*	1.445	21
0.8 to 99.5	1000	2.5	Transmission peaks	22
99.5 to 100	3	0.25	2.946	21
99.5 to 100	20	2.5	2.946	23
99.7 to 100	4	2.5	2.946	23

*The window in this case is of glass; all others are of CaF_2.

The samples for examination range in size, as a rule, from 0.5 to 1 cm^3, and the times involved range from 1 to 10 min per operation.

Infrared spectrophotometry calls for careful sample purification. Foreign substances, especially organic matter, greatly complicate the absorption spectra.

Since the density of pure heavy water differs from that of natural water by about 10%, clearly isotopic analysis can be done by means of sufficiently accurate density measurements. This kind of measurement calls for considerable equipment, i.e., very accurate scales, a thermostat sensitive to 0.01°C, etc., as well as very careful sample purification. Aside from the elimination of impurities, it should be remembered that, in all density-measurement procedures, the ^{18}O (^{17}O is generally negligible) also contributes to the density, as well as the D: 1 γ (1 wppm) of increment of density can be attributed to 8.75 ppm mol of $^{18}O/^{16}O$ or to 9.27 ppm mol D/H. Thus, if the sample has undergone any enrichment in ^{18}O, it must be eliminated (e.g., by electrolysis) or taken into account.

With the pycnometric method it is not difficult to obtain precision of ±1 γ (or around 10 ppm mol D/H), but the procedure is very tedious; every single measurement takes about 6 hr.

The float is one density method which, while offering high precision, is much quicker. The method consists in measuring the temperatures at which the unknown sample and a standard sample have densities equal to that of a small glass or quartz float. These temperatures may be determined by observing when the float in the liquid achieves neutral equilibrium. The concentration of deuterium in the sample is a univocal and known function of the difference between the two neutral-equilibrium temperatures.

To eliminate the need for overdelicate thermostat equipment, Cerrai, Marchetti, and Silvestri[26] developed a method suggested by Sapirstein,[27] which consists in reading the neutral-equilibrium temperatures by determining the point at which the float starts to rise in the water as the temperature is gradually lowered.

The float used in the experiments[26] is a small hollow glass sphere to which a solid glass stem is attached. The dimensions of the float are about 10 mm in length and about 5 mm in diameter at the fattest part.

The capsule containing the sample takes a volume of 0.8 to 1.5 cm^3 of water for each reading. The water sample, after normal purification, is distilled three times in a vacuum in a three-stage still, and the sample is gathered directly into the capsule containing the float. When the sample is ready for the reading, the capsule is placed (close to a thermometer) in a water thermostat equipped with an agitator.

The thermostat is heated until the density of the water in the capsule is lower than that of the float, and the float lies on the bottom of the capsule. At this point the heating is stopped, the thermostat is allowed to cool by natural convection, and the temperature at which the float rises from the bottom is noted. At this temperature the density of the water to be analyzed is the same as that of the float. The operation is repeated with natural distilled water, and a new reading for the neutral equilibrium temperature is obtained. Naturally the rate at which the thermostat temperature drops must be such as to ensure thermal equilibrium between the thermometer bulb and the sample being examined.

The following equation is used for calculating the deuterium content with this method:

$$N = \frac{(d_0/cd_1') - 1}{[(M_2/M_1) - 1] - [(M_2 d_1/M_1 d_2) - 1]\, d_0/cd_1'}$$
$$-\,\beta\,\frac{3(t - t_0)\, d_0/cd_1'}{(M_2/M_1)\,[1 - (d_1/d_2)]} \qquad (2.5)$$

where d_0 = density of natural water at temperature t_0

$\quad\quad d_1'$ = density of natural water at temperature t

$\quad\quad d_1$ = density of pure hydrogen oxide at temperature t

$\quad\quad d_2$ = density of pure deuterium oxide at temperature t

$\quad\quad \beta$ = coefficient of linear expansion of the float per degree centigrade

M_1 and M_2 = molecular weights of H_2O and D_2O, respectively

$\quad\quad c$ = ratio of the density of pure hydrogen oxide to the density of natural water (its numerical value is 0.999984 and may be considered independent of the temperature)

Using floats made of glass like pyrex or other borosilicates, having a takeoff temperature in natural water of about 25°C and with samples of water containing deuterium up to 10 mol %, we can obtain a level of precision of ±0.00003 mol D_2O (30 ppm mol D/H). The method can be improved by using quartz floats with a takeoff temperature in natural water of around 8°C.

The low-temperature method allows measurement of the deuterium content of water samples containing up to 0.1 mol % deuterium, with a precision as high as ±2 to 3 ppm mol D_2O. Natural water can be analyzed with this method at a precision level of ±2% of the value of the deuterium concentration. It takes about 30 min for a complete determination of the deuterium content in a water sample by this method.

The difference in thermal conductivity among H_2, HD, and D_2 can be exploited for the analysis of deuterium in gaseous hydrogen. If we arrange four metallic filaments in a Wheatstone bridge so that two of the filaments are in a natural-hydrogen atmosphere and two are in the gas to be analyzed, it is then possible, since the cooling conditions and hence the electrical resistances will differ, to translate the difference in deuterium content into the difference in potential (along the diagonal of the bridge).

An instrument based on this principle, with which it is possible to perform analyses throughout the entire span of deuterium concentration with an accuracy of at least ±100 ppm mol, has been developed by Silvestri and Adorni.[28]

The essential part of this instrument is a conductivity cell of the Gow–Mac type, consisting of a brass block with four holes drilled in it to hold four tungsten filaments. The four filaments are connected so as to form a Wheatstone bridge.

The filaments on two opposite sides are in a hydrogen atmosphere of known isotopic concentration, and the other two are in a hydrogen atmosphere whose concentration is to be measured.

In each hole there is the following relation between the temperature T_1 of the filament and that of the wall of the cavity (T_2):

$$T_1 = T_2 + (\phi/Ak) \tag{2.6}$$

in which ϕ is the heat flow through the gas, k is the thermal conductivity of the gas in the hole, and A is a constant depending on the geometry of the hole.

As we know, if k_1 and k_2 are the thermal conductivities of two components of a binary mixture and N_1 and N_2 are the molar fractions of the two components, the thermal conductivity k of the mixture is given by the equation

$$k = \frac{k_1}{1 + a_{1.2}(N_2/N_1)} + \frac{k_2}{1 + a_{2.1}(N_1/N_2)} \tag{2.7}$$

in which $a_{1.2}$ and $a_{2.1}$ are constants depending on the physical characteristics of the two gases.

For mixtures of H_2 and HD, since the thermal conductivity of the mixture may be made up additively without introducing any significant error, we can write

$$k = k_1(1 - N) + k_2 N = k_1 - N\Delta k \tag{2.8}$$

in which N is the molar fraction of HD and $\Delta k = k_1 - k_2$.

The values of k for the H_2 and HD molecular species are, respectively, k_{H_2} = 4.6 x 10^{-4} cal cm^{-1} sec^{-1} °C^{-1}, and k_{HD} = 3.76 x 10^{-4} cal cm^{-1} sec^{-1} °C^{-1} at a temperature of approximately 37.5°C. Hence Δk is 8.4 x 10^{-5} cal cm^{-1} sec^{-1} °C^{-1}.

If a constant voltage, V, is applied to the bridge, and if R is the resistance of the two branches of the bridge in contact with the reference gas and $R + \Delta R$ is the resistance of the two branches of the bridge in contact with the gas to be analyzed, the difference in potential along the diagonal of the bridge, ΔV, can be expressed by

$$\Delta V \cong 0.2 \frac{a}{A} \frac{\Delta k}{k_1^2} \frac{V^3}{R} N \quad (mV) \tag{2.9}$$

in which a is the temperature coefficient of the resistance. Note that R is not a constant, but varies slightly as a function of V.

The results of concentration measurements taken on gas samples containing as much as 5 mol % deuterium agree with the empirical equation

$$\Delta V = 4.56_8 (N - 0.00015) \quad (mV) \tag{2.10}$$

Concentration measurement by thermal conductivity can also be done on water samples, exploiting thermal-conductivity differences between H_2O and D_2O vapors, each in equilibrium with its own corresponding ice, at a constant temperature.

It is not feasible here to conduct a complete review of the many methods for deuterium analysis, on the basis of the most disparate and various physical properties (mechanical, optical, thermal, etc.) in which the deuterated substances are distinguished from the nondeuterated. For further information in this field, we refer the reader to the specialized literature (see the reference section of this chapter).

Table 2.2

PRECISION LEVELS OBTAINABLE WITH SEVERAL METHODS OF
DEUTERIUM ANALYSIS

Method	Interval, mol D (H + D)	Precision, ppm mol D/H
Mass spectrometry	0 to 0.0006	±0.1
Infrared	0 to 0.0003	±1
Pycnometry	0 to 1	±10
Float	$\sim 10^{-4}$ to 0.001	±2
Thermal conductivity	$\sim 10^{-4}$ to 0.05	±100

Table 2.2 is a summary of the precision levels that are possible in practice for the various methods described in the foregoing paragraphs.

The usual practice for obtaining measurements of high precision is to compare the unknown sample with a standard sample of known concentration that is fairly close to the concentration of the unknown sample. In the specific case of mass spectrometry, this also helps to avoid memory effects that would distort subsequent measurements of samples with very different concentration levels.

Measurements are often taken in the low-concentration field, even when the unknown sample is highly concentrated. This can be done by diluting the sample with water down to a low concentration or even to an impoverished state of known concentration.

Standards of known concentration can be obtained by mixing the proper proportions of practically pure deuterium oxide with practically deuterium-free protium oxide. By repeating the operation several times, we can get below 1 ppm mol D/H.

Currently available are standards prepared by the National Bureau of Standards (NBS-1 and NBS-1A), and just recently the Bureau has been considering the adoption of SMOW (Standard Mean Ocean Water) as a universal standard.[29] According to measurements taken at Chalk River, the absolute deuterium content of SMOW is 157.6 ± 0.5 ppm mol D/H. Measurements taken in various other laboratories agree with this value to within ±1 ppm.

REFERENCES

1. J. Robotz, *Introduction to Mass Spectroscopy: Instrumentation and Techniques,* Interscience Publishers, Inc., New York, 1968.
2. G. Nief and R. Botter, *Advances in Mass Spectrometry,* Pergamon Press, Inc., Elmsford, New York, 1959.
3. C. P. Keim and C. R. Baldock, *Mass Spectrometry at Oak Ridge National Laboratory: Electromagnetically Enriched Isotopes and Mass Spectrometry,* p. 145, Butterworth & Co. (Publishers, Ltd.), London, 1956.
4. G. H. Palmer, *Isotopic Abundance Measurements by Mass Spectrometry: Electromagnetically Enriched Isotopes and Mass Spectrometry,* p. 166, Butterworth & Co. (Publishers, Ltd.), London, 1956.
5. G. P. Barnard, *Modern Mass Spectrometry,* The Institute of Physics, London, 1953.

Special Procedures for ^{235}U Analysis

6. L. Debevec, Mass Spectrometric Measurements of UF_6, "*J. Stefan*" *Inst. Rep. (Ljubljana),* **5**: 49 (1958).
7. V. L. Warren and L. A. Smith, Measurements of the Isotopic Enrichment of Uranium by a Direct Comparison Mass Spectrometer Method, USAEC Report K-1369, June 28, 1958.
8. C. D. Tabor, *Mass Spectrometry for Uranium Isotopic Measurements,* Review Series, No. 5, International Atomic Energy Agency, Vienna, 1960 (STI/PUB/15/5).
9. R. F. Smith, R. E. Eby, and C. W. Turok, Improved ^{235}U Measurements at the Paducah Plant Through Refinements in the Gravimetric Oxide Dilution Procedure, USAEC Report KY-349, July 25, 1960.
10. A. H. Gillieson, *Some Alternatives to Mass Spectroscopy for Isotopic Abundance Determinations: Electromagnetically Enriched Isotopes and Mass Spectrometry,* p. 190, Butterworth & Co. (Publishers, Ltd.), London, 1956.
11. R. Capitini, M. Ceccaldi, J. P. Leicknam, and J. Rabec, Isotopic Analysis of ^{235}U by Emission Spectroscopy. II. Determination of the ^{235}U/^{238}U Ratio Using a Spectrograph and Electrodeless Lamps, French Report CEA-R-3457(2), February 1970.
12. E. L. Gamer, L. A. Machlan, and W. R. Shilds, *Uranium Isotopic Standard Reference Materials,* National Bureau of Standards, Special Publication 260-27, Superintendent of Documents, U. S. Government Printing Office, Washington, April 1971.

Special Methods for Analyzing Deuterium

13. I. S. Kirshenbaum, *Physical Properties and Analysis of Heavy Water,* H. C. Urey and G. M. Murphy (Eds.), McGraw Hill Book Company, Inc., New York, 1951.
14. A. I. Shatenstein et al., *Isotopic Analysis of Water,* Akad. Nauk *SSSR,* 1957.
15. B. Brigoli, *Energ. Nucl. (Milan),* **4**: 483 (1957); *ibid.,* **5**: 317 (1958).
16. G. Nief and R. Botter, Mass Spectrometric Analysis of Simple Hydrogen Compounds, French Report CEA-1583, 1960.
17. R. V. Krishna Murphy and B. S. Prohallada Rao, An All-Metal Spectrometer for Isotopic Analysis of Hydrogen at Material Concentration Levels, *Indian J. Pure Appl. Phys.,* **1**: 73 (1963).
18. W. M. Thurston, Automatic Mass Spectrometric Analysis of the Deuterium to Hydrogen Ratio in Natural Water, *Rev. Sci. Instrum.,* **41**: 963 (July 1970).
19. W. M. Thurston, Steam-Film Sampling of Water for Mass Spectrometric Analysis of the Deuterium Content, *Rev. Sci. Instrum.,* **42**: 700 (May 1971).
20. J. G. Bayly, V. B. Kartha, and W. H. Stevens, The Absorption Spectra of Liquid Phase H_2O, HDO, and D_2O from 0.7 μm to 10 μm, in *Infrared Physics,* Vol. 3, p. 211, Pergamon Press, Inc., New York, 1963.

21. J. Gaunt, Infrared Methods for the Analysis of Heavy Water, in *Proceedings of the International Conference on the Peaceful Uses of Atomic Energy, Geneva, 1955,* Vol. 8, p. 422, United Nations, New York, 1956.

22. J. G. Bayly, W. H. Stevens, and W. M. Thurston, An Infrared Method for Determining Variations in the Deuterium Content of Natural Water, Canadian Report AECL-2076 (January 1964).

23. W. H. Stevens and W. M. Thurston, The Determination of the D_2O Content of Heavy Water by Infrared Spectrometry, Canadian Report CRC-568, March 1954 (Reprint, June 1956).

24. W. H. Stevens, J. G. Bayly, W. M. Thurston, and V. B. Kartha, Heavy-Water Analysis in the 1% to 99% D_2O Range by Infrared Spectrophotometry, Canadian Report AECL-1391, September 1961.

25. B. Brigoli, E. Cerrai, and M. Silvestri, *Energ. Nucl. (Milan),* **4**: 43 (1957).

26. E. Cerrai, C. Marchetti, and M. Silvestri, *Nuovo Cim.,* **9**: 530 (1952).

27. L. A. Sapirstein, *J. Lab. Clin. Med.,* **35**: 793 (1950).

28. M. Silvestri and N. Adorni, *Rev. Sci. Instrum.,* **27**: 388 (1956).

29. H. Craig, Standard for Reporting Concentrations of Deuterium and Oxygen-18 in Natural Waters, *Science,* **131**: 1833-1834 (1961).

THE PHYSICAL PRINCIPLES
OF ISOTOPE SEPARATION

GENERAL REMARKS

Isotope separation is made possible by the diversity of isotopes' chemical and physical properties dependent on mass.

There are two types of properties that depend directly on mass and are therefore usable for separation. One type has to do with the "individual" diversity of movement of molecules of different masses (e.g., when the molecules are subjected to a gravitational field or, in the case of ions, to an electrical field). The other type has to do with the varying "statistical" behavior of molecular species of differing masses (e.g., in a gaseous mixture in thermal equilibrium, the square of the mean velocity of the various molecules is inversely proportional to the square root of the mass).

The diverse statistical behavior of isotopic molecular species, to which we owe a separation effect, is often only indirectly connected with the diversity of their masses through the zero-point energies. Slight differences in the levels of such zero-point energy affects (as we shall see shortly) the volatility, the constants of chemical equilibrium, the reaction speed, and other properties of the isotopic species.

The degree of separation obtainable by any process can be expressed on the basis of a quantity typical of the particular process and dependent on the conditions under which it is brought about, known as the *elementary separation factor.*

Assume that we have L mols of a substance, in which we want to enrich an isotopic species already present with the molecular fraction N. After a small quantity,

δL, of the substance has undergone the physicochemical transformation to which the separation effect is due (e.g., it has undergone a change of state, from liquid to vapor; or a change in chemical bonds, from water to hydrogen in water electrolysis), the process is stopped. Let N' be the mol fraction of the species in question in the enriched fraction (e.g., in δL) and N'' be the mol fraction in the impoverished fraction (e.g., in the residue $L - \delta L$). We will call the elementary separation factor the quantity

$$q_0 = \frac{N'/(1 - N')}{N''/(1 - N'')} \tag{3.1a}$$

With the introduction of the relative abundance $R = N/(1 - N)$, Eq. 3.1a can also be written

$$q_0 = \frac{R'}{R''} \tag{3.1b}$$

If the quantity δL that has undergone transformation is small enough with respect to the initial quantity L, there will be in the latter no appreciable variation in concentration, and therefore Eqs. 3.1a and 3.1b can, for all practical purposes, be written in the form

$$q_0 \simeq \frac{N'/(1 - N')}{N/(1 - N)} \tag{3.2}$$

In the processes that take place under conditions of thermodynamic and chemical equilibrium, the differences in concentration between one phase and another or between one component and another remain even after the cessation of isotope transfer between the phases or components. In these processes the $q = R'/R''$ ratio between the relative abundances of the enriched and impoverished fractions (generally called the *separation factor*) is constantly equal to the *elementary* separation factor, q_0, even for high values of the $\delta L/L$ ratio between the transformed fraction and the initial quantity of the substance. Of course, for high values of $\delta L/L$, Eq. 3.2 is no longer valid.

In the processes that take advantage of kinetic effects, the differences and gradients of concentration exist only so long as there is a transfer of isotopes from one zone to the other or a transfer between phases or components. In this case, the quantity δL of a binary substance which has undergone transformation can be expressed as the sum, $\delta L = \phi_1 + \phi_2$, of the initial transports or transfers of the two components. Equation 3.1a can then be written in the form

$$q_0 \simeq \frac{\phi_1/\phi_2}{N''/(1 - N'')} \simeq \frac{\phi_1/\phi_2}{N/(1 - N)} \tag{3.3}$$

In the following paragraphs we shall review the more significant methods of isotope separation, i.e., those which have hitherto been most widely applied or tested.

DISTILLATION

Distillation is a process used for centuries to separate the components of a liquid substance which have different levels of volatility. (As early as the 16th century, our knowledge of distillation was substantial. That was the century in which the first exhaustive treatise on the art, *Das grosse Distillierbuch,* was published by Brunwig in Strasbourg in 1500. This is one of the earliest works on applied chemistry published in a language other than Latin.) The same principle is used to separate the isotopic components of a chemically pure substance, with the single difference that—except for a few special cases—there is very little difference in the volatility levels of these components. Volatility is defined for component 1 of a liquid mixture at a given temperature by the ratio

$$v_1 = \frac{p_1}{N} \qquad (3.4)$$

between its partial pressure p_1 in the vapor present and the mol fraction N of the same component in liquid. Calling n the mol fraction of the considered component in the vapor phase and p the total pressure, we obtain (through Dalton's law)

$$v_1 = p\frac{n}{N} \qquad (3.5)$$

For a single substance ($n = N = 1$), the volatility will be equal to the vapor pressure, $v_1 = \bar{p}_1$. The same equality also exists in the case of ideal mixtures. In fact, according to Raoult's law, $p_1 = \bar{p}_1 N$; from Eq. 3.4, we still have $v_1 = \bar{p}_1$. But if we are dealing with other than ideal mixtures, the volatility will usually vary with the composition and may be greater or lesser than the vapor pressure of the pure component according to whether the partial pressure is greater or lesser than that calculated by Raoult's law. Hence we can write

$$v_1 = \gamma_1 \bar{p}_1 \qquad (3.6)$$

in which $\gamma_1 = p_1/\bar{p}_1 N$; in other words, the volatility of a component is only roughly proportional to its vapor pressure in the pure state. We can also say—still roughly—that volatility varies inversely as the boiling temperature. However, sometimes the component with the highest boiling point is also the most volatile. This happens particularly in the case of two components whose boiling points are not very far apart.

For simplicity's sake, let us consider a binary mixture and assign the index 1 to the relative size of the lighter component and the index 2 to the heavier component.

From Eq. 3.5 we have

$$\frac{v_1}{v_2} = \frac{n_1/n_2}{N_1/N_2} \tag{3.7}$$

Furthermore, the second member of Eq. 3.7 is by definition the elementary separation factor q_0 of the process, and hence we can write

$$q_0 = \frac{v_1}{v_2} \tag{3.8}$$

The ratio v_1/v_2 is commonly called relative volatility.

In the particular case of ideal mixtures, the relative volatility is given by the ratio between the vapor pressures of the two components

$$q_0 = \frac{\bar{p}_1}{\bar{p}_2} \tag{3.9}$$

Vapor pressures vary with temperature, according to Clausius–Clapeyron's law,

$$\frac{d\bar{p}}{\bar{p}} = \frac{\lambda}{RT^2} \, dT \tag{3.10}$$

so that the $\bar{p}_1/\bar{p}_2$ ratio is constant with the temperature only if the two components considered have equal values for latent heat of evaporation, λ. In general, this condition does not occur. Hence the separation factor, q_0, is found to be a function of temperature. Obviously the temperature interval within which the distillation process is physically possible is that between the triple point and the critical temperature.

Table 3.1 shows, for example, the ratios between the vapor pressures of the two molecular species $H_2{}^{16}O$ and $D_2{}^{16}O$ at different temperatures. However, despite the fact that the diverse isotopic species of the water constitute ideal mixtures, these cannot be considered binary at any and all concentrations. For example, deuterium is almost always found in only the HDO form at low concentrations but is found in both the HDO and D_2O forms at medium and high concentrations. Hence the $\bar{p}_{H_2O}/\bar{p}_{D_2O}$ ratios listed in Table 3.1 do not directly give the values of the separation factor, which are, however, readily derived from them. We shall see in Chap. 9 that the separation factor is equal to $(\bar{p}_{H_2O}/\bar{p}_{D_2O})^{1/2}$.

From Table 3.1 we see that the vapor-pressure ratio decreases as the temperature increases (this is behavior common to any pair of isotopic substances) and that, furthermore, between 220 and 230°C this ratio descends below unity, i.e., the heavier component becomes more volatile than the lighter one. Different binary systems at

Table 3.1

VAPOR-PRESSURE RATIOS FOR $H_2{}^{16}O$ AND $D_2{}^{16}O$

Temp., °C	$\bar{p}_{H_2O}/\bar{p}_{D_2O}$	Temp., °C	$\bar{p}_{H_2O}/\bar{p}_{D_2O}$
10	1.196	150	1.022
30	1.148	200	1.005
50	1.112	220	1.001
70	1.081	230	0.999
100	1.052	240	0.996

different temperatures have similar inversion points, and in some systems the heavier component is actually the more volatile all along the temperature span, from the triple point to the critical temperature. This is the case with the $^{10}BF_3-^{11}BF_3$ system.

Listed in Table 3.2 are the values of the $\bar{p}_1/\bar{p}_2$ ratio for several pairs of isotopic substances at the triple-point temperature and at the boiling point. Again, these values do not always coincide with the separation factor, either because the mixtures are not ideal (the case of the H_2/HD system) or because the molecular species indicated cannot coexist in a binary system, as has been shown for H_2O and D_2O. For separation of deuterium by ammonia distillation, the separation factor is given by the cube root of $\bar{p}_1/\bar{p}_2$, whereas, for separating ^{15}N by nitrogen distillation, the separation factor is given by the square root of $\bar{p}_1/\bar{p}_2$.

The following remarks can be made from the data in Table 3.2:

1. For any isotopic system, the separating effect decreases as temperature increases.

2. For any isotope, the separating effect is generally smaller for increasing molecular weights of the substance of which it is a part: e.g., the H_2, NH_3, H_2O, CH_4 series for deuterium or the H_2O, CO series for ^{18}O.

3. In any substance the separating effect is smaller for the isotopes of the heaviest element, e.g., D and ^{15}N in ammonia, D and ^{18}O in water, and ^{13}C and ^{18}O in CO.

This latter point is merely a consequence of the general decrease of the separating effect with the increase in the mass of the isotopes to be separated, i.e., in the decrease of the differences in relative mass. Table 3.2 shows that for Xe, with a 6% difference in mass, the separation factor is less than $\frac{1}{1000}$ away from unity. When uranium hexafluoride is distilled at 75°C, the separation factor of ^{235}U from ^{238}U is 1.0006. Hence it is clear that, with the heavy elements, distillation is not practically suitable for isotope separation.

We can better understand the separating effect of distillation if we consider the molecular interactions in which it originates. Assume that two isotopic molecules vibrating around their position of equilibrium in the liquid (or solid) lattice are subjected to an identical van der Waals field. Their potential energy, E, in other words,

Table 3.2

VAPOR-PRESSURE RATIOS FOR SOME PAIRS OF ISOTOPIC SUBSTANCES

Molecular species	Triple point			Boiling point		Data published by
	p, torr	T, °C	$\overline{p}_1/\overline{p}_2$	T, °C	$\overline{p}_1/\overline{p}_2$	
$o\text{-}H_2/HD$	54	-259.4	3.61	-252.9	1.73	H. T. Hoge, 1951
NH_3/ND_3	45.6	-77.7	1.26	-33.6	1.11	I. Kirshenbaum and H. C. Urey, 1942
H_2O/D_2O	4.6	0.0	1.254	100.0	1.052	I. Kirshenbaum, 1951
CH_4/CH_3D	87.5	-182.5	1.0016	-161.9	0.9965	G. T. Armstrong, 1953
$^3He/^4He$	38.6*	-271.0*	7.0	-268.9		J. G. Daunt, 1952
$^{10}BF_3/^{11}BF_3$	69	-127		-100	0.9925	P. T. Nettley et al., 1957
$^{12}CO/^{13}CO$	111.3	-205.7	1.011	-191.3	1.0071	F. T. Johns, 1957
$^{14}N_2/^{15}N_2$	96.4	-209.9	1.012	-195.8	1.008	H. C. Urey, 1947
$^{14}NH_3/^{15}NH_3$	45.6	-77.7	1.0055	-33.6	1.0025	H. C. Urey, 1947
$^{16}H_2O/^{18}H_2O$	4.6	0.0	1.010	100.0	1.0046	H. C. Urey, 1947
$^{16}CO/^{18}CO$	111.3	-205.7	1.008	-191.3		F. T. Johns et al., 1950
$^{16}O_2/^{16}O^{18}O$	2	-218.4	1.043	-183	1.0054	F. T. Johns, 1957
$^{20}Ne/^{22}Ne$	325	-248.6		-245.9		W. H. Keeson, 1933–1934
$^{36}Ar/^{40}Ar$	540	-189.2	1.002	-185.7		J. T. Phillips et al., 1971
$^{128}Xe/^{136}Xe$	317	-111.8	1.000	-109.1		W. Groth and P. Harteck, 1940
$^{235}UF_6/^{238}UF_6$	1134	64.05	0.9999†			J. W. Grizard and G. D. Oliver, 1951

*λ point.
†Relative volatility at 92°C.

will be the function of their distance, d, from the interacting molecule, as shown in Fig. 3.1. The vibration frequency ν_1, typical of the lighter molecule, is higher than the frequency ν_2 of the heavier molecule. In fact, if we discard in a first approximation the harmonic effects, we have

$$\nu_1 = \frac{1}{2\pi}\left(\frac{k}{\mu_1}\right)^{\frac{1}{2}} \text{ and } \nu_2 = \frac{1}{2\pi}\left(\frac{k}{\mu_2}\right)^{\frac{1}{2}}$$

where k is the elastic constant (equal, under our hypothesis, in both molecules) and μ_1, μ_2 are the two reduced masses ($\mu_1 < \mu_2$).

It then follows that the zero-point energy (at absolute zero temperature) $E_0 = \frac{1}{2} h\nu$ is greater for the light molecule; hence the heat of evaporation, λ, is less for the light molecule (see Fig. 3.1). Under these conditions, the lighter molecular species is the more volatile. The effect described persists even at temperatures other than absolute zero. Applying Boltzmann's statistics to a system of molecules, considered as quantum harmonic oscillators, we find for the mean energy the expression

$$\bar{E} = \frac{1}{2} h\nu + \frac{h\nu}{e^{h\nu/kT} - 1} \tag{3.11}$$

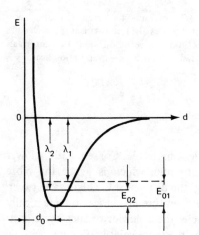

Fig. 3.1 Interaction energy (E) and zero-point energies (E_0) of two isotope molecules (1,2) in the case of equal van der Waals fields; d is the distance between the two molecules, and λ is the evaporation heat.

For two isotope species the difference $\bar{E}_1 - \bar{E}_2$ is thus, in general, other than zero. The difference has a maximum value $E_{01} - E_{02} = \frac{1}{2} h(\nu_1 - \nu_2)$ for $T = 0$ and hence declines as temperature increases, disappearing when $T \to \infty$, in practice, as is shown in Eq. 3.11 written for the two molecular systems, when $kT \gg h\nu$. In this case the heat of evaporation becomes almost equal for the two molecular species, and hence their volatilities become practically equal.

Actually the hypothesis of the identity of the van der Waals field to which light and heavy molecules are subjected is not exactly verified. Various reasons, such as the anharmonicity of the vibrations of the atoms making up the molecule and the electromagnetic interaction between the molecule and some of its atoms, cause the potential to be different for the two isotopic species. If this difference is slight enough, the above-mentioned situation remains qualitatively unchanged and the lighter molecular species turns out to be the more volatile. But if the field of interaction is appreciably different, as it is, for example, in Fig. 3.2, the basic energy level for the

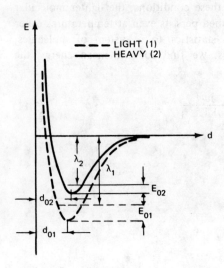

Fig. 3.2 Interaction energy (E) and zero-point energies (E_0) of two isotope molecules (1,2) in the case of different van der Waals fields; d = distance; λ = evaporation heat.

heavy molecule may be higher than that of the light molecule. Consequently a lower evaporation heat is obtained for the heavier molecule, which is hence the more volatile. Even in this case, with Eq. 3.11 applying, the difference in volatility between the two molecular species diminishes as the temperature increases and practically vanishes for fairly high temperatures. This explains the behavior of such systems as $^{10}BF_3/^{11}BF_3$, in which the heavier component is the more volatile. For any isotopic system the separating effect of distillation may be thought of as resulting from two contrasting effects: (1) the "normal," which tends to make the lighter component the more volatile, and (2) the "inverse."

Both effects decline as the temperature increases, but the inverse effect, if it is due primarily to electromagnetic interaction between the molecule and one of its atoms, disappears at higher temperatures since the vibration frequency of an atom in the molecule is always higher than the vibration frequency of the molecule in the liquid or solid lattice. Thus, as the temperature rises, the inverse effect may prevail over the normal, causing an inversion of the volatility levels, as was seen for the $H_2^{16}O/D_2^{16}O$ and CH_4/CH_3D systems (see Tables 3.1 and 3.2).

Distillation is a process by which it is particularly easy to multiply the elementary separation effect by inducing a countercurrent flow in the distillation columns (or towers). These columns are cylindrical containers within which contact is made between the two phases: (1) the liquid phase that flows by gravity from top to bottom and (2) the vapor phase that, produced in a reboiler at the base of the column, flows from bottom to top. The temperature of the process, aside from the temperature drop connected with the pressure drop across the column, is determined by the temperature at which the condenser at the top of the column is operated. A diagram of the apparatus is shown in Fig. 3.3. Extraction of the portion or "fraction" rich in the desired component (hence the term "fractionation" which is used in distillation technical nomenclature to indicate the separation process) is performed at the top or bottom of the column depending on whether the desired component is the more or less volatile one. At the end opposite from the withdrawal of the rich fraction, the impoverished fraction is extracted, but the feed point of the liquid or vapor can be selected according to feed concentration. If the feed is at an intermediate point in the column, the portion of the column in which the concentration levels are higher than that of the feed is called the enrichment section, and the other part is called the stripping section.

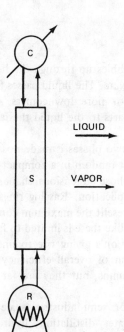

LIQUID

S   VAPOR

Fig. 3.3 Scheme of a distillation process. R = reboiler; S = column; C = condenser.

Distillation columns can be divided into two basic categories: plate columns and packed columns. In the former, there is repeated contact between the two phases, whereas the latter operates on the principle of continuous contact.

A typical and extremely common example of a plate column is the bubble-cap column, whose operating principle is shown in Fig. 3.4. Each plate consists of a platform with openings for the vapor to pass through, usually in the form of a flue capped with a dome (bubble-cap plates). Through these openings (Fig. 3.4 shows only

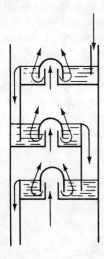

Fig. 3.4 Operating principle of plate columns.

one opening per plate, for simplicity's sake) the vapor bubbles up through the liquid contained in the plate and moves up to the next higher plate. The liquid passes from one plate to the one below by overflowing through one or more downcomers. As it passes through each plate, the vapor condenses and imparts to the liquid the latent heat necessary to make it evaporate.

In packed columns, continuous contact between the two phases is made possible by the presence of a quantity of solid bodies arranged at random in a compact and uniform bulk. A film of liquid flows over these bodies (whose dimensions, shape, and material may vary widely according to the particular application: Raschig rings are very common) toward the base of the column so as to present the maximum contact surface to the vapor. The area of application of columns like these is limited to fairly modest dimensions in order to obviate an overlarge section's giving rise to uneven distribution of the liquid, with a consequent diminution of overall efficiency. Of course, there are similar limitations for bubble-cap columns, but they are far less restrictive.

The distillation method is used on an industrial or semi-industrial scale for separating various isotopes, principally deuterium (water distillation; hydrogen distillation), ^{10}B (BF_3 distillation) and ^{18}O (water distillation).

MOLECULAR DISTILLATION

In the preceding section we considered the separating effect of distillation under conditions of dynamic equilibrium of the two phases involved. This equilibrium is produced by the equality (for each component of the mixture) of the number of molecules that evaporate per unit of time and the number of molecules that condense in that same unit of time after diffusing through the gaseous phase. This number, proportional to vapor density, is larger at higher vapor pressures and hence temperatures.

With fairly high vapor pressures (and hence temperatures), even in a nonadiabatic process, in which liquid is continuously kept boiling at constant temperature, it is thus possible to achieve, for all practical purposes, the conditions of dynamic equilibrium previously described. The only requirement is that the quantity of liquid, B, transformed into vapor per unit of time, which works out to the difference

$$B = \phi_{ev.} - \phi_{cond.} \qquad (3.12)$$

between the quantity of substance evaporated ($\phi_{ev.}$) and the quantity condensed ($\phi_{cond.}$) in that same unit of time, be negligible in comparison with $\phi_{ev.}$ and $\phi_{cond.}$. Under these conditions the vapor in contact with the surface of a boiling liquid is practically saturated.

If this same process is run at a much lower temperature but with the quantity B kept unchanged, we find that B is no longer negligible by comparison with $\phi_{cond.}$. The vapor in contact with the surface liquid is under pressure appreciably lower than the vapor pressure corresponding to the process temperature, and hence the process can no longer be considered as being in dynamic equilibrium.

If all the evaporated molecules were removed from the space bordering the surface of the liquid, e.g., by immobilizing all the molecules on a condensing surface placed facing the liquid surface, at most we would have $\phi_{cond.} = 0$ and hence $B = \phi_{ev.}$.

In this case, if a binary liquid is considered, $\phi_{ev.}$ is given by the sum $\phi_{ev.1} + \phi_{ev.2}$ of the evaporation rates of the light and heavy components, respectively; the elementary separation factor for the process then becomes

$$q_0 = \frac{\phi_{ev.1}/\phi_{ev.2}}{N/(1-N)} \qquad (3.13)$$

in which N is the mol fraction of the light component in the liquid.

To compute the evaporation rate, $\phi_{ev.}$, we first introduce Langmuir's hypothesis, which holds that at low enough temperatures—corresponding with which there would be vapor pressures no greater than a millimeter of mercury—evaporation speed is not affected by the presence of the vapor in the immediate vicinity of the liquid surface. In other words, at low enough temperatures the evaporation rate of a liquid, under no matter how high a vacuum, is the same as it is when the liquid is in the presence of its saturated vapor.

Therefore we can calculate $\phi_{ev.}$ from the condensation rate $\phi_{cond.}$ in conditions of equilibrium. In this way we avoid the difficulty of dealing theoretically with the evaporation mechanism that involves, among other things, a study of molecular diffusion in the liquid phase. The speed of condensation, expressed in mols evaporated per unit of surface and per unit of time, can on the other hand be readily calculated on the basis of the kinetic theory of gases. Consider the vapor to be a perfect gas, and let ν be its molecular crowding factor (the number of molecules per unit of volume). Since there are no preferential directions, we shall have $\frac{1}{2}\nu$ as the number of molecules whose velocities are oriented toward the liquid surface. If $\bar{v}$ is the mean velocity of the molecules, the mean component directed orthogonally toward the liquid surface is $\frac{1}{2}\bar{v}$.

The number of molecules condensing in a unit of time on a unit of surface then becomes $\frac{1}{4}\nu\,\bar{v}$. Using n to indicate the molar density of the vapor (mols per unit of volume; $n = \nu/N_{Av}$, with N_{Av} the Avogadro number), we get as our evaporation velocity ($\phi_{ev.} = \phi_{cond.}$) the equation

$$\phi_{ev.} = \frac{1}{4} n\bar{v} \tag{3.14}$$

On the other hand, we have

$$n = \frac{\bar{p}}{RT} \tag{3.15}$$

and

$$\bar{v} = \left(\frac{8}{3\pi}\right)^{\frac{1}{2}} \bar{\bar{v}} \tag{3.16}$$

in which $\bar{\bar{v}}$ is the mean square velocity. But we have

$$\bar{\bar{v}} = \left(3\,\frac{RT}{M}\right)^{\frac{1}{2}} \tag{3.17}$$

in which M is the molecular weight, and hence

$$\bar{v} = \left(\frac{8RT}{\pi M}\right)^{\frac{1}{2}} \tag{3.18}$$

Substituting Eqs. 3.15 and 3.18 in Eq. 3.14, we have

$$\phi_{ev.} = \bar{p}/(2\pi\,MRT)^{\frac{1}{2}} \tag{3.19}$$

Langmuir used Eq. 3.19 to calculate the vapor pressure of pure metallic elements (tungsten, platinum, and molybdenum), measuring the weight loss in filaments kept at high temperature in a strong vacuum.

The logarithms of vapor pressure thus derived are shown to be a linear function of $1/T$, in agreement with Clausius–Clapeyron's law (Eq. 3.10).

In reality the speed of evaporation is a little less than that given by Eq. 3.19 because of the collisions that inevitably give rise to the condensation on the liquid surface of a small portion of the evaporated molecules and because of possible impurities found on the evaporating surface. We can allow for this by means of an efficiency coefficient α, which enables us to write Eq. 3.19 in the following form:

$$\phi_{ev.} = \alpha\overline{p}/(2\pi\,MRT)^{\frac{1}{2}} \tag{3.20}$$

Measurements by E. W. Washburne of the evaporation speed of mercury at $0°C$ led to determining $\alpha = 0.84$. Elsewhere, Knudsen showed that α can be brought to values very close to unity in molecular distillation of mercury if the evaporating surface is kept clean.

Let us now consider a binary mixture having light and heavy components that are, as usual, indicated by subscripts 1 and 2. Equation 3.19 can be rewritten for each of these two components by substituting for $\overline{p}$ the partial pressures $p_1 = v_1 N$ and $p_2 = v_2(1 - N)$. The ratio $\phi_{ev.1}/\phi_{ev.2}$ then becomes

$$\frac{\phi_{ev.1}}{\phi_{ev.2}} = \frac{v_1}{v_2}\left(\frac{M_2}{M_1}\right)^{\frac{1}{2}}\frac{N}{1-N} \tag{3.21}$$

for which Eq. 3.13 gives

$$q_0 = \frac{v_1}{v_2}\left(\frac{M_2}{M_1}\right)^{\frac{1}{2}} \tag{3.22}$$

and in particular, in the case of ideal mixtures,

$$q_0 = \frac{\overline{p}_1}{\overline{p}_2}\left(\frac{M_2}{M_1}\right)^{\frac{1}{2}} \tag{3.23}$$

In molecular distillation the elementary distillation factor is therefore greater than it is for distillation under conditions of equilibrium by a factor $(M_2/M_1)^{\frac{1}{2}}$, which represents the diffusion contribution to the separation process.

Unlike what happens in distillation under equilibrium conditions, for which (the pressure being fixed) the temperature of the process is univocally determined, molecular distillation can occur (the pressure being fixed) at different temperatures. There is a resulting modification of the separation factor, due to the variation in the ratio $\overline{p}_1/\overline{p}_2$, and of the overall speed of the distillation process, which is faster at high temperatures.

A limitation on the efficiency of the separative process in molecular distillation stems from the absence of boiling, which in ordinary distillation remixes the liquid phase. The liquid flow is suitably laminated with various systems so as to increase the transfer of the more volatile component, which would otherwise be left solely to diffusion in the liquid (slow process).

One system for inducing counterflow with the molecular distillation process was used successfully by Brewer and Madorsky[11] to separate the isotopes of mercury on a laboratory scale. This system is shown in Fig. 3.5. The plates, P (width, 2 cm; length,

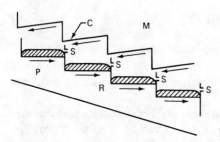

Fig. 3.5 Device for a molecular distillation cascade.

7.5 cm; depth, 0.8 cm), are arranged in a cascade, and they communicate through the overflow lips, S. These plates are gouged out of the steel block, R, which is heated by electrical resistance. Each plate has above it a roof, C, which is in thermal contact with a mass of mercury, M, held at 0°C by means of alcohol flowing through a cooling coil. The mercury is evaporated in a vacuum (less than 10^{-5} torr) at temperatures between 55 and 100°C. As the mercury condenses on each roof, C, it flows to its eaves and drips into the plate preceding the one from which it was evaporated. The liquid, through the overflow lips, S, moves in the opposite direction, producing the counterflow.

With the apparatus of Brewer and Madorsky, an elementary separation factor q_0 of 1.0085 was found for mercury as $^{204}Hg/^{198}Hg$, as against a theoretical value of 1.021.

Small-scale experiments on isotopic separation of lithium by molecular distillation, with temperatures ranging from 500 to 600°C, have given elementary separation values of 1.09 to 1.06.

Aside from the resistance to mass transfer in the liquid phase, there are two major causes of inefficiency in molecular distillation which can largely explain the discrepancy between theoretical and experimental separation factors. These causes are:

1. Return of evaporated molecules onto the evaporating surface as a result of collisions with other evaporated molecules.

2. Return of evaporated molecules onto the evaporating surface as a result of reevaporation from the condensing surface.

To reduce these causes of inefficiency to a minimum, we must:

1. Operate at low enough pressures, so that the mean free travel distance will not be much less than the distance between the evaporating and condensing surfaces. In practice, this means pressures of a few tenths of a millimeter of mercury.

2. Maintain low enough temperatures on the condensing surface, so that the vapor pressure accordingly will not exceed 10 to 50 μm Hg.

Hence the substance being worked on must have a triple point below these pressure levels; otherwise it would not be easy to induce counterflow. This fact sharply limits the area of applicability for the method.

EXCHANGE REACTIONS

Two isotopes, ^1A and ^2A, of an element A belonging to two different chemical compounds, AB and AC, are distributed between the compounds as a result of the exchange reaction

$$^1AB + {}^2AC \rightleftharpoons {}^2AB + {}^1AC \tag{3.24}$$

whose equilibrium constant K is given by the expression

$$K = \frac{[^2AB]/[^1AB]}{[^2AC]/[^1AC]} \tag{3.25}$$

in which the symbols in brackets indicate the mol concentrations. Of course, symbolic expressions like Eq. 3.24 are conventionally written so that the K constant is greater than 1. Hence, in this instance, Eq. 3.25 means that, under conditions of thermodynamic equilibrium, the ^2A isotope is distributed more abundantly in substance AB than it is in substance AC. If we take N and n to indicate the mol fractions of isotope ^2A in compounds AB and AC, respectively, we can write Eq. 3.25—assuming for simplicity's sake that there are only two isotope species—in this form

$$K = \frac{N/(1-N)}{n/(1-n)} \tag{3.26}$$

Furthermore, Eq. 3.26 coincides with the definition of the elementary separation factor q_0 for equilibrium processes, and hence for the reaction under consideration, we have the identity

$$q_0 \equiv K \tag{3.27}$$

Among the exchange reactions of the type shown in Eq. 3.24, we cite by way of example the following:

$$^{10}BF_3 + ^{11}BF_3 \cdot (C_2H_5)_2O \rightleftharpoons ^{11}BF_3 + ^{10}BF_3 \cdot (C_2H_5)_2O \tag{3.28}$$

in which the rarest isotope of boron, ^{10}B, is distributed between gaseous BF_3 and its compound with ethyl ether in the liquid phase.

In conditions of equilibrium, ^{10}B proves more abundant in the liquid phase (remember, by the way, that in BF_3 distillation too the lighter component is less abundant in the gaseous phase).

Another reaction of the Eq. 3.24 type is of special interest in separating ^{15}N from ^{14}N and is the following:

$$^{15}NO + H^{14}NO_3 \rightleftharpoons ^{14}NO + H^{15}NO_3 \tag{3.29}$$

which takes place between the gaseous nitrogen monoxide and nitric acid in aqueous solution.

Thus far we have considered only exchange reactions between molecules in which the substance, A, to be separated into its isotopes, is present with only a single atom. In the more common case, in which reaction occurs between molecules containing more than one A atom, the relation between the separation factor and the equilibrium constant is not so simple, unless one of the two isotopes to be separated (we shall continue to assume that we are dealing with binary isotopic mixtures) is present in low concentrations. Consider, for example, a reaction of the following type:

$$(^{1}A)_\mu B + (^{1}A)_{\nu-1}{}^{2}AC \rightleftharpoons (^{1}A)_{\mu-1}{}^{2}AB + (^{1}A)_\nu C \tag{3.30}$$

in which the ^{2}A isotope, assumed to be present only in low concentration, shifts from compound $(A)_\nu C$ to compound $(A)_\mu B$, in each of which only one atom appears. The equilibrium constant for Eq. 3.30 is

$$K = \frac{[(^{1}A)_{\mu-1}{}^{2}AB]/[(^{1}A)_\mu B]}{[(^{1}A)_{\nu-1}{}^{2}AC]/[(^{1}A)_\nu C]} \tag{3.31}$$

using N and n as the mol fractions of isotope ^{2}A in compounds $(A)_\mu B$ and $(A)_\nu C$, respectively, we have

$$\frac{N}{1-N} = \frac{[^{2}A]}{[^{1}A]} = \frac{[(^{1}A)_{\mu-1}{}^{2}AB]}{(\mu-1)[(^{1}A)_{\mu-1}{}^{2}AB] + \mu[(^{1}A)_\mu B]}$$

$$= \frac{[(^{1}A)_{\mu-1}{}^{2}AB]/[(^{1}A)_\mu B]}{\mu + (\mu-1)[(^{1}A)_{\mu-1}{}^{2}AB]/[(^{1}A)_\mu B]} \tag{3.32}$$

Furthermore, since we have assumed that the concentration of ^2A will be low, the second addend to the denominator for Eq. 3.32 is negligible by comparison with μ, and hence we can write

$$\frac{N}{1-N} \simeq \frac{1}{\mu} \frac{[(^1A)_{\mu-1}\,^2AB]}{[(^1A)_\mu B]} \tag{3.33}$$

Similarly we have

$$\frac{n}{1-n} \simeq \frac{1}{\nu} \frac{[(^1A)_{\nu-1}\,^2AC]}{[(^1A)_\nu C]} \tag{3.34}$$

The separation factor q_0, by definition, is obtained by dividing Eq. 3.33 by Eq. 3.34, which—remembering Eq. 3.31—gives us

$$q_0 \simeq \frac{\nu}{\mu} K \tag{3.35}$$

Hence, when $\mu = \nu$, we have approximately $q_0 \equiv K$: this is the case in the reaction

$$H_2O + HD \rightleftharpoons HDO + H_2 \tag{3.36}$$

in which we have $\mu = \nu = 2$. This reaction may be considered either in the homogeneous (gaseous) or heterogeneous (gaseous hydrogen–liquid water) phase.

Another example of the Eq. 3.30-type exchange reaction is the following:

$$NH_3 + HD \rightleftharpoons NH_2D + H_2 \tag{3.37}$$

in which we have $\mu = 3$ and $\nu = 2$, hence $q_0 \simeq \frac{2}{3}K$.

The equilibrium constant K of an exchange reaction is a decreasing function of the temperature and, similar to what we have seen for the relative volatility, will, as the temperature moves toward infinity, tend to take on a value such as to nullify the separative effect. Hence, at the limit for $T \to \infty$, we have $K = 1$ for Eq. 3.36 and $K = \frac{3}{2}$ for Eq. 3.37.

The behavior of the equilibrium constant in Eq. 3.36 with the temperature is shown in Table 3.3, in which the various values are interpolated from a series of experimental data.

Table 3.4 contains the values for the separation factors of a number of exchange reactions usable for isotopic separation of various elements. The equilibriums considered refer both to homogeneous gaseous-phase systems and to gas–liquid systems.

Specifically, if the liquid is a solution and the solute is dissociated, we can assume that there is chemical equilibrium between ions in solution and neutral molecules in the gaseous phase.

Table 3.3

EQUILIBRIUM CONSTANTS FOR THE H_2O + HD $\rightleftharpoons$ HDO + H_2
REACTION IN THE GASEOUS PHASE

Temp., °C	K	Temp., °C	K
50	3.06	400	1.52
100	2.53	500	1.39
200	2.00	600	1.31
300	1.66	700	1.22

For uranium, which has no volatile compounds with convenient physicochemical properties, isotope exchange has been considered in a liquid–liquid system. Chemical equilibrium in liquid–solid systems also makes isotope separation possible. Particularly interesting are the systems in which the solid phase consists of special resins called ion-exchange resins. A brief summary is given in the following section.

As for the exchange reactions listed in Table 3.4, it can be remarked that, in most instances, the heavy isotope tends to be concentrated in the heavier component. It is clearly shown that the separation effect has a tendency, on the average, to decline as the atomic weight of the element whose isotopes we are trying to separate increases. This fact is analogous with what we have seen in relation to distillation.

The explanation of the separation effect in isotope-exchange reactions stems from the existence of discrete quantum levels of the molecular energy and the relevant statistics.

Assume first that this separation effect, which can be derived from the equilibrium constant K, should be theoretically findable with the procedures of standard thermodynamics. We know that for a typical reaction

$$\alpha A + \beta B \rightleftharpoons \gamma C + \delta D \tag{3.38}$$

in which we assume that the reacting substances A, B, C, and D are perfect gases, the equilibrium constant

$$K = \frac{[C]^{\gamma} \cdot [D]^{\delta}}{[A]^{\alpha} \cdot [B]^{\beta}} \tag{3.39}$$

is findable from the expression (see A. Sommerfeld, *Lectures on Theoretical Physics,* Vol. 5, *Thermodynamics and Statistical Mechanics,* Chap. 2, paragraph 13, Wiesbaden, 1952)

$$RT \ln K = -\Delta F \tag{3.40}$$

Table 3.4

SEPARATION FACTORS FOR SOME ISOTOPE-EXCHANGE REACTIONS

Reaction	Temp., °C	q_0	References
$H_2O(liq.) + HDS(gas) \rightleftharpoons HDO(liq) + H_2S(gas)$	25	2.34	K. Clusius, 1939; 1946
$NH_3(gas) + HD(gas) \rightleftharpoons NH_2D(gas) + H_2(gas)$	25	3.88	I. Kirshenbaum, 1951
$H_2O(liq.) + HD(gas) \rightleftharpoons HDO(liq.) + H_2(gas)$	25	3.87	H. C. Urey, 1947
$^{11}BF_3 \cdot (C_2H_5)_2O(liq.) + {}^{10}BF_3(gas) \rightleftharpoons {}^{10}BF_3 \cdot (C_2H_5)_2O(liq.) + {}^{11}BF_3(gas)$	20	1.034	R. W. McIlroy, 1957
$^{11}BF_3 \cdot H_2O(liq.) + {}^{10}BF_3(gas) \rightleftharpoons {}^{10}BF_3 \cdot H_2O(liq.) + {}^{11}BF_3(gas)$	20	1.025	S. V. Ribnikar, 1957
$^{13}HCN(gas) + {}^{12}CN^-(aq.) \rightleftharpoons {}^{12}HCN(gas) + {}^{13}CN^-(aq.)$	22	1.026	H. C. Urey, 1947
$^{15}NH_3(gas) + {}^{14}NH_4^+(aq.) \rightleftharpoons {}^{14}NH_3(gas) + {}^{15}NH_4^+(aq.)$	25	1.034	H. C. Urey, 1947
$^{15}NO(gas) + H^{14}NO_3(aq.) \rightleftharpoons {}^{14}NO(gas) + H^{15}NO_3(aq.)$	25	1.053	T. I. Taylor, 1957
$C^{16}O_2(gas) + 2H_2^{18}O(liq.) \rightleftharpoons C^{18}O_2(gas) + 2H_2^{16}O(liq.)$	0	1.046	H. C. Urey, 1947
$^{34}SO_2(gas) + H^{32}SO_3^-(aq.) \rightleftharpoons {}^{32}SO_2(gas) + H^{34}SO_3^-(aq.)$	25	1.013	G. Stiel, 1969
$^{238}UF_6 \text{ (Freon soln.)} + NO^{235}UF_6 \text{ (HF soln.)} \rightleftharpoons {}^{235}UF_6 \text{ (Freon soln.)} + NO^{238}UF_6 \text{ (HF soln.)}$		1.0016	A. J. Saraceno, 1972

in which Δ is the algebraic sum of the free energy ($F = H - TS$) of the various components, referred to a standard state:

$$\Delta F = \gamma F_C + \delta F_D - \alpha F_A - \beta F_B \qquad (3.41)$$

In the case of isotopic reactions, the ΔF quantities are very small and it is not possible to calculate them from Eq. 3.41, since the uncertainties with which the molar free energies of the various isotopic species are known are generally greater than ΔF.

Furthermore, in statistical thermodynamics we can demonstrate that, for one mol of perfect gas,

$$U = RT^2 \left(\frac{\partial \ln Z}{\partial T} \right)_V \qquad (3.42)$$

where

$$Z = \Sigma_i g_i e^{-E_i/kT} \qquad (3.43)$$

is the partition function for the system under consideration (g_i is the statistical weight of the energy level E_i). (For the demonstration, see A. Sommerfeld,† *op. cit.,* Chap. 4, paragraphs 29 and 33; or S. Glasstone, *Textbook of Physical Chemistry,* 2nd ed., Chap. IV, p. 333, and Chap. XIII, pp. 870–882, Van Nostrand Reinhold Company, New York, 1940–1946.)

Since, in addition, we have

$$S = RT \left(\frac{\partial \ln Z}{\partial T} \right)_V + R \ln \frac{Z}{N} + R \qquad (3.44)$$

from Eqs. 3.42 and 3.44 we have, for the free energy ($F = U + pV - TS = U + RT - TS$), the expression

$$F = -RT \ln \frac{Z}{N} \qquad (3.45)$$

and hence

$$\Delta F = -RT \, \Delta \ln \frac{Z}{N} \qquad (3.46)$$

Comparing Eq. 3.46 with Eq. 3.40, we have

$$K = \frac{Z_C^\gamma Z_D^\delta}{Z_A^\alpha Z_B^\beta} \qquad (3.47)$$

Statistical mechanics thus permits the calculation of equilibrium constants through the partition functions, Z, relevant to the reaction of various molecular species.

Since the total energy for each level can be broken down into the terms relating to the different degrees of freedom, we find that

$$Z = Z_{trans.} Z_{rot.} Z_{vibr.} Z_{el.} Z_{nucl.} e^{-E_0/kT} \tag{3.48}$$

in which the first five factors refer in order to the degrees of translational, rotational, vibrational, electronic, and nuclear degrees of freedom, and the final term expresses the zero-point energy E_0.

For isotope-exchange reactions of the general type

$$\nu AX_\mu + \mu BX_\nu^* \rightleftharpoons \nu AX_\mu^* + \mu BX_\nu \tag{3.49}$$

in which X and X* are two isotopes of the same element, the equilibrium constant is

$$K = \frac{(Z^*/Z)_{AX_\mu}^\nu}{(Z^*/Z)_{BX_\nu}^\mu} \tag{3.50}$$

with the meanings of the symbols being obvious. On the other hand, for isotopic molecules, the terms $Z_{nucl.}$ and $Z_{el.}$ are reduced when making the ratios that appear in Eq. 3.50. In addition, we assume with fair approximation that the zero-point energies differ only in the vibrational terms, calculable from the basic frequencies. Neglecting anharmonicity gives

$$E_0 = \frac{1}{2} h \sum \nu \tag{3.51}$$

where the sum is extended to all the basic frequencies of the molecule; hence, introducing the notation $u = h\nu/kT$, we can write the Z^*/Z ratios that appear in Eq. 3.50 as

$$\frac{Z^*}{Z} = \left(\frac{Z^*}{Z}\right)_{trans.} \left(\frac{Z^*}{Z}\right)_{rot.} \left(\frac{Z^*}{Z}\right)_{vibr.} \times \exp\frac{1}{2}\left(\sum u^* - \sum u\right) \tag{3.52}$$

We also have

$$Z_{trans.} = const \times \frac{M^{3/2} T^{5/2}}{p} \tag{3.53}$$

in which M is the molecular weight and p is the pressure, and

$$Z_{rot.} = const \times \frac{IT}{s} \tag{3.54a}$$

for biatomic or linear polyatomic molecules (I is the moment of inertia, and s is the molecule's symmetry number,† or

$$Z_{rot.} = const \times \frac{(ABC)^{\frac{1}{4}} T}{s}$$ (3.54b)

for nonlinear polyatomic molecules (A, B, and C are the principal moments of inertia). The partition function for the vibrational degrees of freedom is given by

$$Z_{vibr.} = \prod \left[\frac{1}{(1 - e^{-u})} \right]$$ (3.55)

in which the product is extended to all the basic frequencies of the molecule. For biatomic molecules, with only a single basic frequency, we obtain from Eqs. 3.53, 3.54a, and 3.55:

$$\frac{Z^*}{Z} = \frac{s}{s^*} \left(\frac{M^*}{M} \right)^{\frac{3}{2}} \frac{I^*}{I} \frac{e^{-u^*/2}}{1 - e^{-u^*}} \frac{1 - e^{-u}}{e^{-u/2}}$$ (3.56)

whereas for nonlinear polyatomic molecules, we obtain from Eqs. 3.53, 3.54b, and 3.55:

$$\frac{Z^*}{Z} = \frac{s}{s^*} \left(\frac{M^*}{M} \right)^{\frac{3}{2}} \left(\frac{A^*B^*C^*}{ABC} \right)^{\frac{1}{2}} \prod \left(\frac{e^{-u^*/2}}{1 - e^{-u^*}} \frac{1 - e^{-u}}{e^{-u/2}} \right)$$ (3.57)

Nonlinear molecules made up of n atoms have $3n - 6$ degrees of freedom, whereas linear ones have $3n - 5$ degrees of freedom. For the latter group in Eq. 3.57, every product ABC must be replaced with the single moment of inertia, I.

Normally we have experimental data for the typical frequencies and moments of inertia for only one isotopic species: i.e., the more abundant. In this case the quantities relating to the other isotopic species can be found, for biatomic molecules, from the ratios $\nu^*/\nu = (\mu/\mu^*)^{\frac{1}{2}}$ and $I^*/I = \mu^*/\mu$, in which μ is the reduced mass of the molecule. For polyatomic molecules the difficulties can be overcome in many cases by making use of the rule of the product of frequencies, stated by Teller and Redlich [see O. Redlich, *J. Phys. Chem.*, 28: 376 (1935); *Z. Elektrochem.*, 43: 661 (1937)], which gives

$$\left(\frac{M^*}{M} \right)^{\frac{3}{2}} \left(\frac{A^*B^*C^*}{ABC} \right)^{\frac{1}{2}} = \prod \left(\frac{u^*}{u} \right)$$ (3.58)

---

†By the symmetry number of a molecule, we mean the number of identical positions that the molecule assumes in rotating 360° around each of its axes of symmetry.

Equation 3.57 then becomes

$$\frac{Z^*}{Z} = \frac{s}{s^*} \prod \left(\frac{u^*}{u} \frac{e^{-u^*/2}}{1 - e^{-u^*}} \frac{1 - e^{-u}}{e^{-u/2}} \right) \tag{3.59}$$

This equation is also applicable to biatomic molecules, yielding results very close to those obtained with Eq. 3.56. Equation 3.59, developed in series of powers of $\Delta u = u^* - u$ and approximated except for terms of a higher order than the first, becomes

$$\frac{Z^*}{Z} = \frac{s}{s^*} e^{-\Sigma G(u) \Delta u} \tag{3.60}$$

with $G(u) = \frac{1}{2} - (1/u) + 1/(e^u - 1)$. Tabulation of the $G(u)$ function, which varies from 0 to $\frac{1}{2}$ for u variable between 0 and ∞, makes it far simpler to calculate the equilibrium constants.

As an example in calculating the equilibrium constant, consider the exchange reaction

$$DCl + H_2 \rightleftharpoons HCl + HD \tag{3.61}$$

In Table 3.5 are shown the numerical values of the quantities required for the calculation. The basic frequencies of the molecules are known from the spectroscopic data.

Table 3.5

MOLECULAR CONSTANTS OF HYDROGEN
AND HYDROCHLORIC ACID

	H_2	HD	HCl	DCl
M	2.016	3.023	35.99	37.00
μ	0.504	0.669	0.981	1.901
ν_0/c	4405.3	3817.1	2989.0	2143.5
uT	6349	5489	4298	3082
s	2	1	1	1

Specifying the quantities of Eq. 3.50, we have

$$K = \frac{Z_{HCl} Z_{HD}}{Z_{DCl} Z_{H_2}} = \frac{s_{DCl} s_{H_2}}{s_{HCl} s_{HD}} \frac{u_{HCl} u_{HD}}{u_{DCl} u_{H_2}}$$

$$\times \left\{ \exp \left[-\frac{1}{2} (u_{HCl} + u_{HD} - u_{DCl} - u_{H_2}) \right] \right\} f(u) \tag{3.62}$$

where we have placed

$$f(u) = \frac{(1 - e^{-u}DCl)}{(1 - e^{-u}HCl)} \times \frac{(1 - e^{-u}H_2)}{(1 - e^{-u}HD)}$$

Substituting the values shown in Table 3.5, we have

$$K = \frac{(1)(2)}{(1)(1)} \frac{(4298)(5489)}{(3082)(6349)} \times \left\{ \exp\left[-\frac{1}{2} T (4298 + 5489 - 3082 - 6349) \right] \right\} f(u)$$

and neglecting the factor $f(u)$, which at $1000°K$ differs from unity by less than 4%, we have, finally,

$$K = 2.417 \, e^{-178/T} \tag{3.63}$$

In Table 3.6 the values of K as calculated with Eq. 3.63 are compared, for various temperatures, with the corresponding experimental values. (The calculations are taken from A. I. Brodskiy, *Himiya Isotopov*, 2nd edition, p. 343, Akademiya Nauk SSSR, Moscow, 1957.)

Table 3.6

CALCULATED AND EXPERIMENTAL VALUES FOR THE EQUILIBRIUM
CONSTANT OF THE DCl + H$_2$ ⇌ HCl + HD REACTION[1 3]

	390°K	599°K	876°K	944°K
$K_{calc.}$	1.531	1.779	1.930	1.950
$K_{exper.}$	1.45	1.73	1.93	1.94

From Eq. 3.59 we see that, as the temperature tends toward infinity, since the u quantities correspondingly tend to disappear, we have $Z^*/Z = s/s^*$, and hence the equilibrium constant (Eq. 3.50) tends toward the limiting value

$$K_0 = \frac{(s/s^*)_A^\nu \, X_\mu}{(s/s^*)_B^\mu \, X_\nu} \tag{3.64}$$

thus canceling the separation effect, and the distribution of isotope X^* among the molecular species in the system is purely probabilistic. The constant K_0 is usually called the "classic constant" for short.

Now we should recall that when a compound, AX_μ, reacts with a second compound, BX_ν^*, all the molecular species are present in equilibrium: $AX_{\mu-i} \, X_i^* \, (i = 0,1, \ldots , \mu)$ and $BX_{\nu-i} \, X_i^* \, (i = 0,1, \ldots, \nu)$. In the same compound the concentrations of the various molecular species are determined by the equilibrium constants of the various exchange reactions of the following type (taking $\mu = 4$, for example):

$$AX\, X_3^* + AX_3 X^* \rightleftharpoons 2AX_2 X_2^*$$

Assuming that the distribution of X^* is purely probabilistic, we show that the concentrations of the various molecular species $AX_{\mu-i}X_i^*$ are determined by the following relations of proportionality

$$[AX_{\mu-i}X_i^*] \propto (1-n)^{\mu-i} n^i \frac{\mu!}{(\mu-i)!\, i!} \tag{3.65}$$

in which n is the mol fraction of isotope X^* in the compound AX_μ.

For example, in hydrogen containing deuterium with a molar fraction n, the molar fractions of the various molecular species will have the following proportions to each other:

$$[D_2] : [HD] : [H_2] = n^2 : 2n(1-n) : (1-n)^2 \tag{3.66}$$

With these simplifying hypotheses let us calculate the separation factor for the chemical exchange of deuterium between hydrogen and ammonia, which in Eq. 3.37 has been considered only in the case of small concentrations of deuterium. We can consider any of the many possible reactions among the various molecular species, e.g.,

$$NH_3 + 3DH \rightleftharpoons ND_3 + 3H_2 \tag{3.67}$$

since all the other reactions are in equilibrium if this one is. Applying Eq. 3.65 to the ammonia molecules, we have

$$[ND_3] : [ND_2 H] : [NH_2 D] : [NH_3]$$
$$= N^3 : 3N^2(1-N) : 3N(1-N)^2 : (1-N)^3 \tag{3.68}$$

in which N indicates the mol fraction of deuterium in the ammonia. The equilibrium constant of Eq. 3.67 is

$$K = \frac{[ND_3]\, [H_2]^3}{[NH_3]\, [HD]^3} \tag{3.69}$$

Expressing the concentration ratios that appear in Eq. 3.69 by means of Eqs. 3.66 and 3.68, we have

$$K = \frac{N^3}{(1-N)^3} \frac{(1-n)^3}{2^3 n^3} \tag{3.70}$$

from which, recalling the definition of the elementary separation factor, we have

$$q_0 = 2K^{1/3} \tag{3.71}$$

If for K we take the classic value $K_0 = (\frac{1}{2})^3$, Eq. 3.71 gives us $q_0 = 1$, as might have been expected. Equation 3.71, however, can also be written in the more meaningful form

$$q_0 = \left(\frac{K}{K_0}\right)^{\frac{1}{3}} \tag{3.72}$$

More generally, for equations like 3.49 we have

$$q_0 = \left(\frac{K}{K_0}\right)^{1/\mu\nu} \tag{3.73}$$

In the foregoing discussion we examined only the case of exchange reactions in the gaseous phase, whereas we often have to deal with equilibriums in other phases (see Table 3.4), particularly in liquid–gas systems. For these systems the constants of equilibrium are easy to find, once the corresponding equilibrium constants in the gaseous phase are known. Take, for example, the reaction

$$H_2O(\text{liq.}) + HD(\text{gas}) \rightleftharpoons HDO(\text{liq.}) + H_2(\text{gas}) \tag{3.74}$$

whose constant is

$$K = \frac{[HDO](\text{liq.})[H_2](\text{gas})}{[H_2O](\text{liq.})[HD](\text{gas})} \tag{3.75}$$

On the other hand, we have, by applying Raoult's law:

$$\frac{[HDO](\text{liq.})}{[H_2O](\text{liq.})} = \frac{p_{HDO}}{p_{H_2O}} \times \frac{\bar{p}_{H_2O}}{\bar{p}_{HDO}} = \frac{[HDO](\text{gas})\,\bar{p}_{H_2O}}{[H_2O](\text{gas})\,\bar{p}_{HDO}} \tag{3.76}$$

which permits us to write Eq. 3.75 as follows:

$$K = K(\text{gas}) \times \frac{\bar{p}_{H_2O}}{\bar{p}_{HDO}} = K(\text{gas})\, q_0(\text{distill.}) \tag{3.77}$$

Obviously the calculation can be extended to equilibrium reactions between substances in solution.

The multiplication of the elementary separation effect obtained with chemical equilibrium is particularly handy when we are dealing with gas–liquid systems. In this case, which is quite a common one, counterflow can be achieved with the use of distillation columns. Usually the reboiler and the condenser are replaced with apparatus in which the conversion of the liquid product to the gaseous—and vice versa—takes place.

Exchange reactions are used particularly for the separation of large quantities of deuterium, ^{10}B, and ^{15}N. To produce deuterium by means of water–hydrogen exchange, the water at the base of the column can be converted to hydrogen by an electrolytic cell (or a battery of them). If the exchange reaction occurs in the gaseous phase between hydrogen and the water that saturates it, we use, as will be shown in Chap. 12 of this volume, columns somewhat different from the conventional ones. Basically water can also be converted into hydrogen with chemical reactions, such as in the oxidation of iron.

Again, for separating ^{15}N by exchange between nitric acid and nitrogen oxide (see Table 3.4), the conversion is done chemically by treating the nitric acid with SO_2 and with water. We then get the following reactions:

$$3SO_2 + 2HNO_3 + 2H_2O \rightarrow 3H_2SO_4 + 2NO$$

$$SO_2 + 2HNO_3 \rightarrow H_2SO_4 + 2NO_2$$

The process of exchange between ammonia ions in solution and gaseous ammonia for separating ^{15}N can be started by using, for example, a solution of ammonium nitrate (NH_4NO_3) which, at the bottom of the column, is converted to ammonia by a solution of NaOH; the resulting $NaNO_3$ is thus withdrawn.

As for the exchange reactions for separating ^{10}B, the conversion of complex BF_3 in the liquid phase to gaseous BF_3 can be obtained by simple thermal dissociation in a reboiler. In this case the process is totally analogous to that of fractional distillation.

ION-EXCHANGING RESINS

As was pointed out in the preceding section, chemical exchange in liquid–solid systems has some very interesting applications with the exchanging resins. These can be used in the form of a solid porous bed immersed in the solution of the substance on which we wish to effect isotope separation.

The physical principle that gives rise to the separating effect is absolutely identical with that of chemical exchange in gas–liquid systems or in the homogeneous gas phase, described in the preceding section. For example, if an aqueous solution of ammonium hydroxide is placed in contact with a suitable exchanging resin, the following exchange reaction occurs:

$$^{14}NH_4^+ + {}^{15}NH_4OH \rightleftharpoons {}^{15}NH_4^+ + {}^{14}NH_4OH \qquad (3.78)$$

$$\text{resin} \qquad \text{solution} \qquad \text{resin} \qquad \text{solution}$$

as a result of which, under conditions of equilibrium, the heavy nitrogen, by means of the ammonium ion, is distributed more abundantly in the solid phase, which is the resin. At ambient temperature and using Dowex 50-X12 resin, Spedding and Powell[19] found, in 1955, the value $K = 1.0257 \pm 0.0002$ for the equilibrium constant in Eq. 3.78 which in this case is equivalent to the elementary separation factor.

Ion exchange with resins has also been studied for separating the isotopes of uranium. For example, using an aqueous solution of $UO_2(NO_3)_2$ with IR-100 Amberlite, at ambient temperature, H. Clewett and W. B. Schaap (1947) found, for the following reaction:

$$^{235}UO_2^{2+} + {}^{238}UO_2^{2+} \rightleftharpoons {}^{238}UO_2^{2+} + {}^{235}UO_2^{2+} \qquad (3.79)$$

resin   solution   resin   solution

the equilibrium constant to be $K = 1.0004$.

Although the nature of the separation effect in ion exchange with resins does not differ materially from that of any other chemical equilibrium, the methods used to multiply the elementary effect generally have some special characteristics, thanks to the fact that—since one of the two phases is a solid—it is not possible to bring about counterflow according to the usual patterns.

One typical method for multiplying the elementary effect is that described by Spedding and Powell[19] for separating ^{15}N by Eq. 3.78. The Dowex 50-X12 resin, (a cationic resin of the type $R \cdot SO_2O^- - R \cdot SO_2O^- - R \cdot SO_2O^-$) arranged in a column, is first treated by passing a dilute acid through it until the bed is completely saturated with H^+, and the resin is then washed with water. Thus prepared, the resin will present, along the entire length of the column, the structures shown schematically in Fig. 3.6(a). At the top of the column, a quantity of a dilute solution of NH_4OH is now added until a band of ammonia of the desired length $Z_2 - Z_1$ is formed [see Fig. 3.6(b)]. So that the end of the band will be quite clear, there must be a chemical reaction that moves strongly in one direction. This is what happens with ammonium hydroxide, thanks to the (considerably exothermic) reaction

$$H^+ + NH_4OH \rightleftharpoons NH_4^+ + H_2O \qquad (3.80)$$

resin   solution   resin   solution

whose equilibrium constant is $\sim 10^9$. Once the band of the desired length has been formed, it is moved from the top of the column to the bottom by feeding the head of the column with an eluant solution of NaOH.

At this point, the following reaction takes place:

$$NH_4^+ + NaOH \rightleftharpoons Na^+ + NH_4OH \qquad (3.81)$$

resin   solution   resin   solution

which, having an equilibrium constant of about 10^5, in turn guarantees a very clear rear end to the band. The addition of each equivalent of NaOH shifts into solution an equivalent of NH_4^+ at the rear end of the $Z_2 - Z_1$ band; thanks to Eq. 3.80, the

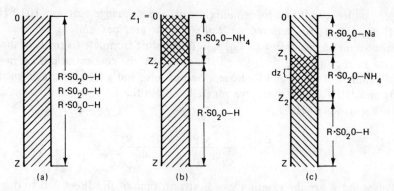

Fig. 3.6 Diagram of the resin bed in the exchange column: (a) after treatment with dilute acid; (b) after formation of the ammonia band; (c) during downward shift of the ammonia band.

consequence is adsorption of an equal quantity of NH_4^+ at the front end. The band of adsorbed ammonia thus shifts downward, still between two clear limits, as shown in Fig. 3.6(c), and along its entire length it is in equilibrium with a solution of NH_4OH (from 0 to Z_1 there is NaOH solution, and from Z_2 to Z there is only water). If every segment dz of the band of adsorbed ammonia stays in contact with the ammonium hydroxide solution long enough, equilibrium of the isotope-exchange reaction will be achieved (Eq. 3.78). With elution speeds on the order of 1 m/hr, such equilibrium is practically reached. In addition, the movement of the solution toward the bottom gives rise to a counterflow of the resin and solution phases, which means that, as the band gradually drops, the ^{15}N tends to accumulate toward the rear end and the ^{14}N toward the front end. In practice, ammonia bands 2 or 3 m in length are used, and they are rinsed over distances of some hundreds of meters before the separated products at the two ends of the band are withdrawn. This can readily be achieved even with a few short columns that are operated by attaching them in cyclic series. From the connecting valves between the columns, withdrawal and feeding can be done whenever the ammonia band passes from one column to the next.

From the foregoing it is clear that chemical exchange with resins is a separation method mainly suited for producing, in laboratory quantities, isotopes of elements that are not too heavy. In addition to ^{15}N, both ^7Li and ^{33}S have been separated in the laboratory using exchanging resins. The isotope ^{33}S is used to produce ^{33}P (particularly valuable in medical and biochemical research) by irradiating ^{33}S in a reactor; ^{33}P is produced by the reaction (n,p).

CHEMICAL EXCHANGE AND REACTION SPEED

In a manner that is similar to what we have seen in distillation under conditions of equilibrium, chemical equilibrium too is the result of dynamic equilibrium. For example, under conditions of equilibrium in the exchange reaction $HD + H_2O \rightleftharpoons H_2 + HDO$ (Eq. 3.36), referred to earlier, there are, per unit of time, as many reactions occurring, according to Eq. 3.36 in the shift from left to right, as there are occurring in the opposite direction. Calling a and b the concentrations (in mols per unit of volume) of water and hydrogen, respectively, and x and y the concentrations [HDO] and [HD], respectively, we generally obtain the following expression for the speed of formation of HDO:

$$\frac{dx}{dt} = v\frac{(a-x)y}{ab} - v'\frac{x(b-y)}{ab} \tag{3.82}$$

in which v and v' are the reaction speeds at zero time of the direct (left to right) and inverse reactions, respectively. These speeds, which have the dimensions of a concentration divided by the time, are those which the process would have if the reacting system were constituted solely of H_2O and HD molecules with constant concentrations a and b, or solely of HDO and H_2 molecules with the same concentrations.

Equation 3.82 can also be written in the form

$$\frac{dx}{dt} = k(a-x)y - k'x(b-y) \tag{3.83}$$

where $k = v/ab$ and $k' = v'/ab$ are quantities called velocity constants or coefficients of velocity or specific reaction speeds.

At equilibrium we have $dx/dt = 0$; hence from Eq. 3.82 or Eq. 3.83 we have

$$K = \frac{x(b-y)}{(a-x)y} = \frac{v}{v'} = \frac{k}{k'} \tag{3.84}$$

meaning that the equilibrium constant is equal to the ratio between the specific direct and inverse reaction speeds.

The exchange reaction, Eq. 3.36, can also be obtained as the result of a chemical reaction that transforms water into hydrogen or vice versa, e.g., the reaction of oxidation and reduction of iron

$$H_2O + Fe \rightleftharpoons FeO + H_2 \tag{3.85}$$

which, for monodeuterated water, is written

$$HDO + Fe \rightleftharpoons FeO + HD \tag{3.86}$$

From the ratio between the equilibrium constants of Eqs. 3.85 and 3.86, we obtain the equilibrium constant K of the isotope-exchange reaction, Eq. 3.36, and the values for it obtained experimentally in various ways do, in fact, coincide. Hence, for example, if we oxidize iron with natural water, we obtain, at equilibrium, a portion of deuterium-enriched water and a portion of deuterium-poor hydrogen. The separation factor for the process is K.

Several isotope-exchange reactions, although they present equilibrium constants that would favor separation, occur too slowly. It is true that, in each case, as Arrhenius' law shows,

$$k = const \times e^{-\Delta E/RT} \tag{3.87}$$

(where ΔE is the activation energy), the reaction speed can be increased by raising the temperature, but by doing this we also lower the equilibrium constant and hence the separating effect. Thus in many cases we must use catalysts. For reactions in the gaseous phase or in gas–liquid systems, solid catalysts are often used. The reaction occurs in this case on the surface of the catalyst, and it is generally possible to distinguish five phases in the process:

1. Diffusion of the reacting molecules toward the surface.
2. Adsorption of the reacting molecules on the surface with formation of compounds between them and the substance of which the surface is composed.
3. Reaction between the compound molecules on the surface.
4. Desorption of the molecules produced by reaction 3.
5. Withdrawal of these from the surface by diffusion.

Naturally, the overall speed of the process is determined by the slowest of the five above-listed processes. The slowest processes usually turn out to be the two diffusion processes, the one drawing closer to the active surface and the other going away from it.

The greater the surface a given quantity of catalyst can present, the more effective it will be. For this reason it can be used either in finely powdered form or in the form of a deposit on the surface of such a highly porous supporting substance as activated charcoal or silica gel. When the catalyst is a precious metal, this latter system is primarily advantageous from the economic point of view.

Several reactions useful in deuterium separation call for the use of catalysts. For example, the reaction (Eq. 3.36) between water and hydrogen must be catalyzed both in the liquid–gas system and in the gaseous phase. In the liquid–gas system the reaction speed is strongly limited by the slowness of the diffusion processes in the liquid. For the reaction between water and hydrogen, the catalysts most commonly used, in decreasing order of activity, are platinum, palladium, nickel, and iron.

For reaction, Eq. 3.37, between ammonia and hydrogen, also, it is necessary to use a catalyst. In the liquid–gas system potassium amide (KNH_2) in solution in ammonia can be used.

Among the exchange reactions that can be used for deuterium separation, it is worth taking particular note of the reaction between hydrogen sulfide and water, shown in Table 3.4, because even at ambient temperature there is no need for a catalyst.

GASEOUS DIFFUSION

In the process of diffusion of a gaseous mixture through a porous barrier under isothermic conditions, the different mean velocities of the various molecular species in thermodynamic equilibrium are exploited for purposes of separation.

Assume that we have a chamber divided into two areas A and B separated by a porous barrier S [see Fig. 3.7(a)] whose thickness ℓ in an initial simplified hypothesis [see Fig. 3.7(b)] is small by comparison with the mean diameter d of the pores. In

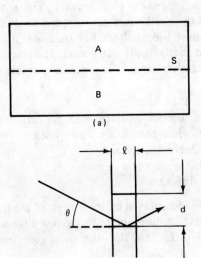

Fig. 3.7 (a) Diffusion chamber shown schematically. (b) Diagram of the passage of a molecule through a pore in a very thin barrier.

area A we have a binary gaseous mixture at a pressure p″ which is low enough that the mean free molecular path λ is long by comparison with the mean diameter d of the pores. From the kinetic theory of gases, we find, for the mean free path (MFP), the expression

$$\lambda = \frac{kT}{(2)^{\frac{1}{2}}\pi(2\sigma)^2 p} \qquad (3.88)$$

in which k is the Boltzmann constant and σ is the molecular radius ($\sim 2.10^{-8}$ cm for most gases). The MFP, as we know, can also be found from the equation

$$\lambda = \frac{3}{4}\eta\frac{(2\pi RT/M)^{\frac{1}{2}}}{p} \qquad (3.89)$$

in which η is the viscosity and the meanings of the other symbols are obvious.

The gas contained in A diffuses through the pores in the barrier S into area B in which a vacuum has been induced and where, during the diffusion process, the gas pressure is held at a level, p', markedly lower than p''. Let us calculate for each component of the gaseous mixture the mol flow rate that passes through a unit of pore section from A to B. Under the hypotheses we have made, all the molecules coming from A and hitting the pore section on the opening, will pass into area B either directly (there are practically no collisions between molecules at the mouth of the pore) or after bouncing off the edge of the pore. If we take n to be the mol density of a gas and $\bar{v}$ as its mean molecular velocity, the mol mass velocity in question is given by

$$\phi = \frac{1}{4} n \bar{v} \tag{3.90}$$

Expressing n for each component as a function of the partial pressure and recalling the expression of mean velocity as a function of the temperature and the molecular weight, we have

$$\phi_1 = \frac{N''p''}{(2\pi M_1 RT)^{\frac{1}{2}}} \tag{3.91}$$

and

$$\phi_2 = \frac{(1 - N'')p''}{(2\pi M_2 RT)^{\frac{1}{2}}} \tag{3.92}$$

in which p'' is the total pressure in A, N'' is the mol fraction of the light component, and the other symbols have the usual meanings. Equations 3.91 and 3.92 are wholly analogous to Eq. 3.19, which gives the evaporation speed. This is obvious, owing to the identity of the derivation.

In an initial phase of the process, the flow of gas in the inverse direction, from B to A, is negligible and the mol fraction N'' remains practically constant; hence the relative abundance of the light component in B is given by $R' = \phi_1 / \phi_2$. Thus from Eqs. 3.91 and 3.92 we have, for the elementary separation factor, the expression

$$q_0 = \left(\frac{M_2}{M_1} \right)^{\frac{1}{2}} \tag{3.93}$$

Equation 3.93 in substance constitutes a formulation that is only formally different from Bunsen's law, obtained experimentally, which establishes, for rarefied gases diffusing through porous walls, proportionality between the densities and the squares of the times of outflow.

Analogous results are reached by considering the molecular flow through pores of length ℓ that is not negligible or even large with respect to d, the mean diameter of the pores. By this we mean flow through capillary conduits that—for simplicity's sake—we shall assume are circular in section.

The flow of a sufficiently rarefied gas through a capillary ($\lambda \gg d$) is governed by Knudsen's law. That statement is based on the hypothesis that the rebound of molecules from a wall is isotropic, meaning that the rebound does not depend on the angle of incidence, which is the opposite of what happens for particles obeying the law of elastic reflection. This can be explained if we picture the reflecting wall as being very rough by comparison with the molecular dimensions, which means that the molecule will be reflected according to a random law and that the overall impact no longer obeys the classic law of reflection. This interpretation is confirmed by the fact that experiments run on perfectly crystalline barriers have not verified Knudsen's law.

To find this law, we must remember first of all that the number of molecules which, in a given unit of time, can impact on one unit of the surface of a barrier is given by $\nu\bar{v}/4$, with the usual significance of symbols. The number of impacts due to the $d\nu$ molecules whose velocities lie between v and v + dv is thus $vd\nu/4$. We now assume that the individual molecules have a certain flow velocity in the capillaries, i.e., a velocity v_1 parallel to the walls of the capillary, given by

$$v_1 = Kv \tag{3.94}$$

with K as the constant of proportionality. Each molecule of mass m which impacts on the wall transfers to the wall a momentum that will not be returned to the molecule, since the molecule is isotropically reemitted. Hence the wall is subject to an impulse equal to the momentum

$$Q = \int_\nu mKv \times \frac{vd\nu}{4} \tag{3.95}$$

in which, assuming a Maxwellian distribution of the velocity,

$$d\nu = \nu \left(\frac{mN_{Av}}{2\pi RT}\right)^{\frac{3}{2}} e^{-(mN_{Av}/RT)v^2} \times v^2\ dv \tag{3.96}$$

in which N_{Av} is the Avogadro number. With substitution and integration we have

$$Q = \frac{3}{4} K \frac{RT}{N_{Av}} \nu \tag{3.97}$$

Letting w be the linear velocity of the gas flow in the capillary, we can write

$$w = K\bar{v} \tag{3.98}$$

in which $\bar{v}$ has the well-known expression

$$\bar{v} = \frac{2(2)^{1/2}}{(\pi)^{1/2}} \left(\frac{RT}{M}\right)^{1/2} \tag{3.99}$$

given by kinetic theory.

Eliminating the constant K with Eq. 3.98 and allowing for Eq. 3.99, Eq. 3.97 becomes

$$Q = \frac{3}{8}\left(\frac{\pi}{2}\right)^{1/2} \times w \times \frac{v}{N_{Av}} (MRT)^{1/2} \tag{3.100}$$

Furthermore, the impulse per unit of time and surface is equivalent to the shear stress applied to the wall of the capillary. Hence the total force is

$$F = \frac{3\pi}{8}\left(\frac{\pi}{2}\right)^{1/2} \times w \times \frac{v}{N_{Av}} (MRT)^{1/2} \times \ell d \tag{3.101}$$

furthermore, under conditions of dynamic equilibrium it is

$$F = \pi \frac{d^2}{4} \Delta p \tag{3.102}$$

in which Δp is the drop in gas pressure. Comparing Eq. 3.101 with Eq. 3.102, we have, for the linear flow velocity, the expression

$$w = \frac{2}{3}\left(\frac{2}{\pi}\right)^{1/2} \times \frac{N_{Av}}{v(MRT)^{1/2}} \times \frac{d}{\ell}\Delta p \tag{3.103}$$

The mol mass velocity through the capillary thus turns out to be

$$\phi = \frac{4/3}{(2\pi MRT)^{1/2}} \times \frac{d}{\ell} \Delta p \tag{3.104}$$

This is Knudsen's law, according to which—with low enough pressures—the flow rate of a gas through a capillary is proportional to the pressure drop Δp and not to its square, as in those cases in which Poiseuille's law applies.

Equation 3.104 can be written independently for each of the two components of a binary mixture, whose mol mass velocities through the pores of a barrier—assuming that the pressure in area B is negligible—are found to be, respectively,

$$\phi_1 = \frac{4/3}{(2\pi M_1 RT)^{1/2}} \frac{d}{\ell} N''p'' \tag{3.105}$$

and

$$\phi_2 = \frac{4/3}{(2\pi M_2 RT)^{1/2}} \frac{d}{\ell} (1 - N'')p'' \tag{3.106}$$

Since, as was shown in an initial phase of the process, it is R' that is equal to ϕ_1/ϕ_2, we again obtain, from the two preceding equations, the same equation that appeared earlier as Eq. 3.93:

$$q_0 = \left(\frac{M_2}{M_1}\right)^{1/2}$$

Since M_2 and M_1 are very close, Eq. 3.93 can be written in the approximate form

$$q_0 \simeq 1 + \frac{M_2 - M_1}{M_2 + M_1} \tag{3.107}$$

Should the pressure p' of the diffused gas in area B no longer be negligible by comparison with p'', we must allow for back diffusion from B to A, which leads—as will be shown in the detailed discussion of the process of gaseous diffusion—to a decrease in the separation factor by comparison with the ideal value given by Eq. 3.93.

For separation it is essential, as we have seen, to have $\lambda \gg d$. As the pressure p'' increases, the flow of gas through each pore in a barrier (again we are assuming the pore to be a cylindrical capillary conduit) tends to obey Poiseuille's law:

$$\phi = \frac{p''^2 - p'^2}{64\eta RT} \times \frac{d^2}{\ell} \tag{3.108}$$

and the separation effect disappears.

In the gas-diffusion process, the elementary separation factor cannot be multiplied by means of a counterflow system in a single apparatus analogous to the distillation columns. As we shall see, diffusion plants are made up of many diffusion vessels (or diffusers) connected in series, in each of which the maximum separation theoretically obtainable is that corresponding to the ideal factor q_0 given by Eq. 3.93.

The process has been used on a vast scale for separating ^{235}U; the choice of raw material is, in this case, limited to UF_6 for all intents and purposes. Since fluorine has only one isotope, with a mass number of 19, the difference in mass between the molecular species of UF_6 is entirely due to the uranium isotopes. The elementary separation factor for the process, calculated with Eq. 3.93, comes out as $q_0 = 1.0043$.

For separating ^{13}C from ^{12}C by diffusion of CH_4, the separation factor $q_0 = 1.0303$.

MASS DIFFUSION

In the mass-diffusion process, the components of a gaseous mixture are separated by using their different diffusion rates in another substance in the gaseous state. This substance is called the "separating agent." For the gaseous mixture whose components are to be separated, the agent and the components must be easily separable, which means that if the former is a gas, the latter must be an easily condensable vapor or vice versa. Now assume that we place in contact a gas consisting of two components, whose molecular weights are M_1 and M_2, and a vapor (separating agent) whose molecular weight is M_0. This contact comes about when the gas to be separated and the vapor acting as the separating agent are placed, respectively, in areas A and B of a container and are separated by a porous barrier S (see Fig. 3.8). Gas and vapor are

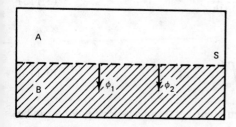

Fig. 3.8 Principle of mass-diffusion separation shown schematically. A = binary gas mixture; B = separating agent.

under the same pressure. The pores of this barrier are far greater in diameter than those of the pores used in the gas-diffusion process (e.g., $10 \, \mu m$), so that any difference in pressure between areas A and B will give rise to a flow in the fluid state. The function of the barrier S thus consists also in preventing a rapid remixing of the two substances brought into contact, through convective and vortex movements.

Once brought into contact through the pores of the barrier S, the separating agent begins to diffuse from B to A, and the binary gas mixture from A to B.

The phenomenon can be visualized if we imagine that the binary mixture initially occupies a semispace, e.g., that of the negative x abscissa, and that diffusion of the two components begins from the plane x = 0 toward the semispace of the x-positives. The diffusion process is governed by the equation

$$\frac{\partial n_i}{\partial t} = D_{io} \frac{\partial^2 n_i}{\partial x^2} \qquad (3.109)$$

where n is the concentration (in mols per unit of volume), D is the diffusion coefficient of a component in the separating agent, and the index i = 1,2 refers to each of the two components.

When Eq. 3.109 is integrated with the initial conditions

$$n_i = 0 \text{ for } t = 0 \text{ and } 0 < x < \infty \tag{3.110}$$

and with the boundary conditions

$$n_i = n_i^0 = \text{const for } x = 0 \text{ and } 0 < t < \infty \tag{3.111}$$

the following solutions are given:

$$n_i = n_i^0 \left[1 - \phi\left(\zeta_i\right)\right], \tag{3.112}$$

in which

$$\zeta_i = \frac{x}{2 \left(D_i t\right)^{\frac{1}{2}}} \tag{3.113}$$

and

$$\phi(\zeta) = \frac{2}{(\pi)^{\frac{1}{2}}} \int_0^\zeta e^{-\zeta^2} \, d\zeta \tag{3.114}$$

The separation achieved at time t between point x = 0 and a generic point x can be expressed by the factor

$$Q = \frac{n_1 / n_2}{n_1^0 / n_2^0} \tag{3.115}$$

Particularizing the indices in Eq. 3.112 and substituting them in Eq. 3.115, we have

$$\ln Q = \ln \left[1 - \phi\left(\zeta_1\right)\right] - \ln \left[1 - \phi\left(\zeta_2\right)\right] \tag{3.116}$$

which, in the case of $D_1 - D_2 \ll D_1$, becomes, approximately,

$$\ln Q = \frac{\partial}{\partial \zeta} \ln \left[1 - \phi\right] \times \frac{\partial \zeta}{\partial D} \left(D_1 - D_2\right) \tag{3.117}$$

Substituting Eqs. 3.113 and 3.114 in Eq. 3.117, we have

$$\ln Q = \frac{D_1 - D_2}{D} \times f \tag{3.118}$$

in which

$$f = \frac{\zeta \exp(-\zeta^2)}{(\pi)^{\frac{1}{2}} [1 - \phi(\zeta)]} \tag{3.119}$$

and D is the overall diffusion coefficient for the binary mixture. The f factor is canceled for $\zeta = 0$ and tends toward ζ^2 for large values of ζ. In this last case, we have approximately the equation

$$f = \ln(v^0/v)$$

in which

$$v = \int_x^\infty n\, dx \quad \text{and} \quad v^0 = \int_0^\infty n\, dx$$

are the quantities of mixture that have gone, respectively, beyond the $x = x$ and $x = 0$ planes. Figure 3.9 shows the behavior of f as a function of ζ. The f factor, in which

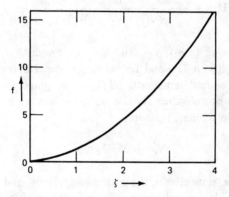

Fig. 3.9 The f factor as a function of the ζ parameter.

only x, t, and D appear, clearly does not depend on the elementary separation factor. The latter can appear in Eq. 3.118 only through the term $(D_1 - D_2)/D$. Taking for D the mean between the diffusion coefficients of the two components, we define the elementary separation factor q_0 by the equation

$$q_0 - 1 = \frac{2(D_1 - D_2)}{D_1 + D_2} \tag{3.120}$$

With the same approximation, we can write

$$q_0 = D_1/D_2 \tag{3.121}$$

Returning to the pattern shown in Fig. 3.8, we observe that, since the diffusion coefficient D_1 is greater than D_2, after a certain span of time from the start of the process, the light component will be more abundant in area B than in area A. Hence we need only to condense the vapor contained in A and in B and to separate the condensate from the gas in order to obtain the enriched fraction and the impoverished fraction.

Clearly, in addition to the property of being easily separable in the gas, the prime requisites for the separating agent are selectivity toward the components to be separated and a high diffusion coefficient in the gas. Selectivity generally increases as molecular weight, but correspondingly the diffusion coefficient in gas decreases. A practical compromise is often struck by choosing a molecular weight close to that of the gas.

For molecular species of simple structure, the diffusion coefficients can be calculated with good approximation in square centimeters per second (cm^2/sec) according to the following formula, developed by J. O. Hirschfelder, C. F. Curtiss, and R. B. Bird:

$$D_{12} = \frac{5.36 \times 10^{-3}\, T^{3/2}\, (1/M_1 + 1/M_2)^{1/2}}{p(V_{C_1}^{1/3} + V_{C_2}^{1/3})^2\, W(T/T_{12})} \tag{3.122}$$

in which p is the pressure (atm), V_{C_1} and V_{C_2} are the critical volumes (cm^3/mol), $T_{12} = 0.75(T_{C_1} T_{C_2})^{1/2}$ (with T_{C_1} and T_{C_2} as the critical temperatures), and finally W is a function of the reduced temperature T/T_{12}, the graph for which is shown in Fig. 3.10. When experimental values for the critical values are not available, they can be calculated by the approximate formula

$$V_c = 0.35 RT_c/p_c$$

in which T_c and p_c are, respectively, the critical temperature and the critical pressure.

An empirical formula for calculating the diffusion coefficient is this one from E. R. Gilliland

$$D_{12} = \frac{4.3 \times 10^{-3} T^{3/2}\, (1/M_1 + 1/M_2)^{1/2}}{p(V_1^{1/3} + V_2^{1/3})^2} \tag{3.123}$$

in which V_1 and V_2 are the molecular volumes (cm^3/mol) of the two components at the normal boiling point.

Since, for isotopic substances, M_1 and M_2 are very close, Eq. 3.120 can be written with good approximation in the following form:

$$q_0 - 1 = \frac{M_2 - M_1}{M_2 + M_1} \times \frac{M_0}{M_0 + (M_1 + M_2)/2} \tag{3.124}$$

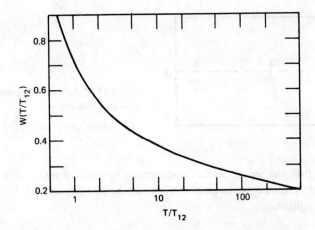

Fig. 3.10 The $W(T/T_{12})$ function for calculating diffusion coefficients.

To establish a comparison with the gas-diffusion process, we use Eq. 3.124 to calculate the separation factors for separating ^{235}U and ^{13}C. For the first process—diffusing UF_6 in $N(C_7F_9)_3$ ($M_0 = 671$)—we get $q_0 = 1.00281$; for the second process—using CH_4 and water vapor as the separating agent—we get $q_0 = 1.0158$.

The separation effect of gas diffusion is thus greater than that of mass diffusion. The latter, however, offers the advantage of greater technical simplicity, which could make it useful for small-scale separation operations. Furthermore, as shown later on, mass diffusion can be done in a counterflow mode in an apparatus similar to a distillation column.

THERMAL DIFFUSION

Consider the ideal case of a receptacle containing a gas that has a molecular weight M and a pressure p; the gas, however, is at two different temperatures T_A and T_B ($T_A > T_B$) in the two regions A and B, respectively, into which the receptacle is divided by the purely ideal separation surface S. The situation is shown schematically in Fig. 3.11.

In region A, let n_A be the mol density and $\bar{v}_A$ the mean molecular velocity; the mol flow which, in one unit of time, crosses one unit of surface of the ideal wall S in the direction of A to B is thus

$$\phi_{AB} = \frac{1}{4} n_A \bar{v}_A$$

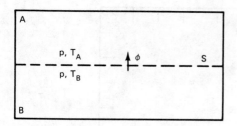

Fig. 3.11 Schematic diagram of the thermal diffusion process.

Assuming that the gas is perfect and expressing each quantity as a function of temperature and pressure, we have, as was seen in the sections on molecular distillation and on gaseous diffusion,

$$\phi_{AB} = \frac{p}{(2\pi MRT_A)^{1/2}}$$

Similarly we have, for the flow from B to A

$$\phi_{BA} = \frac{p}{(2\pi MRT_B)^{1/2}}$$

The net flow $\phi = \phi_{BA} - \phi_{AB}$ is thus found to be

$$\phi = \frac{p}{(2\pi RM)^{1/2}} \left[\frac{1}{(T_B)^{1/2}} - \frac{1}{(T_A)^{1/2}} \right] \tag{3.125}$$

Finally, the gas migrates from the cold zone to the hot zone, and the flow is inversely proportional to the square root of the molecular weight. Hence, in the case of a binary mixture, the greater flow is that of the lighter component which is thus found in greater abundance in the hot region. This is the separation effect of thermal diffusion, a phenomenon long known both on the theoretical[30] and experimental levels (S. Chapman and F. W. Dootson, 1917), but not applied until 1938, when it began to be used for isotope separation on large quantities of material. In this connection, the experiments of Clusius and Dickel[32] were of decisive importance: they obtained multiplication of the elementary effect with counterflows in apparatus similar—in principle—to a distillation column.

The earlier description of thermal diffusion gives a fairly simplistic view of the process, which is governed not only by the masses but also by the potentials for molecular interaction. In fact, thermal diffusion has been used to separate carbon monoxide (CO) and ethylene (C_2H_4), the molecular weights of which are practically equal (F. T. Wall and C. E. Holley, 1940).

To have a quantitative notion of the separating effect of thermal diffusion, we first observe that the specific mol flow ϕ_1 of the light component in a binary mixture across a surface perpendicular to a temperature gradient $\partial T/\partial r$ is given by

$$\phi_1 = D\rho\left[N\,(1-N)\,\frac{\gamma}{T}\frac{\partial T}{\partial r} - \frac{\partial N}{\partial r}\right] \tag{3.126}$$

where D is the diffusion coefficient, ρ is the mol density, and γ is a nondimensional parameter called the "thermal diffusion constant." Clearly the flow ϕ_1 is the result of a positive term proportional to the thermal gradient and of a negative diffusion term proportional to the concentration gradient.

For isotopic mixtures the thermal diffusion constant is positive at high temperatures, declines as the temperature drops, and can become negative at temperatures below the critical point. Furthermore, it is independent from concentrations, and practically independent from pressure up to several atmospheres.

Given the uncertainties to which the theoretical determination of γ leads, it is preferable to use data obtained experimentally. In calculations it is common to use the ratio R_T between the measured constant γ and the theoretical value for rigid spherical molecules without any attractive potential. For isotopic mixtures the following relation exists between γ and R_T:

$$\gamma = \frac{105}{118} \times \frac{M_2 - M_1}{M_2 + M_1}\,R_T \tag{3.127}$$

Table 3.7 shows the values of R_T for several isotopic systems and for various temperatures.

Table 3.7

R_T RATIOS FOR VARIOUS ISOTOPIC SYSTEMS

System	Temp., °K	R_T	Experimenters
H_2-D_2	333	0.50	J. Hirschfelder et al., 1949
$^{12}CH_4-^{13}CH_4$	573–296	0.27	R. C. Jones and W. H. Furry, 1946
$^{14}N_2-^{14}N^{15}N$	623–195	0.33	A. K. Mann, 1948
$^{20}Ne-^{22}Ne$	623–195	0.65	A. K. Mann, 1948
$^{36}Ar-^{40}Ar$	620	0.47	J. Hirschfelder et al., 1949

By integrating Eq. 3.127 between the two limits, N'' and N', to which the two temperatures T'' and T' correspond, the former on the cold wall ($r = 0$) and the latter on the hot wall ($r = d$) of the container in which the gas is confined, we obtain the expression

$$\phi_1 d = D\rho \left[\bar{\gamma}\bar{N}(1 - \bar{N}) \ln \frac{T'}{T''} - (N' - N'')\right] \tag{3.128}$$

in which $\bar{\gamma}$ and $\bar{N}$ are mean values. The values of N'' and N' which occur in conditions of equilibrium for $\phi_1 = 0$ are the ones which determine the elementary separation factor of the process:

$$q_0 = 1 + \left[\frac{N' - N''}{\bar{N}(1 - \bar{N})}\right]_{\phi_1 = 0} = 1 + \bar{\gamma} \ln \frac{T'}{T''} \tag{3.129}$$

Referring again to the case of separating $^{13}CH_4$ from $^{12}CH_4$, which we considered in the discussions of gas diffusion and mass diffusion, we find that, for thermal diffusion with extreme temperatures of $537°K$ and $296°K$, respectively, Eq. 129 gives the separation factor $q_0 = 1.0048$. This value is lower than either that for gas diffusion (1.0303) or that calculated for mass diffusion with water vapor (1.0158).

Also, the thermal diffusion separation factor is further reduced in reality by the fact that the transport of the gas is not governed by the entire temperature drop between the hot wall and the cold wall. Despite the lesser separation effect by comparison with the other diffusion processes, thermal diffusion nevertheless offers some very real advantages in its relative simplicity of operation, particularly when it is not done on too large a scale.

It is interesting to note that separation by thermal diffusion can be obtained even with operation in the liquid phase.

CENTRIFUGATION

There is no need to explain the well-known separating effect of centrifugation here. Let it suffice for now to recall (for a more extensive discussion, see Chap. 6) that the application of this principle to isotope separation—which requires particularly intense gravitational fields—has called for the solution of difficult technological problems, and, as a result, the first successful experiments with it came only in 1936–1937, when Beams and coworkers[40-41] used CCl_4 to separate the isotopes of chlorine.

The idea of using gravitational fields or centrifuges for isotope separation was suggested for the first time by Lindemann and Aston in 1919 [*The Philosophical Magazine*, **37**: 530 (1919)], with the intention of verifying the difference in isotopic composition of neon samples taken at ground level and others taken at an altitude of 30 km.

The difference should be marked. In fact, a gas with molecular weight M_i which is subjected to the uniform gravitational field g will, according to Boltzmann's law of distribution, display the following partial pressure as a function of the altitude h:

$$P_i(h) = p_i(0) e^{-M_i gh/RT}$$

Therefore, for two gases whose molecular weights are, respectively, M_1 and M_2, we will have

$$\frac{p_1(h)}{p_2(h)} = \frac{p_1(0)}{p_2(0)} e^{(M_2 - M_1)gh/RT} \tag{3.130}$$

The separation factor between ^{20}Ne and ^{22}Ne is about 1.4, on the basis of Eq. 3.130, with the difference in altitude considered and with $T = 220°K$.

To set up the calculation of the elementary separation factor, assume first that we have an ideal uniform gas of molecular weight M and mol density ρ in the drum of a centrifuge of radius r' and that this drum rotates with an angular velocity of ω. At a distance r from the axis, the pressure gradient in the gas is given by

$$\frac{dp}{dr} = M\rho\omega^2 r = \frac{Mp}{RT}\omega^2 r$$

Integrating this expression between r'' and 0, we get

$$\frac{p''}{p'} = e^{M\omega^2 r''^2/2RT} \tag{3.131}$$

Analogously, for each of the two components of a binary mixture having molecular weights M_1 and M_2, we get, respectively,

$$\frac{p'' N''}{p' N'} = e^{M_1 \omega^2 r''^2/2RT} \tag{3.131a}$$

$$\frac{p''(1 - N'')}{p'(1 - N')} = e^{M_2 \omega^2 r''^2/2RT} \tag{3.131b}$$

Dividing Eqs. 3.131a and 3.131b part by part, we have the elementary separation factor

$$q_0 = e^{(M_2 - M_1)\omega^2 r''^2/2RT} \tag{3.132}$$

When we compare Eq. 3.132 with Eq. 3.130, we readily see that the only difference between each other lies in the fact that, instead of the gravitational potential gh appearing in the former, we have in the latter the centrifugal potential $\frac{1}{2}\omega^2 r''^2$.

The separation factor in centrifugation thus depends on the square of the peripheral velocity and on the difference in mass of the molecular species to be separated. The separation factor also depends on the temperature and diminishes as the temperature rises, as it logically would if we remember that there is at the same time an increase in the diffusive transport tending to obliterate the concentration gradients.

All other conditions being equal, q_0 is the same for isotopes of light elements as it is for those of heavy elements. Furthermore, it does not depend on the particular chemical compound in which the element whose isotopes are to be separated appears. All these characteristics are peculiar to centrifugation and thus make it appear particularly advantageous by comparison with other methods for separating heavy isotopes.

By way of example, for centrifugal separation of ^{235}U from UF_6 at 300°K in a drum having a 6-cm radius r'' and spinning at a velocity of 667 turns/sec, we obtain as the elementary separation factor

$$q_0 = \exp \frac{3 \times (4190)^2 \times (6)^2}{2 \times 8.315 \times 10^7 \times 300} = 1.0387$$

This value has been confirmed experimentally. When $q_0 - 1$ is $\ll 1$, Eq. 132 gives us the approximate expression

$$q_0 - 1 = \frac{(M_2 - M_1)\omega^2 r''^2}{2RT} \tag{3.133}$$

Of course if the separation takes place in an annular zone of the rotor, lying between radii r'' and r' ($r'' > r'$), the difference $r''^2 - r'^2$ occurs in Eqs. 3.132 and 3.133 in place of r''^2.

Table 3.8 lists the separation factors obtainable by differences of mass from 1 to 3 with various peripheral velocities at ambient temperature (300°K). With $v = 300$ m/sec and $r'' = 10$ cm, we have an acceleration of about 90,000 g.

Table 3.8

ELEMENTARY SEPARATION FACTORS FOR VARIOUS DIFFERENCES
OF MASS AND FOR VARIOUS PERIPHERAL VELOCITIES (T = 300°K)

$M_2 - M_1$	300 m/sec	350 m/sec	400 m/sec	450 m/sec
1	1.018	1.049	1.069	1.085
2	1.037	1.104	1.144	1.177
3	1.057	1.159	1.198	1.278

In Chap. 6 of this volume, we will show that it is possible to multiply the elementary effect in the rotor of a centrifuge by setting up countercurrent in it. This fact makes the process more readily adaptable to production on a large scale. Studies are even now under way for applying this method to the production of ^{235}U.

THE SEPARATION NOZZLE

A method of separation based on diffusive processes was conceived a few years ago by Becker et al.[36] in Germany. [Although the method was described in 1948 in a patent filed in the United States by Dickens[35] and prior to Becker's first publications (1954–1955), the method is generally attributed to Becker by reason of the extent and completeness of his work.]

The principle of the method in its latest version, adapted for isotope separation of uranium, is shown in Fig. 3.12 by means of the separating device in cross section. A metal wall contains a long gutter with a cross section almost semicircular. Above it, but not touching it, are two blades, also metal. The first blade has a suitably shaped profile (as can be seen in Fig. 3.12), and the second is shaped like a knife-edge. The

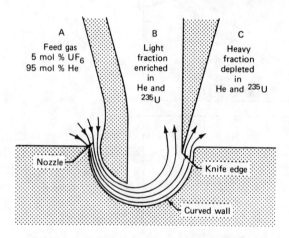

Fig. 3.12 Operating principle of the separating nozzle.

two blades separate the three zones A, B, and C. The profiled blade, along with the concave wall of the gutter, forms a conduit which, seen in cross section, starts with a neck toward the mouth. The conduit cross section has somewhat the shape of a bent Laval nozzle. Typical dimensions of the device in cross section are: (1) diameter of the gutter, 0.2 mm; and (2) width of the neck, 0.03 mm. The length of the gutter may vary; some gutters have been made as long as 2 m.

The input gas, a mixture of UF_6 and helium, comes from zone A. Typical proportions are 5 mol % UF_6 and 95 mol % helium. The total pressure in A is, for example, 600 mm Hg. Zones B and C have considerably lower pressure (about 150 mm Hg), so that the gas flows through the nozzle at a supersonic speed.

The gas that follows the flow line with the greatest curvature enters zone B, and the uranium it contains is enriched in ^{235}U, whereas the remaining fraction goes into zone C, where it is correspondingly enriched in ^{238}U. The elementary separation factor depends, once a certain expansion ratio is set, on the pressure of the feed gas. In Fig. 3.13, we see both this dependency (for a particular separation device) and that of the cut, θ, of the inlet pressure. Comparison of the two curves shows that the elementary separation factor in the separation nozzle is a function of the cut, unlike many other processes in which it is intrinsically constant. (Note that "cut" is the term used for the mol ratio $\delta L/L$ (see pages 35 and 36).

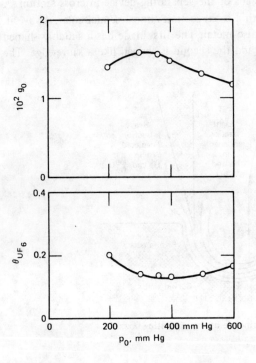

Fig. 3.13 Separation nozzle: typical dependence both of the separation effect $g_0 = q_0 - 1$ and of the cut θ_{UF_6} on inlet pressure p_0.

The separating effect is due primarily to the centrifugal forces set up in the gas jet by the curved wall. The presence of a diluting gas (like helium) with low molecular weight helps increase the speed of flow. The diluting gas contributes to the separating effect in still another way: it delays the establishment of a hypsometric distribution of UF_6 density. This delay temporarily reduces the remingling by diffusion of the isotopes of uranium separated by the centrifugal forces.

The phenomenon is too complex to allow calculation of the separation factor by purely analytical means. Hence we usually rely on the values obtained experimentally. The separation factor of course depends on the particular configuration of the nozzle and on several operative parameters, namely:

• The type of diluting gas (other gases may be used as alternatives to helium) and its abundance in relation to UF_6.
• The inlet absolute pressure (see, for example, Fig. 3.13) and temperature.
• The expansion ratio of the light fraction.
• Absolute pressure of the heavy fraction.

These parameters exactly determine the cut.

Other conditions being equal, the separation factor is an increasing function of the expansion ratio of the light fraction. For example, with a mixture of 1.6 mol % UF_6 + hydrogen, a separation gain $g_0 = q_0 - 1 \simeq 0.04$ is obtained which is 10 times greater than that obtainable with gas diffusion. In practice, however, it is better to work with lower compression ratios (3 to 4) and to settle for lower separation gains (0.01–0.02).

The separation-nozzle process was developed, in its original version, without the use of an auxiliary gas. The separation device is shown schematically in Fig. 3.14. The

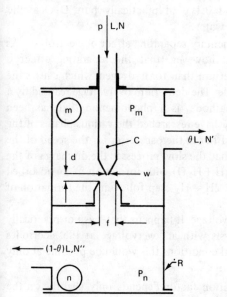

Fig. 3.14 Early version of the separation nozzle.

feed gas L emerged at supersonic speed from the mouth (diameter W) of the nozzle C. The jet expanded into the space d between the nozzle (separation nozzle) and the nosepiece f. The nosepiece separated the θL fraction which had been enriched in light component (by diffusion along the transverse pressure gradient) from the $(1 - \theta)L$ fraction which had been depleted.

The disadvantage of the method was that it operated at very low pressures (p $\simeq$ 10 to 50 mm Hg) and required high compression ratios. These disadvantages were eliminated in the aboved-described new version.

ELECTROLYSIS

In electrolysis of acid or alkaline water or of water containing a salt (with oxygenated anion), hydrogen is developed at the cathode and oxygen at the anode. The hydrogen produced in this way contains less deuterium than did the aqueous solution it came from. As is shown later, the elementary separation factor q_0 of the process, defined as the ratio between the relative abundance R of deuterium in the water and the abundance r of deuterium in the hydrogen given off, has fairly high values, usually greater than 3. Naturally, the process can be based either on the method of reducing the volume of an initial charge of water (in which we get a gradual enrichment of the water remaining in the electrolytic cell) or on the continuous method, in which, because water is constantly feeding the electrolytic cell, the concentrations are unchanging.

The first system was used in 1933 when Lewis and MacDonald[46] first separated heavy water electrolytically. They obtained 0.1 g of practically pure D_2O as the residue of electrolysis of 20 liters of alkaline water.

Even now there is no theory of the elementary separating effect of electrolysis. As for the hydrogen isotopes, it is thought, however, that the separating effect is produced by a greater overvoltage for deuterium than for hydrogen, which causes the hydrogen to be released faster at the cathode. The deuterium overvoltage, caused by a lag in the formation of this gas at the cathode, is a phenomenon that has been intensively studied by electrochemists. They have researched the various phases of the process to find out which is the slowest and hence the pacesetter for the speed of the overall process. In some cases it is argued that the slow process is the discharge of the hydrogen ion at the cathode ($H_3O^+ + e^- \rightarrow H + H_2O$) with formation of an adsorbed atom; in other cases it is believed to be the $2H \rightleftharpoons H_2$ step following the formation of 2H from $2H^+$.

As a consequence of the hydrogen overvoltage, it happens that it is not practically possible to break down water by electrolysis with an overvoltage at the electrodes lower than about 1.7 V, whereas under ideal conditions this would be possible at only 1.23 V.

For heavy water the electrolytic separation factor depends only slightly on the nature and concentration of the electrolyte or on its enrichment in deuterium. (Some researchers have observed that, in general, the separation factor—with electrodes of the same metal—is higher in alkaline solutions than in acid.) It is, however, sensitive to the influence of the following factors: (1) temperature, (2) material and surface treatment of the electrodes, and (3) impurities in the electrolytic solution.

Systematic measurements of the effect of temperature on the separation factor were taken by Brun and Varberg,[47] who electrolyzed water alkalinized with 5 or 20% KOH with a cathode of soft iron and a cathodic current density of 0.05 A/cm². These measurement results are shown in Table 3.9, where we see that the elementary separation factor q_0 rises as the temperature declines. The current density also has an indirect effect on the separation factor: At high cathodic current densities (0.25 to 1

A/cm^2), the temperature of the electrode is markedly higher than that of the solution near the electrode itself, with a consequent lowering of the separation factor.

The effects of the above-cited factors 2 and 3 were also studied by Brun et al.[48] In Table 3.10 are the values that they found for q_0 using cathodes of various materials, but in each case they were working under the following conditions: the cells without

Table 3.9

SEPARATION FACTORS AS A FUNCTION OF
CATHODE TEMPERATURE

Temp., °C	q_0	Temp., °C	q_0
97	5.8	15	12.7
75	7.1	6	13.2
50	8.6	1	14.4
25	10.6	−19	17.5

Table 3.10

ELECTROLYTIC SEPARATION FACTORS[48] FOR DEUTERIUM
WITH CATHODES OF DISPARATE MATERIALS

Cathode*	H$_2$ overvoltage, V	q_0
Electrolytic iron		13.2
Low-carbon steel	0.49	12.2
Platinum	0.75	8.8
Palladium	0.86	7.8
Lead	0.73	10.6
Silver	0.65	10.2
Copper	0.48	10.5
Nickel	0.57	8.0
Zinc	1.00	5.1
Cadmium	0.80	5.9
Tin	1.00	5.5
Zirconium	0.95	4.0

*The cathode surfaces are lapped.

membranes; the current density was 0.05 A/cm^2; the electrolyte temperature was 15°C; the initial concentration of D$_2$O was 10%; and the KOH concentration was 5%. They found very marked differences. Even the condition of the electrode surface affects separation: deposits, incrustations, and deterioration are the cause of lower values in the separation factors obtainable in commercial electrolytic cells.

With cathodes having such high surface catalytic activity as iron with platinum black electroplating, low values are obtained for the separation factors. This is explained by the fact that the cathode catalyzes the $HD + H_2O \rightleftharpoons H_2 + HDO$ exchange reaction, whose equilibrium constant at ambient temperature is about 3.8.

As for impurities found in the electrolytic bath, it was shown that certain heavy-metal compounds, such as zinc, tin, and lead, produce a considerable drop in the separation factor. For example, working with a soft-iron cathode under conditions very close to those referred to in Table 3.9, values of q_0 between 10.8 and 6.7 have been found for ZnO concentrations between 10^{-6} and 10^{-2} mol/liter.

The separation factors by electrolysis are very close to unity for all elements except hydrogen. Shown in Table 3.11 are the results of several experiments on isotopes of different elements.

Table 3.11

ELECTROLYTIC SEPARATION FACTORS FOR SOME ELEMENTS

Systems	Electrolyte and electrode	q_0	Authors
$^6Li-^7Li$	LiCl on platinum	1.055	H. L. Johnston and C. A. Hutchiston, 1940
$^{14}N-^{15}N$	NH_4Cl on mercury	1.006	H. L. Johnston and C. A. Hutchiston, 1942–1945
$^{16}O-^{18}O$	KOH on nickel	1.032	L. Tronstad and J. Brun, 1938
			H. E. Watson, 1953
$^{35}Cl-^{37}Cl$	NaCl on platinum	1.061	H. L. Johnston and C. A. Hutchiston, 1942–1945
$^{39}K-^{41}K$	KCl on platinum	1.055	H. L. Johnston and C. A. Hutchiston, 1942–1945

Note that, given the existence of an electrolysis separation factor of ^{18}O, heavy water produced by electrolysis is also enriched in ^{18}O. We must keep this in mind when calculating the deuterium content on the basis of density.

When Eidinoff[50] electrolyzed an aqueous solution of NaOH containing $10^{-9}\%$ tritium, he found a separation factor for this isotope of 13.4 to 14.7.

ELECTROMIGRATION

Electrolysis makes it possible to achieve isotope separation by taking advantage of an effect other than the one described in the preceding section. We can use—rather than the different rates at which two isotopes are released around an electrode—the difference in mobility between the ions of two isotopic species in their migration toward the electrode.

This separation process, although it was known earlier, was successfully used only in 1946 and 1947 by Klemm,[52-54] and by Brewer, Madorsky, and Westhaver.[51] This process can occur under various conditions: in solution, in molten salts, in molten metal, and in crystals.

As an example of the process in solution, we cite the separation of potassium isotopes (^{39}K and ^{41}K) in the electrolysis of an aqueous solution of KCl. The experimental apparatus, as described by Brewer, Madorsky, and Westhaver,[51] is shown in Fig. 3.15. The 1.67% solution of KCl is electrolyzed between platinum electrodes.

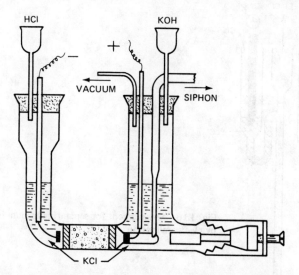

Fig. 3.15 Device for separating potassium isotopes by electromigration.

The potash that forms at the cathode is neutralized with a continuous flow of HCl, and the chlorine formed at the anode is neutralized by adding KOH. The level of the electrolyte is kept constant by means of a siphon. Under the effect of the electrical field, the K^+ ions of the light isotope migrate toward the cathode causing an accumulation of ^{39}KCl. Obviously the introduction of natural KOH limits the possibility of anode enrichment in ^{41}K. A membrane of porous material (sand, glass wool, etc.) is placed between the electrodes to prevent remixing. Such remixings may be due to either retrodiffusion or convection movement caused by the discontinuity in temperature (brought about by the Joule effect) across the section.

Running electrolysis for 450 hr with a cathode space of 11 cm^3, Brewer found in his experiments that the $^{39}K/^{40}K$ mol ratio was raised from the natural level of 14.2 to 20. This corresponds to a value of $q_0 = 1.0022$ for the elementary separation factor.

A similar procedure was used by Klemm[54] to separate ^7Li, electrolyzing molten LiCl. The ^6Li, whose ions have a greater migration velocity, accumulates around the cathode and the ^7Li piles up around the anode. Klemm used the apparatus shown in Fig. 3.16 to conduct his experiments. The metallic lithium formed around the cathode is transformed back to chloride by means of a flow of gaseous chlorine. The electrodes are made of carbon or graphite to withstand the action of chlorine at high temperatures (above 600°C). The apparatus includes the usual filter for separation between the catholyte and anolyte. Also, to cut down as much as possible on the anode space in which the ^7Li is concentrated, Klemm[54] used $PbCl_2$ (which does not enter into the electrolytic process) as the buffer liquid between anolyte and anode.

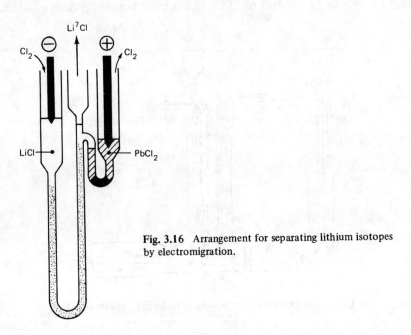

Fig. 3.16 Arrangement for separating lithium isotopes by electromigration.

With a filter 20 cm long, anode collecting volumes of 1 to 2 cm^3, current densities of 9 A/cm^2, he obtained samples of LiCl containing only 0.1% of ^6Li after a lapse of about 300 A-hr.

Electromigration in molten metals was first successfully tried in 1953 in work with the isotopes of mercury.

ELECTROMAGNETIC SEPARATION

The separating effect of a magnetic field on ions of different mass impelled by speeds normal to the field was used by J. J. Thomson as early as 1911 to demonstrate the existence of isotopes in stable elements. By sending a beam of positive neon ions across an electrical field and a magnetic field and then causing the ions to strike a photographic film, J. J. Thomson obtained two different parabolas, one for ^{20}Ne and the other for ^{22}Ne.

The calutron is the apparatus currently used for isotope separation by means of this system. The name is derived from the University of California Cyclotron Laboratory, where the first prototypes were designed and built. The principle of the calutron is shown in Fig. 3.17. In a vacuum container the two slits, F_1 and F_2, between which there is a negative potential difference of V volts, extract a collimated beam of positive ions from the source S. This setup consists, for example, of a chamber into which a volatile compound of the element to be separated is introduced. The

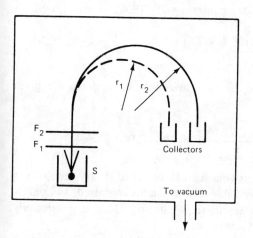

Fig. 3.17 Diagram of the operating principle of the calutron.

molecules are broken down, and the atoms are ionized by thermoelectrons produced by a heated filament. The collimated beam of positive ions enters a magnetic field of H gauss intensity normal to their velocity (in this case, on the plane of the figure), following a circular trajectory whose radius differs according to the ratio between mass and charge. The ions reach their maximum scattering after completing a semicircle. At the end of this trajectory, they are gathered in collectors placed there for that purpose. Under ideal conditions we would have a complete separation between the isotopes of an element which would be tantamount to infinity as a separation factor.

An ion of mass m (grams) and electrical charge Ze emerges from slit F_2 with a kinetic-energy charge of

$$\frac{1}{2}mv^2 = 10^7 \, VZe$$

in which e = 1.6021 × 10^{-19} coulomb is the charge of the electron, and the velocity v is expressed in centimeters per second. This gives us

$$v = \left(2 \times 10^7 \times \frac{VZe}{m}\right)^{\frac{1}{2}}$$ (3.134)

The radius, r (centimeters) of the trajectory within the magnetic field, is determined by the equilibrium between the centrifugal force and the magnetic force. Expressing the forces in dynes, we have

$$\frac{mv^2}{r} = 0.1 \text{ HZ ev}$$

from which, remembering Eq. 3.134 and introducing in place of m/e the M/F ratio (M being the atomic weight, and F the Faraday constant = 96,519.4 coulombs), we have

$$r = \frac{(2 \times 10^9 \text{ MV/ZF})^{\frac{1}{2}}}{H}$$ (3.135)

The maximum scattering of ions, after traversing half of the circumference, is given by

$$2(r_2 - r_1) = \frac{(8 \times 10^9 \times V/ZF)^{\frac{1}{2}}}{H} \left[(M_2)^{\frac{1}{2}} - (M_1)^{\frac{1}{2}}\right]$$

Although separation in the calutron is almost total, the yield is very low: only a small portion of the substance introduced into the apparatus is ionized, and only a fraction of the ions produced ever reach the collector. This is particularly disadvantageous when the feed substance is expensive.

Another limitation of the method is the ion current, which at excessively high values (some work is now being done at levels as high as 500 mA or more) tends to break up the ion beams—with a consequent decline in separation—owing to the effect of the space charge.

Although these facts constitute marked disadvantages for production on a very large scale, there is still the simplicity and versatility of the electromagnetic method (in the sense that with a single piece of apparatus we can perform the separation of almost all the elements) which make it suitable for producing isotopes in quantities on the order of a gram, i.e., for laboratory purposes. The only elements that cause trouble in separation via the calutron method are the noble gases. While the other gaseous substances are trapped in the collectors by means of handy chemical reactions (N_2, for example, is collected on a graphite–magnesium screen, with formation of a magnesium nitrate), this is not feasible in the case of totally inert rare gases.

In 1944, at Oak Ridge, Tennessee, the first large quantities (on the order of kilograms) of ^{235}U were produced in calutrons. Each unit operated with several sources in parallel. The installation, known as Y-12 Plant, operated until 1946, after which—since the process was more costly than gaseous diffusion—the plant was assigned to isotope separation of other elements for scientific purposes.

In conclusion, we are reminded that what we have called the versatility of the electromagnetic method makes it particularly suitable—as was shown in Chap. 2—to the design of such analytical instruments as mass spectrographs.

PHOTOCHEMICAL SEPARATION

The difference in mass between isotopic atoms or molecules means that there are slight differences in frequency in certain lines of the optical spectrum. We saw this also (pages 22 and 23) in the discussion of the emission spectrum of ^{235}U; the differences of the ^{235}U emission spectrum from that of ^{238}U are exploited for analytical purposes.

We might consider making use of such differences in the absorption spectra of isotopic substances to excite a given component in the mixture but not the others. The separation of the excited component could then be managed by taking advantage of, for example, its different susceptibility to ionization, dissociation, or chemical-combination reactions.

Theoretically photochemical separation looks like a highly selective process (meaning that the elementary separation factor is very high), as was the case for electromagnetic separation. In practice, however, the method must satisfy several requirements; namely, it must show:

1. A clear definition of the line shifted by isotopic effect in the absorption spectrum of the substance to be separated.

2. The presence of a radiation source with a very limited frequency field around that line.

3. Sufficient power in the source and good yield from the excitation process.

4. Modest energy exchange between the excited component and the rest of the system, so that the separation process described under item 5 can occur before excitation ends and so that the unwanted species do not become excited by energy transfer and thus cause a reduction in q_0.

5. The presence of a sufficiently selective physical or chemical separation process with a good yield.

Photochemical separation has been tested with some success on mercury, using the hyperfine structure of the line $\lambda = 2537$ Å. This structure is an effect of nuclear spin.

Gunning[43] obtained mercury 90% enriched with ^{202}Hg (the natural concentration is 29.8%) by irradiating a mixture of mercury vapor and oxygen with a discharge lamp without electrodes containing ^{202}Hg. (As an alternative, we can use a source with natural mercury and filter the radiation through mercury vapor). The excited ^{202}Hg oxidizes in the presence of oxygen, whereas the other isotopes do not react to any extent. Adding butadiene to the mixture made it possible to suppress most of the secondary reactions that destroy $^{202}HgO_2$ thus formed. Isotopic enrichment of mercury has also been studied in recent experiments in France.[44]

The method has been tested[45] as well for ^{235}U separation. The separation factor obtained, however, was very small: 1.0005 ± 0.0018. The recent application of laser sources seems to have led to far more encouraging results.

ENERGY CONSUMPTION

Every process of isotope separation consists, to varying degrees, of reversible and irreversible thermodynamic transformations. The energy consumed is almost totally governed by the irreversible transformations; the energy absorbed by separation under reversible conditions is minimal by comparison.

Briefly, we shall call a process reversible or irreversible according to the type of thermodynamic transformation predominant in it. Typical examples are distillation (a reversible process) and gaseous diffusion (an irreversible process).

In a single plate of a distillation column, the evaporation of part of the liquid occurs, using the heat of condensation of some of the vapor coming from the plate below. Because this transformation is reversible, the heat of evaporation can be given up to the system only once for all the plates in the column. This occurs in the evaporator located at the bottom of the column.

Ideally one might recover this heat by condensing the vapor at the top of the column. Practically, however, the fluid in the process also undergoes irreversible transformations that greatly reduce the possibility of recovery. Such irreversible transformations are mainly:

1. Loss of heat because of imperfect insulation.
2. Pressure drop due to attrition in the vapor flow through the column.
3. Limited efficiency of the heat exchangers.

The pressure drop mentioned in item 2 causes the condensation at the top of the column to take place at a temperature lower than that at the bottom, which in itself constitutes a loss of available work. But the greater portion of energy consumption is that cited in item 3 and is due to the temperature drop in the heat exchangers.

Consider L mols of a perfect gas composed of a binary mixture with mol fractions of two components N and $(1 - N)$, respectively.

The entropy of isothermic mixing is

$$\Delta S_{mix.} = -RL[N \ln N + (1 - N) \ln (1 - N)] \tag{3.136}$$

This equation can be used to calculate the demingling entropy for a reversible isothermic transformation which separates the initial L mols into L/2 enriched mols (N′) and L/2 depleted mols (N″).

The available work to be supplied to the system is then given by the free energy

$$E = -\Delta F = T \Delta S_{mix.}$$

By applying Eq. 3.136 to each of the transformed fractions, we arrive at the expression

$$E = \frac{1}{8} L g_0^2 \times RT \times N(1 - N) \qquad (3.137)$$

in which $g_0 = q_0 - 1$.

The energy E absorbed in the elementary process depends on the mol fraction N; it is greatest for $N = \frac{1}{2}$ and becomes nothing at the extremes $N = 0$ and $N = 1$.

This can be understood if we remember that, at the two ends of an ideal distillation column of infinite length, the light and heavy fractions are completely separated and hence each is at a pressure corresponding to its own vapor pressure. Such separation thus requires a degree of compression work. Each individual plate is responsible for only a small fraction in the total pressure drop, and that fraction becomes evanescent at the extremes, coming close to the components in the pure state.

Of course, the pressure drop across a single plate, due to the separation transformation, is very slight by comparison with the frictional pressure drop, which, however, is neither the only cause nor the major cause of inefficiency, as has been mentioned.

The elementary separation factor q_0 that we discussed in this chapter for various effects is an index to the usefulness of each but is not exhaustive for purposes of evaluation. The most important index is the "separative power," δU, which will be discussed extensively in Chap. 4 (see pages 120 to 123).

Here we need only know that δU is a measure of productivity of the process, expressed under optimal conditions as

$$\delta U = \frac{1}{8} L g_0^2 \qquad (3.138)$$

From Eq. 3.137 we can therefore express the energy consumed per unit of separative power:

$$\xi_E = \frac{E}{\delta U} = RT \times N(1 - N) \qquad (3.139)$$

Note that ξ_E does not depend on the elementary separation factor, the reason being that, in the reversible transformation considered, the only variations in entropy are those due to variations in concentration, quite independent of the process used to bring them about.

The energy consumptions calculated for ideal reversible processes are lower by many orders of magnitude than those in the corresponding real processes, even though the real processes are considered "substantially reversible."

For example, to produce 1 g of practically pure D_2O, starting with hydrogen in natural concentration and separating the deuterium from the liquid hydrogen by distillation ($20°K$), we would need 2.2×10^{-6} kWh under ideal reversible conditions, whereas in reality it takes about 3 to 6 kWh/g D_2O.

Next consider gaseous diffusion as a typically irreversible process, in which the energy absorption accompanying the elementary effect is that due to isothermic expansion of the gas through the porous barrier.

If r is the compression ratio, the energy absorbed in the diffusion of $\frac{1}{2}L$ mol is

$$E = \frac{1}{2} LRT \ln r$$

In Chap. 5 (see pages 186 to 191) we shall see that, when operating at very low pressures, the elementary separation factor q_0 given by Eq. 3.93 is affected by an efficiency factor that is a function of r, so that the actual "separation gain" $g = q - 1$ is given by

$$g = g_0 (1 - 1/r)$$

The separative power therefore is

$$\delta U = \frac{1}{8} L g_0^2 (1 - 1/r)^2$$

and the specific energy consumption

$$\xi_E = \frac{E}{\delta U} = \frac{4RT}{g_0^2} \times \frac{\ln r}{(1 - 1/r)^2} \tag{3.140}$$

The second factor appearing in this equation is a function solely of the compression ratio and is minimum for $r = 3.5$. Considering, for example, the diffusion of UF_6 at ambient temperature ($298°K$) with $r = 3.5$, we have

$$\xi_E = 610 \times 2.45 = 1500 \text{ kWh/kg U}$$

in which the kg U represents the unit of separative power. In terms of absorbed power and capacity we have, correspondingly,

$$\xi_E = 0.07 \times 2.45 = 0.17 \text{ kW/(kg U year}^{-1}).$$

The second term appearing in Eq. 140 can be interpreted as an efficiency factor that varies from process to process, whereas the first term,

$$\xi_{E_0} = \frac{4RT}{g_0^2}$$

constitutes an absolute lower limit for any irreversible process. In the case of gaseous diffusion (298°K), we have $\xi_{E_0} = 0.07$ kW/(kg U year^{-1}).

An irreversible process may be preferable to reversible processes for separating a particular isotope, despite the greater energy consumption. This happens when the separation factor is so much greater that the dimensions of the installation can be much smaller. A greater expenditure of energy may thus prove more than compensated for by the lower capital costs. This is especially true in the case of isotopes of heavy elements, for which reversible processes generally offer very small separation factors.

REFERENCES

Surveys

1. M. Benedict et al., Report of Uranium Isotope Separation: Review Ad Hoc Committee, USAEC Report ORO-694, June 1972.
2. H. K. Rae, A Review of Heavy Water Production Processes, Canadian Report AECL-2503 (Rev.), August 1969.

Distillation

3. E. Kirschbaum, *Distillier und Rektifiziertechnik*, Springer-Verlag KG, Berlin, 1950.
4. A. Weissberger (Ed.), *Technique of Organic Chemistry*, Vol. 4, *Distillation*, Chap. 1, Theory, A. and E. Rose, Wiley-Interscience, Inc., New York, 1951.
5. A. Hala, J. Pick, V. Fried, and O. Vilim, *Vapour–Liquid Equilibrium*, Pergamon Press, Inc., London, 1958.
6. P. T. Nettley, D. K. Cartwright, and H. Kronberger, The Production of ^{10}B by Low-Temperature Distillation of Boron Fluoride, in *Isotope Separation*, Symposium Proceedings, Amsterdam, Apr. 23–27, 1957, J. Kistemaker, J. Bigeleisen, and A. O. C. Nier (Eds.), p. 385, North-Holland Publishing Company, Amsterdam, 1958.
7. I. Dostrovsky and A. Raviv, Separation of the Heavy Isotopes of Oxygen by Distillation, *ibid.*, p. 336.
8. J. T. Phillips, C. U. Lindenstrom-Lang, and J. Bigeleisen, Liquid–Vapor Argon Isotope Fractionation from the Triple Point to the Critical Point, USAEC Report UR-3999-12, 1971.

Molecular Distillation

9. A. Weissberger (Ed.), *Technique of Organic Chemistry*, Vol. IV, *Distillation*, Chap. VI, Distillation Under High Vacuum, E. S. Perry, Wiley-Interscience, Inc., New York, 1951.
10. I. Langmuir, *Phys. Rev.*, **2**: 329 (1913).
11. A. K. Brewer and S. Madorsky, *J. Res. Nat. Bur. Stand.*, **38**: 129 (1947).
12. D. B. Trauger, J. J. Keyes, G. A. Kuipers, and D. M. Lang, Some Experiments on the Separation of Lithium Isotopes by Molecular Distillation, in *Isotope Separation*, Symposium Proceedings, Amsterdam, Apr. 23–27, 1957, J. Kistemaker, J. Bigeleisen, and A. O. C. Nier (Eds.), p. 350, North-Holland Publishing Company, Amsterdam, 1958.

Exchange Reactions

13. A. I. Brodskiy, *Himiya Isotopov*, Chap. 7, 2nd edition, Akademiya Nauk SSSR, Moscow, 1957.
14. H. C. Urey, *J. Amer. Chem. Soc.*, **69**: 562 (1947).

15. T. I. Taylor and W. Spindel, Preparation of Highly Enriched Nitrogen-15 by Chemical Exchange of NO with HNO_3, in *Isotope Separation*, Symposium Proceedings, Amsterdam. Apr. 23–27, 1957, J. Kistemaker, J. Bigeleisen, and A. O. C. Nier (Eds.), p. 158, North-Holland Publishing Company, Amsterdam, 1958.
16. S. V. Ribnikar, Chemical Exchange Reactions with Boron and a Laboratory Exchange Column for ^{10}B Enrichment, *ibid.*, p. 204.
17. G. Stiel and K. Mueehle, Enrichment of the Stable Isotope ^{34}S in the System NH_4HSO_3/SO_3, *Isotopenpraxis,* 5: 429 (1969). [Translation, USAEC Report MLM-1920(tr)].
18. A. J. Saraceno and C. F. Trivisonno, Uranium Isotope Separation by Chemical Exchange Between Derivatives of UF_6 and Nitrogen Oxide Complexes, USAEC Report GAT-674, February 1972.

Exchanging Resins

19. F. H. Spedding and J. E. Powell, A Laboratory Method for Separating Nitrogen Isotopes by Ion Exchange, USAEC Report ISC-611, June 1955.
20. F. Menes, E. Saito, and H. Roth, Séparation des Isotopes du Lithium sur Échangeurs d'Ions, in *Isotope Separation*, Symposium Proceedings, Amsterdam, Apr. 23–27, J. Kistemaker, J. Bigeleisen, A. O. C. Nier (Eds.), p. 227, North-Holland Publishing Company, Amsterdam, 1958.
21. S. Forbert et al., Enrichment of Heavy Sulphur Isotopes with an Anion Exchanger, *ibid.*, p. 243.

Reaction Speeds

22. S. Glasstone, *Textbook of Physical Chemistry,* Chap. XIII, Van Nostrand Reinhold Company, New York, 1940–1946.
23. R. B. Bernstein, *J. Phys. Chem.,* 56: 893 (1952).

Gaseous Diffusion

24. A. Sommerfeld, Lectures on Theoretical Physics, Vol. 5, Thermodynamics and Statistical Mechanics, Chap. 3, Wiesbaden, 1952.
25. M. Knudsen, *Ann. Phys.,* 28: 75 (1909).
26. Y. Rocard, *Thermodynamique,* Chap. 1, Part 1, pp. 294-297, M. F. Masson, Paris, 1952.

Mass Diffusion

27. J. Crank, *The Mathematics of Diffusion,* Chap. 2, Clarendon Press, Oxford, 1956.
28. A. Klemm, *Z. Naturforsch.,* 1: 252 (1946).
29. Kirk–Othmer, *Encyclopedia of Chemical Technology.* Vol. 5, p. 119, Wiley-Interscience, Inc., New York, 1965.

Thermodiffusion

30. D. Enskog, *Phys. Z.,* 12(56): 533 (1911).
31. S. Chapman and T. G. Cowling, *The Mathematical Theory of Non-Uniform Gases,* Cambridge University Press, Cambridge, 1939.
32. K. Clusius and G. Dickel, *Z. Phys. Chem.,* 44: 397, 451 (1939).
33. J. Hirschfelder, R. B. Bird, and A. L. Spotz, *J. Chem. Phys.,* 16: 968 (1948).
34. G. Vasara et al., *Thermal Diffusion Column: Theory and Practice with Particular Emphasis on Isotope Separation,* VEB Deutsches Verlag Wissenschaften, Berlin, 1969.

Separation Nozzle

35. S. P. Dickens, C. A. Coghlan, and P. C. Murrow, Separation of Gases from Mixtures Thereof, U. S. Patent No. 2,607,439, July 28, 1948.
36. E. W. Becker et al., *Z. Naturforsch.*, 9a: 975 (1954).
37. B. Nardelli and A. Repani, *Energ. Nucl. (Milan)*, 4: 293 (1957); *ibid.*, 5: 247 (1958).
38. E. W. Becker et al., Separation of Isotopes of Uranium by the Separation Nozzle Process, *Angew. Chem., Int. Ed. Engl.*, 6: 507 (1967).
39. E. W. Becker et al., The Separation Nozzle Process for Enrichment of [235]U, in *Proceedings of the Fourth International Conference on the Peaceful Uses of Atomic Energy, Geneva, 1971*, Vol. 9, p. 3, United Nations, New York, 1972.

Centrifugation

40. J. W. Beams and F. B. Haynes, *Phys. Rev.*, 49: 644(A) (1936); 50: 491 (1936).
41. J. W. Beams and A. V. Masket, *ibid.*, 51: 384(A) (1937).
42. W. Groth and K. Beyerle, Gas Centrifuges, Chap. 6, p. 249, in *Separation of Isotopes*, H. London (Ed.), Newnes Educational Publishing Co. Ltd., London, 1961.

Photochemical Separation

43. H. E. Gunning: *Can. J. Chem.*, 36: 89 (1958).
44. J. P. Morand, Étude de l'Oxydation Photochimique du Mercure: Application à la Séparation des Isotopes du Mercure. (Study of the Photochemical Oxidation of Mercury: Application to the Separation of the Mercury Isotopes), French Report CEA R-4126, August 1971.
45. R. L. Farrar, Jr., and D. F. Smith, Photochemical Isotope Separation as Applied to Uranium, USAEC Report K-L-3054(Rev. 1), March 1972.

Electrolysis

46. G. N. Lewis and R. T. MacDonald, *J. Amer. Chem. Soc.*, 55: 3058 (1933).
47. J. Brun and Th. Varberg, *Kgl. Nor. Vidensk. Selsk. Forh.*, 26(6): 19 (1953).
48. J. Brun, Th. Varberg, W. Gundersen, and R. Solli, *ibid.*, 29(2): 5 (1956).
49. J. Brun, W. Gundersen, and R. Solli, *ibid.*, 29(2): 5 (1956).
50. M. L. Eidinoff, *J. Amer. Chem. Soc.*, 69: 977, 2507 (1947).

Electromigration

51. A. K. Brewer, S. L. Madorsky, and J. W. Westhaver, *Science*, 104: 156 (1946).
52. A. Klemm, *Z. Elektrochem.*, 58: 609 (1954).
53. A. Klemm, *Z. Naturforsch.*, 1: 252 (1946).
54. A. Klemm, *J. Chem. Phys.*, 49: 18 (1952).

Electromagnetic Separation

55. C. J. Zilverschoon, An Electromagnetic Isotope Separator, Thesis, Amsterdam, 1954.
56. C. P. Keim, *J. Appl. Phys.*, 24: 1255 (1953).

4 THE THEORY OF CASCADES

CONTINUOUS AND DISCONTINUOUS PROCESSES

We have shown in Chap. 3 that the elementary separation effect in isotope-separation processes is generally very slight. Thus this effect must be suitably multiplied to produce material at the desired concentration. Even when the elementary separation factor is not small, as in the case of deuterium separation by water electrolysis, the difference between the initial concentration and the desired concentration is often such that the latter cannot be achieved without multiplying the elementary effect.

Theoretically this can be done in two different ways: (1) with discontinuous processes or (2) with continuous, multistage processes. The discontinuous process consists of introducing into the separation unit (such as an electrolytic cell or battery of cells, or a still) an initial charge of the mixture to be separated. This same charge is then subjected to the physicochemical transformation planned (electrolysis or evaporation, respectively), and the transformed substance (electrolytic gas or vapor, respectively) is removed as it is formed, but the separation unit is not fed during the process. Its charge is thus continuously reduced, and its concentration is correspondingly increased. The process is interrupted when the remaining charge has reached the desired concentration. It is then removed from the separation unit, which is then fed another charge, and the whole process is repeated. Hence the designation "discontinuous process" refers not so much to the interruptions of operation of the separation unit, which may be relatively brief by comparison with the actual operating time, but rather to the discontinuity of loading.

98

Continuous processes, on the contrary, are characterized by substantial constancy of all the flow rates, particularly input and product. Generally the flow rates are not varied, except to minimize the concentration variations in the product.

STAGES, CASCADES, AND SEPARATING ELEMENTS

In continuous processes the multiplication of the separative effect is achieved by hydraulic connection in series of a number of separation units, each of which is called a "stage." A fraction of the material fed into one stage comes out of it enriched ("head"), and the remaining fraction comes out depleted ("tail"). The enriched fraction goes on to feed the next stage, so that the successive stages in the series are fed with increasingly smaller flows.

The complex of stages arranged in series is called a cascade. In fact, the visualization of the feed flow as a function of the numerical order of the stages resembles a picture of a waterfall with several steps in it.

The successive stages in a cascade, since they are called upon to handle smaller and smaller loads, become consequently smaller and smaller themselves. However, a stage is not always composed of a single separation unit. In a distillation plant, for example, the feed flow of the early stages can be larger than even the biggest column practically feasible (9 to 10 m in diameter) can hold. When this happens, there can be several columns in the same stage, fed in parallel.

Also, for purposes of standardization, it might be desirable to have the individual stages in a cascade made up of a variable number of identical separation units, connected in parallel with each other inside the same stage. For example, a centrifuge installation typically consists of identical machines. Blocks of centrifuges connected in parallel form the stages, which are in turn connected in series to form the cascade.

In general, the name "separating element" is given to the unit of standard dimensions used in the construction of a cascade, e.g., a distillation column of a certain diameter (or even the single plates of the same diameter), a centrifuge, or an electrolytic cell. A typical cascade is shown in Fig. 4.1.

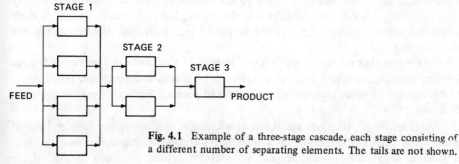

Fig. 4.1 Example of a three-stage cascade, each stage consisting of a different number of separating elements. The tails are not shown.

CASCADE SCHEMES

There are cascades in which the tail coming from a single stage is not processed further and leaves the cascade. In other cases, however, the tail of the single stage is recycled through the preceding stages and processed again. This second type of cascade is called a "countercurrent" cascade, to indicate that the tails flow in the cascade in the opposite direction from that of the heads.

Normally the countercurrent cascades make it possible to get—with the same feed flow, separation factor, and number of stages—a larger quantity of the product than can be obtained from cascades without recycling. The latter are generally used when the desired isotope is a by-product and recycling would entail an intolerable decrease of the main product. A typical example is the separation of deuterium as a by-product of electrolytic hydrogen. In that process, recycling involves burning some of the main product.

The simplest recycling scheme is that in which the tail of each stage is recycled to the entry of the preceding stage and the head goes on to feed the successive stage. Such designs are called "symmetrical," and a diagram of one is shown in Fig. 4.2(b). Figure 4.2(a) is a diagram of a cascade without recycling.

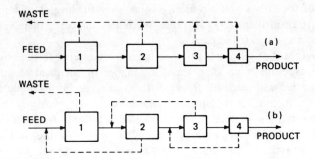

Fig. 4.2   (a) Cascade without recycling, and (b) symmetrical countercurrent cascade.

In other possible schemes the tail emerging from each stage is recycled to two or more stages upstream instead of back to the entrance of the immediately preceding stage. Similarly we can also consider introducing the head of each stage two or more stages downstream rather than into the very next one. Examples of such cascades are shown in Fig. 4.3.

We can see that schemes in which the reentry of the heads and tails of each stage involves jumping an equal number of stages downstream and upstream, respectively, really amount to several symmetrical cascades in parallel. Such schemes are therefore fictitious.

"Asymmetrical" schemes are those in which the reentry of the head and tail of each stage occurs after jumping a different number of stages downstream than upstream. Asymmetrical cascades can be useful for such processes as that of the separation nozzle, in which the distribution of loads required by a symmetrical scheme would not match the optimal operating conditions of the individual separating elements. However, the cases in which it might prove advantageous to choose an asymmetrical cascade are quite rare.

In the following pages, unless specifically stated otherwise, we shall be talking about symmetrical cascades with recycling, which are the most important.

When we desire a certain production level and wish to economize on feed as much as possible, it is best to choose a countercurrent cascade in which the tail of the first stage is further processed in a series of stages operating at steadily lower concentrations with respect to the feed concentration. Such a series of stages is called the "stripping section" of the cascade, whereas the stages that produce enriched fractions at higher concentrations than the feed are known as the "enrichment section."

A symmetrical cascade with a stripping section is shown in Fig. 4.4. The first stage of the stripping section produces an enriched fraction with the same concentration as the feed and is then cycled back into the feed at the entry to the first stage of the enrichment section.

Stripping sections are used in all processes in which the feed consists of material costly enough to suggest its maximum exploitation; a typical case is the enrichment of uranium hexafluoride. Generally, however, there are no stripping sections in those deuterium separation processes in which the feed is natural water.

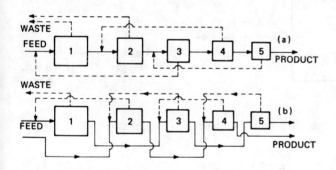

Fig. 4.3 Examples of asymmetrical cascades: (a) with recycling two stages upstream and (b) with feed two stages downstream.

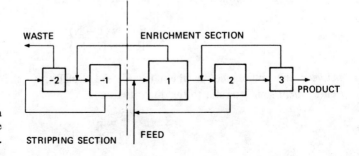

Fig. 4.4 Example of a symmetrical cascade with a stripping section.

STAGE EQUATIONS

Consider next a generic stage of a cascade in the stationary mode of feed and concentrations. Figure 4.5 shows the nomenclature of the concentrations and flows both for feed and for the enriched and depleted fractions.

In analogy with the definitions given on pages 35 and 36 in Chap. 3 and keeping in mind the relations between the terms N and R, we shall use "stage separation factor" to refer to the ratio

$$q = \frac{R'}{R''} = \frac{N'(1-N'')}{N''(1-N')} \tag{4.1}$$

between the relative abundances of the desired isotope in the head and tail of the stage. This factor coincides with the elementary separation factor q_0, provided that, within that stage, there is no remixing or there are no processes occurring which multiply the elementary effect.

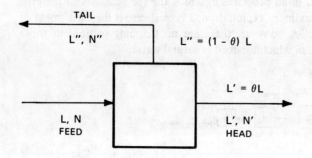

Fig. 4.5 Generic stage in a cascade. L = flow rate; θ = cut; N = mol fraction.

We shall use the term "separation gain" in referring to the quantity

$$g = q - 1 = \frac{R'}{R''} - 1 \tag{4.2}$$

The "stage enrichment factor" is defined by the ratio

$$\alpha = \frac{R'}{R} = \frac{N'(1-N)}{N(1-N')} \tag{4.3}$$

between the abundances in the tail and feed. Finally, we shall use the expression "enrichment gain" to refer to the quantity

$$\epsilon = \alpha - 1 = \frac{R'}{R} - 1 \tag{4.4}$$

From these definitions we derive the equations for stage enrichment:

$$R' - R'' = gR'' \qquad (4.5)$$

$$R' - R = \epsilon R \qquad (4.6)$$

or, in terms of mol fractions,

$$N' - N'' = gN'' (1 - N') \qquad (4.7)$$

$$N' - N = \epsilon N (1 - N') \qquad (4.8)$$

Again, from the definitions of the separation and enrichment factors and noting that, furthermore,

$$\frac{R}{R''} = \frac{q}{\alpha} \qquad (4.9)$$

we can see that the mol fractions of the head, the tail, and the feed have the following interrelations:

$$N' = \frac{qN''}{1 - N'' + qN''} = \frac{\alpha N}{1 - N + \alpha N} \qquad (4.10)$$

$$N'' = \frac{N'}{q(1 - N') + N'} = \frac{\alpha N}{q(1 - N) + \alpha N} \qquad (4.11)$$

$$N = \frac{N'}{\alpha(1 - N') + N'} = \frac{qN''}{\alpha(1 - N'') + qN''} \qquad (4.12)$$

The conservation of the material and of the desired isotope can be expressed as

$$L = L' + L'' \qquad (4.13)$$

$$LN = L'N' + L''N'' \qquad (4.14)$$

By calling the ratio $\theta = L'/L$ the "cut," we can write Eq. 4.14 thus:

$$N = \theta N' + (1 - \theta)N'' \qquad (4.15)$$

or

$$N' - N = (1 - \theta)(N' - N'') \qquad (4.16)$$

A ratio between g and ϵ is obtained by combining enrichment Eqs. 4.7 and 4.8 with conservation Eq. 4.16:

$$N' - N'' = \frac{\epsilon}{1 - \theta} N(1 - N') \tag{4.17}$$

or

$$\epsilon = (1 - \theta) \frac{gN''}{N} \tag{4.18}$$

Expressing the mol fractions as a function of N' by means of Eqs. 4.11 and 4.12, we have

$$\epsilon = \frac{(1 - \theta)g}{1 + \theta g (1 - N')} \tag{4.19}$$

Note that $\epsilon \simeq g$ for very small cuts, whereas it becomes zero as θ tends toward unity. Note also that, in general, an intrinsic dependence on concentration appears when ϵ is expressed as a function of g (and hence when α is expressed as a function of q). This dependence disappears when we operate at very low concentrations (N, N', N'' $\ll$ 1): in this case the following approximate equations apply:

$$q \simeq \frac{N'}{N''} \tag{4.20}$$

$$\alpha \simeq \frac{N'}{N} \tag{4.21}$$

$$\epsilon \simeq \frac{(1 - \theta)g}{1 + \theta g} \tag{4.22}$$

This last equation can also be written in the form

$$\alpha \simeq \frac{q}{1 + \theta(q - 1)} \tag{4.23}$$

or

$$q \simeq \frac{1 - \theta}{(1/\alpha) - \theta} \tag{4.24}$$

The dependence of α on the cut in Eq. 4.23 is shown graphically in Fig. 4.6 for three different values of q.

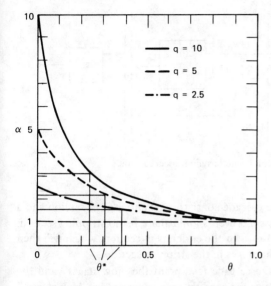

Fig. 4.6 Dependence of α on the cut for three different values of the separation factor q. The θ^* values of the cut are those in which α = the square root of q.

As q diminishes, it tends to become linear. In fact, Eqs. 4.7, 4.8, and 4.19 are simplified in another case as well, i.e., for gains that are very small in relation to unity ($g \ll 1$; $\epsilon \ll 1$). This is conventionally called the "infinitesimal case."

These equations can thus be written in the order

$$N' - N'' \simeq gN(1 - N) \qquad (4.25)$$

$$N' - N \simeq \epsilon N(1 - N) \qquad (4.26)$$

$$\epsilon \simeq g(1 - \theta) \qquad (4.27)$$

This last one is indeed a linear simplification of Eq. 4.22.

It should be noted that, in the second member of Eqs. 4.25 and 4.26, N can be replaced by any concentration that differs from N by small quantities on the order of ϵ: by so doing, an error on the order of ϵ^2 is made.

We can quickly see that the treatment set forth in this section for the typical stage holds good also for the single separating elements of which that stage might conceivably be made up.

EQUATIONS FOR THE GENERIC SYMMETRICAL CASCADE

Consider a generic symmetrical cascade that, fed with the flow F at a concentration of N_F, yields a product P whose concentration is N_P and a quantity of waste, W, whose concentration is N_W (Fig. 4.7). These flows and concentrations (mol fractions) are called the "external parameters" of the cascade.

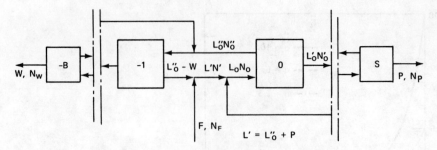

Fig. 4.7 Schematic of a generic symmetrical cascade.

In general, we can assume that the cascade consists of an enrichment section and a stripping section, but the argument is valid even should there be no stripping section.

We will number the stages from 0 to S in the enrichment section, which will then add up to S + 1, and from −1 to −B the stages in the stripping section.

We shall call the stages closer to the cascade feed point the "low stages" and the stages closer to the withdrawal points for the product and the waste the "high stages."

For conservation of the material and the desired isotope, we have

$$F = P + W \tag{4.28}$$

$$FN_F = PN_P + WN_W \tag{4.29}$$

Hence it is possible to express the feed and waste flows as functions of the four other external parameters

$$F = P \frac{N_P - N_W}{N_F - N_W} \tag{4.30}$$

$$W = P \frac{N_P - N_F}{N_F - N_W} \tag{4.31}$$

The name "internal parameters" is given to the number of stages in the cascade, as well as to the flow rates and concentrations of the feed, the head, and the tail of each stage.

The calculation of a cascade usually consists of finding these internal parameters, once the values for the four external parameters are set.

In this connection, consider a portion of the enrichment section of a typical symmetrical cascade, like the one shown in Fig. 4.8.

The conservation equations for the portion of the cascade after the typical stage s, including the stages from s + 1 to S, are written

$$\theta_s L_s - (1 - \theta_{s+1})L_{s+1} = P \tag{4.32}$$

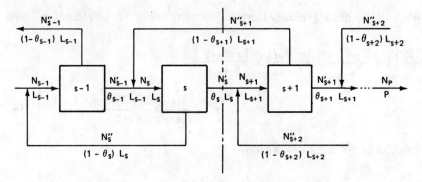

Fig. 4.8 Portion of the enrichment section of a generic symmetrical cascade.

$$\theta_s L_s N_s' - (1 - \theta_{s+1}) L_{s+1} N_{s+1}'' = P N_P \qquad (4.33)$$

From these we obtain

$$N_s' - N_{s+1}'' = \frac{P}{(1 - \theta_{s+1})L_{s+1}} (N_P - N_s') \qquad (4.34)$$

Furthermore, writing the first part of Eq. 4.11 for the $s + 1$ stage,

$$N_{s+1}'' = \frac{N_{s+1}'}{1 + g(1 - N_{s+1}')} \qquad (4.35)$$

and combining this latter with Eq. 4.34, we have

$$N_{s+1}' - N_s' = \frac{g N_{s+1}' (1 - N_{s+1}')}{1 + g(1 - N_{s+1}')} - \frac{P(N_P - N_s')}{(1 - \theta_{s+1})L_{s+1}} \qquad (4.36)$$

In the most common case, the cut θ_s can be considered an arbitrary function of s, and only its definition makes the cascade calculation possible.

Once the cuts θ_s are established, we find that for a given value of P all the flow rates L_s are unequivocally determined. In fact, from Eq. 4.32 we have

$$L_s = \frac{P}{\theta_s} + \frac{1 - \theta_{s+1}}{\theta_s} L_{s+1} \qquad (4.37)$$

and thus

$$L_{s+1} = \frac{P}{\theta_{s+1}} + \frac{1 - \theta_{s+2}}{\theta_{s+1}} L_{s+2} \qquad (4.38)$$

When the s index is gradually increased by unity until s = S, combining will give

$$L_s = \frac{P}{\theta_s} \left[1 + \frac{1 - \theta_{s+1}}{\theta_{s+1}} + \frac{1 - \theta_{s+1}}{\theta_{s+1}} \times \frac{1 - \theta_{s+2}}{\theta_{s+2}} + \dots \right.$$

$$\left. + \frac{1 - \theta_{s+1}}{\theta_{s+1}} \times \frac{1 - \theta_{s+2}}{\theta_{s+2}} \dots \frac{1 - \theta_S}{\theta_S} \right] \quad (4.39)$$

Specifically, for θ = const, we have

$$L_s = \frac{P}{\theta} \frac{\left(\dfrac{1 - \theta}{\theta}\right)^{1+S-s} - 1}{\dfrac{1 - \theta}{\theta} - 1} \quad (4.40)$$

and, for $\theta = 1/2$,

$$L_s = 2P(1 + S - s) \quad (4.41)$$

Using Eqs. 4.36 and 4.39, we can calculate progressively the concentrations of the heads of the successive stages. Correspondingly, the tail and feed concentrations can be calculated using Eqs. 4.11 and 4.12.

For low concentrations ($N'_{s+1} \ll 1$, $N'_s \ll 1$), Eq. 4.36 becomes linear:

$$N'_{s+1} - N'_s = \frac{g}{1+g} N'_{s+1} - \frac{P(N_P - N'_s)}{(1 - \theta_{s+1})L_{s+1}} \quad (4.42)$$

When in addition $N'_s \ll N_P$, which occurs at the low stages, Eq. 4.36 is further simplified:

$$\frac{1}{g} N'_{s+1} - N'_s = - \frac{PN_P}{(1 - \theta_{s+1})L_{s+1}} \quad (4.43)$$

Thus the search for $N' = N'(s)$ consists in solving an equation whose differences are finite and nonhomogeneous with constant coefficients (see Appendix C). Since the equation is of the first order, the problem is defined by a single boundary condition; e.g., $N'_S = N_P$.

From Eqs. 4.34 and 4.42, we see immediately that, when $P = 0$, it is always $N'_s = N''_{s+1}$, i.e., $R'_s = R''_{s+1}$. However, since by definition $R''_{s+1} = R'_{s+1}/q$, we deduce that

$$R'_{s+1} = qR'_s \quad (4.44)$$

From this recurrent equation we derive the pattern of concentrations

$$R'_s = R'_0 q^s \tag{4.45}$$

and·hence

$$s = \frac{\ln R'_s/R'_0}{\ln q} \tag{4.46}$$

Next we will consider the infinitesimal case, with any concentration, even high. Equation 4.36 is simplified as follows:

$$N'_{s+1} - N'_s \simeq gN'_{s+1} (1 - N'_{s+1}) - \frac{P(N_P - N'_s)}{L''_{s+1}} \tag{4.47}$$

If $P/L''_{s+1} \leqslant g$, with the same approximation we can put the N factor in the place of N' and the dN/ds derivative in the place of the incremental ratio

$$\frac{N'_{s+1} - N'_s}{(s + 1) - s}$$

which is equal to the first term of Eq. 4.47. This means that it can then be written

$$\frac{dN}{ds} = gN (1 - N) - \frac{P(N_P - N)}{L''} \tag{4.48}$$

where, in general, $L'' = L''(s)$.

In the infinitesimal case the cascade calculation consists in solving Eq. 4.48, once the function $L'' = L''(s)$ is specified, with a boundary condition, e.g., $N(0) = N_0$.

For zero production, or $P = 0$, the concentration gradient along the cascade becomes

$$\frac{dN}{ds} = gN(1 - N) \tag{4.49}$$

and hence

$$dR = gR \, ds$$

and the concentration pattern will be

$$R = R_0 e^{gs} \tag{4.50}$$

by analogy with that expressed by Eq. 4.45. Thus we have

$$s = \frac{1}{g} \ln \frac{R}{R_0} \tag{4.51}$$

From Eq. 4.48 we also see that, at the end of the cascade, where $N = N_P$, we have

$$\left(\frac{dN}{ds}\right)_{N=N_P} = gN_P(1 - N_P) \tag{4.52}$$

Since the second term of the second member of Eq. 4.48 is negative and decreasing in absolute value, we see that the concentration gradient increases monotonically along the cascade up to the maximum value given by Eq. 4.52.

From Eq. 4.32 it is shown that, if the flows and cuts vary very little from stage to stage, and furthermore, if we are at some distance from the outlet of the cascade, which means that $P/L \ll 1$, we have $\theta_s \simeq 1/2$, and Eq. 4.48 can be written

$$\frac{dN}{ds} \simeq gN(1 - N) - \frac{2P}{L}(N_P - N) \tag{4.53}$$

This last equation, substituting the function $L(s)$ given by Eq. 4.41, enables us to calculate the low stages of the infinitesimal cascade in the particular case where $\theta = 1/2$.

All that has been said about an enrichment section of a generic symmetrical cascade is equally valid for a stripping section. We need only to substitute $-W$ for P, R_0'' for R_0, and R_W for R_P and then to vary s from -1 to $-B$.

EQUATIONS FOR THE IDEAL SYMMETRICAL CASCADE

A cascade is referred to as "ideal" when, at the points of confluence of the heads and recycled tails from the stages further downstream, there is no remixing of materials with different isotopic concentrations. This calls for a proper definition of the cuts and flows all along the cascade.

For the typical stage s, we can write Eq. 4.15 as

$$\theta_s = \frac{N_s - N_s''}{N_s' - N_s''} = \frac{R_s - R_s''}{R_s' - R_s''} \times \frac{1 + R_s'}{1 + R_s} \tag{4.54}$$

Furthermore, by definition,

$$R_s' = \alpha R_s \tag{4.55}$$

also we impose the conditions of nonremixing which, for a symmetrical scheme, are written

$$R''_{s+1} = R'_{s-1} = R_s \tag{4.56}$$

Comparing this latest expression with Eq. 4.55, we have

$$R_{s+1} = \alpha R_s \tag{4.57}$$

Again, from Eq. 4.56 we see that $R''_s = R_{s-1}$ and so, using Eq. 4.57,

$$R''_s = \frac{R_s}{\alpha} \tag{4.58}$$

Since, by definition, we have $R'_s/R''_s = q$, when we compare Eq. 4.55 with Eq. 4.58, we see that in the ideal cascade

$$\alpha = q^{\frac{1}{2}} \tag{4.59}$$

Substituting Eqs. 4.55 and 4.58 in Eq. 4.54, we have the cut of the ideal cascade:

$$\theta_s = \frac{1 + \alpha R_s}{(1 + \alpha)(1 + R_s)} \tag{4.60}$$

Combining Eqs. 4.32 and 4.33, we have

$$L_s = \frac{P(N_P - N''_{s+1})}{\theta_s(N'_s - N''_{s+1})} \tag{4.61}$$

Now, if in this equation, which is universally valid, we replace θ_s with Eq. 4.60, we have, allowing for Eq. 4.56,

$$L_s = \frac{(\alpha + 1) P(N_P - N_s)}{(\alpha - 1)N_s(1 - N_s)} \tag{4.62}$$

and we find that, at the end of the cascade, $L_s \rightarrow (\alpha + 1) P(1 + R_P/\alpha)/(1 + R_P)$.

The concentration pattern is immediately found from the recurrent Eq. 4.57, by which

$$R_s = R_0 \alpha^s \tag{4.63}$$

and hence

$$s = \frac{\ln R_s/R_0}{\ln \alpha} \tag{4.64}$$

by analogy, respectively, with Eqs. 4.45 and 4.46, which are applicable to general symmetrical cascades with zero production.

The total number of stages is therefore

$$S + 1 = \frac{\ln R_P/R_0}{\ln \alpha} \tag{4.65}$$

For the case of low concentrations, the above-cited equations are fairly well applicable, even if N is written instead of R.

Specifically, we have

$$\theta_s \simeq \frac{1 + \alpha N_s}{1 + \alpha}$$

and

$$L_s = \frac{\alpha + 1}{\alpha - 1} P \frac{N_P - N_s}{N_s}$$

or else

$$L_s = \frac{\alpha + 1}{\alpha - 1} \frac{PN_P}{N_s}$$

far from the withdrawal point.

In the infinitesimal case the preceding equations are written

$$\epsilon \simeq \frac{g}{2} \tag{4.66}$$

$$\theta \simeq \frac{1}{2} \left[1 - \frac{\epsilon}{2} (1 - 2N) \right] \tag{4.67}$$

$$L \simeq \frac{2P(N_P - N)}{\epsilon N(1 - N)} \tag{4.68}$$

$$R \simeq R_0 \, e^{\epsilon s} \tag{4.69}$$

$$s \simeq \frac{\ln R/R_0}{\epsilon} \tag{4.70}$$

$$S + 1 \simeq \frac{\ln R_P/R_0}{\epsilon} \tag{4.71}$$

Substituting Eqs. 4.66 to 4.68 in the enrichment Eq. 4.48, we have

$$\frac{dN}{ds} = \epsilon N(1 - N) \tag{4.72}$$

Comparing this with Eq. 4.49, we see that the concentration gradient along an ideal infinitesimal-gain cascade is half that which we have in any nonideal cascade with zero production. And even when, at nonzero production, an ideal cascade is compared with a corresponding nonideal one, the same ratio pertains between the maximum gradients, at the withdrawal point.

It is also observed that

$$\lim_{N \to N_P} (N_P - N) = \left(\frac{dN}{ds}\right)_{N=N_P} = \epsilon N_P(1 - N_P)$$

Hence Eq. 4.68 shows that, toward the withdrawal point of the cascade, $L \to 2P$.

When it comes to handling the stripping section of an ideal symmetrical cascade, the statements made at the end of the preceding section of this chapter (page 110) are valid. Since in an ideal cascade $R_0' = R_0/\alpha$, the number of stages of the stripping section is

$$B = \frac{\ln R_0/R_W}{\ln \alpha} - 1 \tag{4.73}$$

and hence, in the infinitesimal case

$$B = \frac{\ln R_0/R_W}{\epsilon} - 1 \tag{4.74}$$

Returning to Eq. 4.67, we see that, from the low concentrations all the way to the equimolar mixtures ($N = 0.5$), $\theta < 1/2$ and that, thereafter, θ becomes greater than $1/2$.

Figure 4.9, using the above equations for an ideal cascade with $\epsilon = 0.002$, shows the internal parameters and the F and W flows corresponding to the following external parameters:

$$N_F = 0.007 = N_0$$

$$N_P = 0.20; \quad P = 26.25 \text{ mols hr}^{-1}$$

$$N_W = 0.002$$

The production rate of desired isotope is $PN_P = 5.25$ mols hr^{-1}. With a weight of 0.238 kg mol^{-1} and assuming an actual operation of 8000 hr year^{-1}, we have $PN_P = 10$ tons year^{-1}.

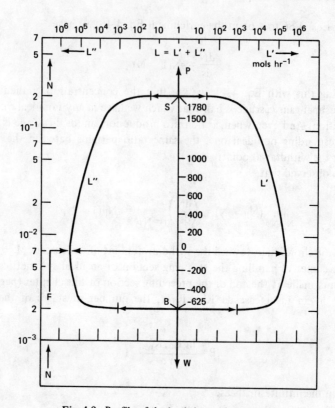

Fig. 4.9 Profile of the loads in an ideal cascade.

In Fig. 4.9 the external flows (P, F, and W) are shown by segments of proportional length on the flow chart. Specifically we have

$$W = 1013 \text{ mols hr}^{-1}$$

$$F = P + W = 1040 \text{ mols hr}^{-1}$$

In the low stages we have $L' \simeq L'' \simeq L/2$, whereas at the withdrawal points we have, respectively,

$$L'_{S-1} = L_S \simeq 2P \ (L''_{S+1} = 0)$$

and

$$L''_{-B+1} = L_{-B} \simeq 2W \ (L'_{-B-1} = 0)$$

From Eq. 4.70 we see that the logarithmic scale of the mol fractions corresponds to a linear scale of the number of stages s until $R \simeq N$. As shown in Fig. 4.9, the deviation begins to make itself felt practically when $s > 1000$.

Obviously the particular flow profile shown in Fig. 4.9 is due to the logarithmic representation.

Using linear scales, we see from Eq. 4.68 that the flow profile in the enrichment section would display a roughly hyperbolic pattern in relation to the N axis. For the stripping sections we have

$$L \simeq \frac{2W(N - N_W)}{N(1 - N)}$$

In particular, for the low concentrations

$$L \simeq \frac{2W}{\epsilon} \left(1 - \frac{N_W}{N}\right)$$

from which we see that the hyperbolic profile in the stripping section becomes concave toward the N axis.

Qualitatively, an ideal cascade can thus be represented as it is shown in Fig. 4.10.

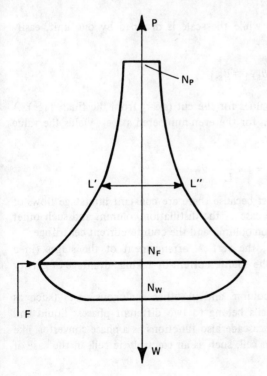

Fig. 4.10 Qualitative representation of an ideal cascade (N on the linear scale).

EQUATIONS FOR THE SQUARE CASCADE

The square cascade is characterized by a feed flow

$$L_s = \text{const} = L \tag{4.75}$$

equal for all the stages with the possible exception of the last, because of the lack of a recycling flow. Only cascades of symmetrical design will be considered here, even though theoretically it is possible to have asymmetrical square cascades, e.g., with recycling of the tails two stages back.

It can readily be seen from Eq. 4.32 that there can be two cases. In case 1 the cut θ is constant and takes on the value

$$\theta = \frac{1}{2}\left(1 + \frac{P}{L}\right) \tag{4.76}$$

For the final stage, however, we have $\theta_s = P/\theta L$. In case 2 the cut θ is not constant, and Eq. 4.32 can be written in the form

$$\theta_{s+1} + \theta_s = 1 + \frac{P}{L}$$

This recurrent expression, rewritten while the scale is dropped by one unit, easily shows that

$$\theta_{s+1} = \theta_{s-1}$$

Hence there are only two possible values for the cut (apart from the final stage). A fixed value for θ_0 set arbitrarily, e.g., for the even-numbered stages, yields the value for all the odd-numbered stages of

$$\theta_1 = 1 + \frac{P}{L} - \theta_0$$

Case 1 is of more practical interest because there are constant interstage flows of θL all along the cascade. This is the case of the distillation columns and such other separation units as the thermal diffusion column and the countercurrent centrifuge.

In the above-mentioned devices, the vertical arrangement of the stages (in a column) makes it possible to achieve the countercurrent by taking advantage of gravity and the laws of natural convection.

In the case of the distillation column and in other analogous cases (such as chemical exchange), the heads and tails belong to two different phases: liquid and vapor (or gas). The final stage of the cascade also functions as a phase converter, like the boiler in distillation (or a reaction cell, such as an electrolytic cell, in the case of chemical exchange).

Square cascades can, however, be built even with the stages arranged horizontally. This occurs, as is shown later, in the individual sections of gaseous diffusion installations. In the gaseous diffusion process the heads and tails belong to the same phase (gas), and the countercurrent is achieved by means of suitable compressors.

We should point out that, in square cascades, there is remixing at the points of confluence of heads and tails, except for the stage in which flows and concentrations coincide with those of the ideal cascade. So for the moment we can say that the square cascade is, on the whole, less efficient than the ideal cascade. In fact, some of the separative work done by one individual stage is lost at the next remixing point.

In columnar installations the remixing occurs within an individual stage (for example, if we are dealing with a distillation column, on a single "plate"), but the result is absolutely the same. The analogy between the two situations—remixing at the point of confluence and remixing within the stage—is shown schematically in Fig. 4.11.

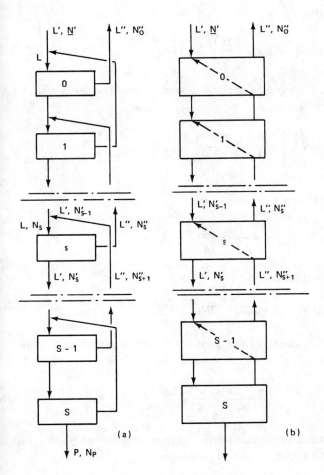

Fig. 4.11 Schematic for square cascades: (a) confluence of the flows outside the individual stage; (b) confluence of the flows inside the individual stage (column arrangement).

From Eq. 4.76 we see that when P = 0, we have

$$\theta = \frac{1}{2}$$

whereas for the final stage, the absence of withdrawal means that $\theta_s = 0$.

Hence this extreme case does not coincide with the one described on page 108, of the cascade with $\theta = 1/2$ for all stages, including the last. In fact, in the second case the flow, rather than being constant, proves to decline linearly as s. For $P/L \ll 1$, the two cases, L = const and $\theta = 1/2$, tend to approach one another only in the low stages of cascades made up of many stages.

The concentration pattern in a square cascade is found by substituting the values of Eqs. 4.75 and 4.76 in Eq. 4.36 and integrating or using, when suitable, the simplified expressions for low concentrations.

Since we assumed, for Eq. 4.48 relating to the infinitesimal case, that $P/L'' \ll 1$, we find that $P/L'' \simeq 2P/L$; thus

$$\frac{dN}{ds} = gN(1 - N) - \left(\frac{2P}{L}\right)(N_P - N) \qquad (4.77)$$

Separating the variables and integrating with the boundary condition $N(0) = N_0$, we have

$$s = \frac{2}{g\Delta(\psi)} \tanh^{-1}\left[\frac{(N - N_0)\,\Delta(\psi)}{(N + N_0)(1 + \psi) - 2NN_0 - 2N_P\psi}\right] \qquad (4.78)$$

where the dimensionless parameter

$$\psi = \frac{P}{L''g} = \frac{2P}{Lg}$$

expresses a normalized production and

$$\Delta(\psi) = [1 + 2\psi(1 - 2N_P) + \psi^2]^{\frac{1}{2}}$$

Given N_0, N_P, and ψ, Eq. 4.78 assists in finding the concentration pattern all along the cascade. For s = S, N = N_P,

$$S = \frac{2}{g\,\Delta(\psi)} \tanh^{-1}\left[\frac{(N_P - N_0)\,\Delta(\psi)}{(N_P + N_0)(1 + \psi) - 2N_PN_0 - 2N_P\psi}\right] \qquad (4.79)$$

This expression also constitutes an implicit relation between enrichment N_P, N_0, and normalized production ψ in a square cascade with S stages.

It is easy to prove that, for P = 0, Eq. 4.77 is reduced to Eq. 4.49 and Eq. 4.78 is reduced to Eq. 4.51.

In the special case of low concentrations, in which $N_0 < N_P \ll 1$, Eq. 4.79 is simplified as follows:

$$S = \frac{1}{g(1 + \psi)} \ln \frac{N_P}{N_0 - (N_P - N_0)\psi} \qquad (4.80)$$

or indeed,

$$a = \frac{N_P}{N_0} = \frac{(1 + \psi) \, e^{gS(1+\psi)}}{1 + \psi \, e^{gS(1+\psi)}} \qquad (4.81)$$

The effect of normalized production ψ on total enrichment a is shown in Fig. 4.12 for various values of the parameter $A = \exp(gS)$, which expresses the enrichment obtainable with zero production ($\psi = 0$).

From Eq. 4.78, simplified if need be for low concentrations, it is possible to find the concentration pattern $N = N(s)$ along a cascade of S stages, as many as are necessary to get the product PN_P from a feed of N_0 concentration.

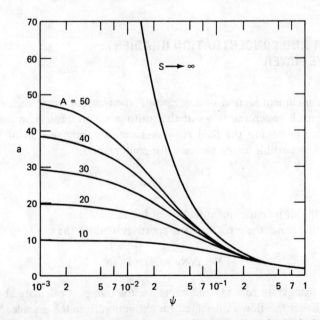

Fig. 4.12 Enrichment a vs. normalized production ψ for square cascades in the infinitesimal case at low concentrations.

It is shown in Fig. 4.12 that, for relatively high values of ψ, it is impossible to obtain any marked enrichment even with a very large number of stages. In particular, for $\psi = 1$, there is a maximum enrichment of a $\simeq 2$.

However, for $\psi \ll 1$, as the number of stages S increases, enrichment can reach very high levels, since we have a $\simeq 1 + 1/\psi$.

It is easy to see from Eq. 4.77 that when $(dN/ds) \to 0$ and then $S' \to \infty$, it is

$$L \to \frac{2P(N_P - N)}{gN(1 - N)} = L_{min}$$

Recalling that Eq. 4.68 expresses the flow L_{id} of a corresponding ideal cascade (which is a cascade with equal enrichment) and since $\epsilon = g/2$, we have

$$L_{id} = 2L_{min}. \tag{4.82}$$

Also from Eq. 4.77, we see that, for $L \to \infty$ (or $2P/L = 0$), we have the case, already dealt with, of the maximum concentration gradient. It involves the minimum number of stages $S_{min.}$ required to obtain enrichment a. Hence the equation

$$S_{id} = 2S_{min}. \tag{4.83}$$

applies.

TRANSPORT AND CONCENTRATION GRADIENT: SEPARATIVE POWER

For the enrichment section of any cascade, the transport, τ, of the desired isotope is the difference between the flows of that isotope which traverse, in the direction of the withdrawal point and the feed point, respectively, any section of that cascade. Disregarding any possible losses, we have, for conservation:

$$\tau = PN_P$$

constant for the entire enrichment section of the cascade.

On the other hand, the term "net transport" is used for the quantity

$$\tau - PN = P(N_P - N) = L''(N - N'')$$

which varies from stage to stage and expresses the transport calculated by subtracting from the L' heads the flow P, destined for extraction from the cascade. Note that the net transport $\tau - PN$ of the desired isotope is matched by an equal transport but with an opposite sign (directed, that is, toward the entry) of the other isotope of the binary system. For P/L much smaller than unity and for the low stages of the cascade, transport and net transport practically coincide.

As far back as Eq. 4.36, which is valid for all symmetrical cascades, and therefore as far back as Eq. 4.48, which applies to the infinitesimal case, we can see that the concentration gradient is the result of the difference between two terms. The first term gives the "separative effect" of the stage $(N' - N'')$, and the second corresponds to the net transport per unit of flow of the tail:

$$f = \frac{P(N_P - N)}{L''} = N - N''$$

When the concentration gradient is zero, we have (in the infinitesimal case)

$$f = f_{max.} = gN(1 - N)$$

The operation of a single stage in a cascade therefore shows the following extreme cases:

$$\frac{dN}{ds} = 0, \qquad gN(1 - N)$$

$$f = gN(1 - N), 0$$

The optimum operating conditions for the individual stage are those which achieve the best compromise between concentration gradient and net transport. This is achieved by maximizing the product

$$E = \frac{dN}{ds} \times fL'' = (N' - N) \times (N - N'')L''$$

which we can call the "separative work" of the stage. Since from Eq. 4.48

$$\frac{dN}{ds} = f_{max.} - f$$

we find that

$$E = (f_{max.} - f) fL''$$

whose maximum in relation to f is found by

$$f = \frac{1}{2} f_{max.} = \frac{g}{2} N (1 - N) \qquad (4.84)$$

Correspondingly, we find

$$\frac{dN}{ds} = \frac{g}{2} N(1 - N) = \frac{1}{2} \left(\frac{dN}{ds}\right)_{max.} \qquad (4.85)$$

and hence

$$E_{max.} = \frac{1}{4} g^2 [N(1 - N)]^2 L'' \qquad (4.86)$$

Whereas the separative work depends on the concentration, we see that this dependence disappears for the quantity

$$\delta U = \frac{E}{N^2 (1 - N)^2} = \frac{N' - N}{N(1 - N)} \times \frac{\tau - PN}{N(1 - N)} \qquad (4.87)$$

which we shall call the "separative power" of the stage, and which represents an intrinsic property of that stage. From Eq. 4.86 we see that

$$\delta U_{max.} = \frac{1}{4} g^2 L'' = \epsilon^2 L'' = \frac{1}{2} \epsilon^2 L \qquad (4.88)$$

Comparing Eq. 4.85 with Eq. 4.72, we can see that each individual stage of the ideal cascade functions under optimal conditions and hence with maximum separative power. In each stage, dN/ds and f are the same and equal to half the maximum value.

For a square cascade, on the contrary, it is not possible for the separative power to be held at the maximum value in all the stages, because of the constance of the flows.

In fact, Eq. 4.77 shows that in the square cascade the conditions at the feed point are

$$\left(\frac{dN}{ds}\right)_0 = gN_0(1 - N_0) - \left(\frac{P}{L''}\right)(N_P - N_0)$$

$$f_0 = \left(\frac{P}{L''}\right)(N_P - N_0)$$

whereas at the withdrawal point they are

$$\left(\frac{dN}{ds}\right)_P \simeq gN_P(1 - N_P)$$

$$f_P \simeq 0$$

In the final stage the concentration gradient is therefore always twice the optimum (ideal cascade), whereas the net transport is practically zero, as is the separative power. Obviously such conditions will exist all along the cascade for $P = 0$.

Hence there is a single stage for which we have $f = (\frac{1}{2})gN(1 - N)$: the stage where the flow coincides with the flow (Eq. 4.68) of an ideal stage functioning at the same concentration.

While the optimum operating conditions for an ideal cascade coincide with the optimum conditions for the single stage, the same cannot be said of a square cascade. For the latter, as is shown later on, optimum operation corresponds to a suitable mean of the properties of the various stages.

Thus far we have considered only the enrichment section of a cascade, but what we have said is easily extended to the stripping section. For this, the net transport of the desired isotope is negative all along the cascade.

YIELD

Definitions

In general, the "yield" of a cascade is defined as the ratio between the transport of the desired isotope and the amount of it contained in the feed

$$\eta = \frac{\tau}{L'N'} \tag{4.89}$$

The same concept applies to any section or part of a cascade.

In particular, for the enrichment section of a cascade (see Fig. 4.7), $\tau = PN_P$, and hence the yield can be written

$$\eta_a = \frac{PN_P}{L'N'} \tag{4.90}$$

For an entire cascade with enriching and stripping sections, the "overall yield" is defined analogously:

$$\eta_T = \frac{PN_P}{FN_F} \tag{4.91}$$

and obviously η_T is greater than η_a.

From the foregoing we see that the yield is a parameter that.is defined in the interval $0 \leqslant \eta \leqslant 1$.

Yield of an Ideal Cascade

In the case of an ideal cascade with low inlet concentration ($R''_0 \simeq N''_0 \simeq N_0/\alpha$), we can write

$$PN_P = (L'' + P)N_0 - L_0'' \frac{N_0}{\alpha}$$

and hence Eq. 4.90 becomes

$$\eta_a = 1 - \frac{1/\alpha}{1 + P/L_0''} \tag{4.92a}$$

If the number of stages is high enough so as to produce a total separation:

$$Q_a = \frac{N_P(1 - N_0)}{N_0(1 - N_P)} \gg \alpha$$

it is $P/L_0'' \ll 1$. For example, for the cascade shown in Fig. 4.9, we find that $P/L_0'' = 7.3 \times 10^{-6}$. So now Eq. 4.92a can be written

$$\eta_a \simeq \frac{\alpha - 1}{\alpha} \tag{4.92b}$$

In the infinitesimal case, Eqs. 4.92a and 4.92b become

$$\eta_a = \frac{\epsilon + P/L_0''}{1 + P/L_0''} = \frac{g}{2} \frac{1 + 2P/gL_0''}{1 + P/L_0''} \tag{4.93a}$$

and

$$\eta_a = \epsilon = \frac{g}{2} \tag{4.93b}$$

And so, if the number of stages S is increased beyond a certain limit, the yield remains constant. In fact, the total enrichment increases, but the P/L' ratio declines proportionately, as can be seen from Eq. 4.68.

If S is not high enough for the difference between L' and L_0'' to be negligible, the yield η_a varies, declining with increasing S (and hence with increasing Q_a). In the case of low concentrations,

$$\eta_a \simeq (\alpha\theta)^S \simeq \left(\frac{\alpha}{1 + \alpha}\right)^S$$

or $\eta_a \simeq (0.5)^S$ in the infinitesimal case. Therefore the maximum yield is found in the extreme case in which the cascade consists of only a single stage (S = 1).

Ideal Cascade with Stripping Section

Confining ourselves to the infinitesimal case with low feed concentrations, remember that, from Eqs. 4.90 and 4.93b,

$$PN_P = \eta_a \, L'N' = \epsilon L_0''N_0''$$

This can also be obtained from Eq. 4.68, which is approximate for low concentrations.

Although the yield of the desired isotope does not vary with the increasing concentration at the withdrawal point N_P, the yield χ_a of the other isotope in the binary mixture does vary and tends to disappear for $N_P \to 1$. In fact

$$\chi_a = \frac{P(1 - N_P)}{L_0''(1 - N_0)} = \frac{PN_P}{L_0''N_0} \times \frac{N_0(1 - N_P)}{N_P(1 - N_0)} = \frac{\epsilon}{Q_a} \qquad (4.94)$$

(in which $Q_a \gg 1$).

The stripping section of an ideal cascade can be considered substantially like an enrichment section for the other isotope and hence (if B is sufficiently large) it will have a constant yield of χ_r for the second isotope:

$$\chi_r = \frac{W(1 - N_W)}{L_0''[1 - N_0(1 - \epsilon)]} \simeq \frac{W(1 - N_W)}{L_0''(1 - N_0)} = \epsilon$$

The yield η_r of the desired isotope in the stripping section then proves to be

$$\eta_r = \frac{WN_W}{L_0''N_0(1 - \epsilon)} \simeq \frac{WN_W}{L_0''N_0} = \epsilon \frac{N_W(1 - N_0)}{N_0(1 - N_W)} = \frac{\epsilon}{Q_r} \qquad (4.95)$$

in which Q_r ($\gg 1$) is the overall enrichment of the other isotope in the stripping section. For $N_W \to 0$, we have $\eta_r \to 0$.

From Eqs. 4.29, 4.89, 4.93b, and 4.95, the total yield of an ideal cascade in the infinitesimal case, and for $Q_r \gg 1$, becomes

$$\eta_T = \frac{PN_P}{PN_P + WN_W} = \frac{\eta_a}{\eta_a + \eta_r} = \frac{Q_r}{Q_r + 1} \qquad (4.96)$$

Hence, as we increase Q_r, we can bring η_T as close to 1 as we like.

Obviously the extreme condition $\eta_r = 0$ (i.e., $N_W = 0$) determines the minimum feed flow

$$F_{min.} = P + W_{min.}$$

which, with Eq. 4.30 in mind, can be written as

$$F_{min.} = P \frac{N_P}{N_F}$$

The presence of the stripping section makes it possible to considerably increase the yield obtainable with only the enrichment section. Consider, for example, the case in which $\epsilon = 0.01$. With $Q_r = 4$, the total yield is $\eta_T = 80\%$, obtainable with $S = \ln 4/0.01 = 140$ stages in the stripping section.

From Eq. 4.96 we see that the increase in yield $d\eta_T$ obtainable with the increase in enrichment dQ_r is

$$\frac{d\eta_T}{\eta_T} = \frac{dQ_r}{Q_r} \times \frac{\eta_T}{Q_r} \tag{4.97}$$

For example, a 10% increase in enrichment $Q_r = 10$ will increase the total yield $\eta_T = 0.91$ by less than 1%.

Thus, in general, it is understandable that, for stripping sections, the values Q_r (and hence B) are sometimes lower than they are for enrichment sections. Cascades thus frequently take the form seen in Fig. 4.9 (in which $Q_a = 35.7$ and $Q_r = 3.5$), and in Fig. 4.10.

Yield of the Square Cascade

For an ideal cascade with S stages without stripping section, the yield η is determined unequivocally. In contrast, for a square cascade with the same number of stages, the yield will vary as a function of the P/L' ratio. The yield when $P/L' = 0$ is nothing, but then it rises toward unity when $P/L' \rightarrow 1$.

Since

$$\eta = \frac{\tau}{L'N_0} - \frac{PN_P}{L'N_0} = \frac{P'/L''}{1 + P/L''} a = \frac{g\psi}{1 + g\psi} a$$

where the enrichment $a = a(\psi)$ is given by Eq. 4.81. As we have already seen, with ψ fixed, enrichment increases with S, and, for $S \rightarrow \infty$, we have $a \rightarrow (1 + \psi)/\psi$. The yield accordingly takes on the extreme value

$$\eta_\infty = \frac{g(1 + \psi)}{1 + g\psi} \simeq g(1 + \psi) \tag{4.98a}$$

or, in the special case of $\psi \ll 1$,

$$\eta_\infty \simeq g \tag{4.98b}$$

This last equation, compared with Eq. 4.92, shows that, for equal and very high S, the square cascade has a yield about twice that of the ideal cascade because the concentration gradient and hence the total enrichment are just about double.

The "relative yield" of a cascade is the ratio

$$\rho = \frac{\eta}{\eta_\infty}$$

Hence we have $0 \leqslant \rho \leqslant 1$.
From Eqs. 4.97 and 4.98,

$$\rho \simeq \frac{a\psi}{1 + \psi} \qquad (4.99a)$$

or, for $\psi \ll 1$,

$$\rho \simeq a\psi \qquad (4.99b)$$

Keeping in mind Eq. 4.99, we can now write Eq. 4.80 in the form

$$s = \frac{a - \rho}{ag} \ln \frac{a - \rho}{1 - \rho} \qquad (4.100a)$$

When $\psi \ll 1$ and also $\rho \ll a$, we have

$$S \simeq \frac{1}{g} \ln \frac{a}{1 - \rho} \qquad (4.100b)$$

Second-Species Withdrawal

From the preceding section, and particularly from Eq. 4.99b, we see that, when $\psi \ll 1$, a square cascade will have a relative yield ρ not very small only when the enrichment a is sufficiently high.

However, there is the possibility that, even when $\psi \ll 1$, the square cascade may have a high ρ for modest values of a. This high ρ can occur when ψ is low, not because very little enriched material is withdrawn from the cascade, but because, even if considerable quantities are drawn off, a quantity only slightly smaller, but at lower concentration, is cycled back into the cascade. Such a situation occurs when several cascades are connected in series to form a composite cascade as shown in Fig. 4.13, generally known as a "step cascade" or "squared-off" cascade. Each step consists of a square cascade, and Fig. 4.13 shows the last two steps. For the first steps of the cascade, it is clear that we can have $\psi \ll 1$ without the involvement of a high enrichment and a low yield for the individual step.

In the first steps there is a process, called by some authors "second-species withdrawal," which is extraction of the desired isotope without any appreciable flow extraction. The transport of the desired isotope (τ), which determines the yield in the

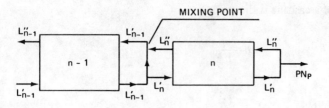

Fig. 4.13 Flow diagram in the final part of a cascade made up of n steps. Each step is a square cascade.

$$L'_0 - L''_0 = L'_n - L''_n = P$$

steps, is not due to the net flow extraction but to the difference in concentration between the enriched flow extracted and the depleted flow returned. The transport τ can be considered even in the extreme case in which there is no net flow extraction.

On the contrary, a "first-species withdrawal" takes place in the final step, in which the transport is entirely obtained by flow extraction.

With first-species withdrawal, even though $P/L''_0 \lesssim g$, there can be more than negligible ψ with respect to unity. With second-species withdrawal we have $\psi \ll 1$, but the relative yield

$$\rho = \frac{\tau}{gL'N_0}$$

is not bound to ψ. For $N \ll N_P \ll 1$, Eq. 4.77 can be written as

$$\frac{dN}{ds} = gN - \frac{\tau}{L'}$$

from which we obtain

$$S = \frac{1}{g} \ln \frac{a - \rho}{1 - \rho} \tag{4.101}$$

VALUE FUNCTION AND SEPARATIVE WORK

In any cascade the quantity

$$\sum_{-B}^{S} {}_i L_i$$

is called the "total flow." Specifically, for a square cascade with S stages, we have

$$\sum_i L_i = SL$$

The total flow is important because it is proportional to several global parameters of the cascade which substantially determine the cost of production.

For example, in such a substantially irreversible process as gaseous diffusion, the total flow is proportional to the volume of the installation (barrier area and compressor sections) and to the power absorbed by the compressors.

In such substantially reversible processes as distillation in a countercurrent column, the total flow is proportional to the volume of the column (i.e., to section x number of plates) and to the irreversible component of energy consumption: the one bound to pressure drop. The reversible component, bound to the absence of recovery of the evaporation heat, is not proportional to the total flow, SL, but to the flow $L'' = (1 - \theta_S)L$; in fact, the evaporation heat is supplied from the outside only once for the entire square cascade.

Consider next the enrichment section of an ideal cascade in the infinitesimal case. We can write

$$\sum_{i=0}^{S} L_i = \int_0^S L \, ds = \int_{N_0}^{N_P} L \frac{ds}{dN} \, dN$$

and hence, from Eqs. 4.68 and 4.72,

$$\sum_{i=1}^{S} L_i = \frac{2P}{\epsilon^2} \int_{N_0}^{N_P} \frac{N_P - N}{N^2(1-N)^2} \, dN$$

$$= \frac{2}{\epsilon^2} \times P \left[(2N_P - 1) \ln \frac{R_P}{R_0} + \frac{1 - 2N_0}{1 - N_0} \frac{N_P - N_0}{N_0} \right]$$

Clearly the total flow can be expressed as a ratio between two terms. The first term is

$$\Delta U = P \left[(2N_P - 1) \ln \frac{R_P}{R_0} \frac{1 - 2N_0}{1 - N_0} \frac{N_P - N_0}{N_0} \right]$$

a function solely of the flow rate P and of the product (N_P) and feed (N_0) concentrations.

The second term is

$$\frac{\epsilon^2}{2} = \frac{\delta U}{G} \tag{4.102}$$

in which δU, as defined by Eq. 4.88, is the separative power of the separating element fed by flow G.

Like this second term, the first term will also have its own intrinsic physical significance. If we interpret the separative power of the separating element as the increment produced by the element in the quantity U, a function solely of concentration and flow rate, we see that ΔU is the increment produced by the entire cascade made up of n separating elements. Thus we have

$$\sum L_i = Gn = G \frac{\Delta U}{\delta U} \qquad (4.103)$$

The definition of U, which we shall call "value function," can be approached by first assuming that it enjoys the property

$$U(P,N) = PV(N) \qquad (4.104)$$

We shall call $V = V(N)$ the "separative potential."

The separative power of a typical separating element fed by flow G at a concentration N, using the standard symbols, is

$$\delta U = \theta GV(N') + (1 - \theta) GV(N'') - GV(N) \qquad (4.105)$$

Developing $V(N')$ and $V(N'')$ in a Taylor series, we see that the coefficients of $V(N)$ and of dV/dN cancel out for the conservation Eqs. 4.13 and 4.16. Discarding terms of an order higher than the second and assuming $\theta = 1/2$, we have

$$\frac{\delta U}{G} = \frac{\epsilon^2}{2} [N(1 - N)]^2 \frac{d^2 N}{dN^2} \qquad (4.106)$$

Hence it must be true that

$$\frac{d^2 V}{dN^2} = \frac{1}{[N(1 - n)]^2} \qquad (4.107)$$

This equation can be integrated (Dirac) with the arbitrary boundary condition

$$V(N_0) = 0$$

$$\left(\frac{dV}{dN}\right)_{N_0} = 0$$

As a result, we find

$$V(N) = (2N - 1) \ln \frac{R}{R_0} + (1 - 2N_0) \frac{N - N_0}{N_0(1 - N_0)} \qquad (4.108)$$

and so

$$\Delta U = PV(N_P) \qquad (4.109)$$

The arbitrariness of the boundary conditions is related to the fact that only the ΔU increments of the value function have intrinsic physical significance, but not the absolute values of U or even of V. We shall call ΔU the "total separative power" of the cascade. When the flow rates that appear in ΔU are replaced by the total weights (flow rate $\times$ operating time), ΔU expresses the corresponding "separative work."

Shifting the above-mentioned boundary conditions to the point of equimolarity ($N = 0.5$) lets the separative potential assume the simplest (elementary) form,

$$V'(N) = (2N - 1) \ln R \tag{4.110}$$

independent of the specific natural composition of the isotopic mixture. Thus defined, the separative potential is a symmetrical function with respect to the axis $N = 0.5$ as shown in Fig. 4.14. A tabulation of $V'(N)$ is given in Appendix D.

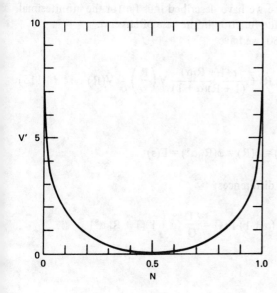

Fig. 4.14 The separative potential in elementary form.

For a cascade with a stripping section, making use of $V(N)$, we have

$$\Delta U = PV(N_P) + WV(N_W) \tag{4.111}$$

whereas, if we use $V'(N)$, we must write

$$\Delta U = PV'(N_P) + WV'(N_W) - FV'(N_0) \tag{4.112}$$

However, recalling the conservation ratios of Eqs. 4.28 and 4.31, we will easily verify that both Eqs. 4.111 and 4.112 reduce to the common expression

$$\Delta U = P(2N_P - 1) \ln R_P + W(2N_W - 1) \ln R_W - F(2N_0 - 1) \ln R_0 \tag{4.113}$$

If there is no stripping section, N_W is very close to N_0, and so Eq. 4.112 becomes

$$\Delta U = PV'(N_P) + (W - F) V'(N_0) - W(N_0 - N_W) \left(\frac{dV'}{dN}\right)_{N_0}$$

$$= P\left[V'(N_P) - V'(N_0) - (N_P - N_0) \left(\frac{dV'}{dN}\right)_{N_0}\right] \qquad (4.114)$$

Developing this, we see that Eq. 4.114 coincides with Eq. 4.109, in which $V(N_P)$ is given by Eq. 4.108. Thus the arbitrary boundary conditions used in defining the separative potential have no effect whatsoever on the calculation of the increments of the value function.

A procedure analogous to the one we have described thus far for the infinitesimal case can be followed to define the value function in the case of larger α.

Recalling Eqs. 4.55, 4.58, and 4.60, we have

$$\frac{\delta U}{G} = \frac{1 + \alpha R}{(1 + R)(\alpha + 1)} V(\alpha R) + \frac{\alpha(1 + R/\alpha)}{(1 + R)(\alpha + 1)} V\left(\frac{R}{\alpha}\right) - V(R) \qquad (4.115)$$

Assuming that

$$(1 + R)V(R) = \phi(R) = \phi(R_0 \alpha^s) = F(s)$$

we obtain the equation for the finite differences:

$$F(s + 1) + \alpha F(s - 1) - (\alpha + 1) F(s) = \frac{\delta U}{G} (\alpha + 1)(1 + R_0 \alpha^s)$$

The general solution

$$F(s) = \frac{\delta U}{G} \frac{\alpha + 1}{\alpha - 1} s (R_0 \alpha^s - 1) + A\alpha^s + B$$

obtainable with the method summed up in Appendix C, can be written so as to retrieve the variable R:

$$V(R) = \frac{\delta U}{G} \frac{\alpha + 1}{\alpha - 1} \frac{2N - 1}{\ln \alpha} \ln \frac{R}{R_0} + A \frac{N}{R_0} + B(1 - N)$$

We will arbitrarily assume the boundary conditions $V(R_0)$ and $V(R_0/\alpha) = 0$, with which

$$V(R) = \frac{\delta U}{G} \frac{\alpha + 1}{(\alpha - 1)\ln \alpha} \left[(2N - 1) \ln \frac{R}{R_0} + \frac{\ln \alpha}{\alpha - 1} \times \frac{\alpha - (\alpha + 1) N_0}{N_0(1 - N_0)} (N - N_0)\right]$$

The second term, analogous to what was seen in Eq. 4.108, reflects the arbitrary nature of the boundary conditions, and hence its dependence on α is not significant. A substantial independence of V(R) from α is thus obtained by defining the separative power of the separating element as follows:

$$\delta U = G \frac{(\alpha - 1) \ln \alpha}{\alpha + 1} \tag{4.116}$$

and so

$$V(R) = (2N - 1) \ln \frac{R}{R_0} + \frac{\ln \alpha}{\alpha - 1} \frac{\alpha - (\alpha + 1) N_0}{N_0(1 - N_0)} (N - N_0) \tag{4.117}$$

It is easily verified that, even for arbitrary α, Eq. 4.110 is valid as an expression of the separative potential in elementary form.

As for the separative power, it varies as $(\alpha - 1)^2$ for α not much greater than 1, whereas for large α it grows only logarithmically.

It is well to conclude these general remarks on the value function with the remark that its definition was based on a symmetrical scheme.

In the infinitesimal case, it is still easy to prove that the definition does not change for asymmetrical schemes, since all equations for the ideal symmetrical cascade remain substantially valid. It should be remembered, however, that the enrichment gain is given by

$$\epsilon \simeq g(1 - \theta)$$

in which the value of $\theta (\neq 1/2)$ is typical of the scheme we are considering. For example, with recycling of the heads one stage forward and the tails two stages back, the conditions for nonremixing give $\theta \simeq 2/3$. This means that such an ideal asymmetrical cascade has a concentration gradient $(g/3)N(1 - N)$, rather than the $(g/2)N(1 - N)$ of the symmetrical cascade.

If the quantity $\delta U/G$ is derived from Eq. 4.105 by retaining the generic value θ in it, we see that, in general,

$$\frac{\delta U}{G} = \frac{\theta}{1 - \theta} \frac{\epsilon^2}{2} = \theta(1 - \theta) \frac{g^2}{2} \tag{4.118}$$

In the symmetrical scheme, $\delta U/G = g^2/8$, whereas in the asymmetrical scheme we have $\delta U = g^2/9$. Since the symmetrical scheme ensures the maximum separative power in the separating element, as a general rule asymmetrical schemes are not suitable.

There can, however, be cases in which g shows an intrinsic dependence on the cut (a possibility we have neglected thus far) so as to make an asymmetrical scheme desirable. This occurs, as will be seen later, in the separation nozzle process.

EQUILIBRIUM TIME

Cascades for isotope separation are often very large, and hence the time required to reach the equilibrium concentrations at every point of the cascade (equilibrium time) can be considerable. However, the flow regime is reached in practice rather quickly after the start of operations.

Confining our considerations to the infinitesimal case, we observe (see Eq. 4.48) that

$$\tau = \epsilon \, LN(1 - N) + PN - \frac{1}{2} L \frac{dN}{ds} \qquad (4.119)$$

valid in stationary conditions, can describe the transient only if $PN_P = \tau$ is no longer considered constant but, rather, variable with time. So it will be better to write $\tau = PN'_S$, in which N'_S (head concentration of the final stage) comes close to N_P (nominal outlet concentration) for $t \simeq t_e$ (equilibrium time).

If, from the beginning, the nominal flow P is extracted from the outlet of the cascade, the initial outlet transport is $\tau = PN_0 < PN_P$. Actually it is usually preferable not to extract product from the cascade until the concentration in the final stage has reached its nominal value. As of that moment (t_P), the extracted flow L'_S is gradually increased (in such a way that N_P remains constant) until reaching the nominal value P. A qualitative description of the transient is shown in Fig. 4.15, which also shows a definition of the equilibrium time t_e, one among many possible definitions.

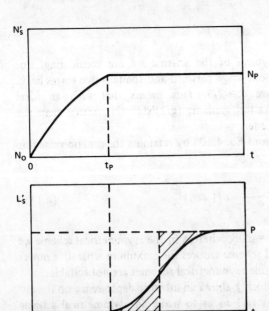

Fig. 4.15 Concentration at the cascade outlet and withdrawal during the initial transient.

With this procedure the transport at the outlet is held at zero for time t_P and is then gradually increased until it reaches the nominal value PN_p.

On the contrary, at the inlet of the cascade we have initially (when $L_S' = 0$):

$$\tau_{in} = \tau_{max.} = L\epsilon N_0(1 - N_0) \qquad (4.120)$$

meaning that the maximum transport is used to accumulate the isotopic content of the cascade in excess of the natural content.

In a square cascade, such a maximum transport is held initially along the entire length of all the stages, only to vanish suddenly in the final one. This provides an isotope source at the end of the cascade, resulting in the formation of a strong gradient dN/ds in the high stages. Consequently there is a corresponding decline in transport. The zone of diminished transport gradually spreads back toward the low stages. The situation in the initial transport is qualitatively shown in Fig. 4.16.

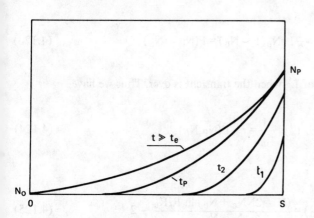

Fig. 4.16 Qualitative representation of the initial concentration transient along the stages of a square cascade ($t_1 < t_2 < t_P$).

In an ideal cascade, however, the increase of concentrations with time is more uniformly distributed over the stages. This increase occurs because the flow decreases from the feed point to the withdrawal point and involves a progressive decrease of the transport in the same direction. In fact, the situation is as if isotope sources are distributed all along the cascade.

The equilibrium time for any cascade can be found as the ratio

$$t_e = \frac{H}{\bar{\tau}} = \frac{1}{\bar{\tau}} \int_0^S hL_s(N_s - N_0)\, ds \qquad (4.121)$$

between the net holdup (i.e., above the natural holdup) of the desired isotope and a suitable mean $\bar{\tau}$ of transport.

Equation 4.121 is written on the assumption that the content of material of the generic stage s is proportional to the feed L_s of the stage according to the constant h, valid for the entire cascade. The constant h expresses the transit time of the material across the single stage.

The difficulty of finding a precise value for the equilibrium time lies in the definition of the mean transport $\bar{\tau}$. However, very good approximations of t_e can be obtained by replacing the mean transport with a representative value for transport at the inlet of the cascade.

For an ideal cascade, using Eqs. 4.68 and 4.69, we have

$$H = \frac{2hP}{\epsilon^2} \left[(N_P - 2N_P N_0 + N_0) \ln \frac{R_P}{R_0} - 2(N_P - N_0) \right] \qquad (4.122)$$

The inlet transport τ_{in} decreases during the initial period (when $L'_S = 0$), starting with the maximum value (Eq. 4.120) but never dropping below the rating value. This means that

$$\tau_{in} \geqslant \frac{1}{2} L\epsilon N_0 (1 - N_0) = P(N_P - N_0) \qquad (4.123)$$

where P is the nominal value of L'_S when the transient is over. Thus we have

$$t_e \simeq \frac{H}{\tau_{in}} = \frac{2h}{\epsilon^2} E(N_P, N_0) \qquad (4.124)$$

in which is placed

$$E(N, N_0) = \frac{(N - 2NN_0 + N_0) \ln R/R_0}{N - N_0} - 2 \qquad (4.125)$$

In the case of uranium,[1] for example, where $N_0 = 0.0071$, the function $E(N, N_0)$ is shown in Fig. 4.17. Until uranium reaches very high concentrations the value of $E(N, N_0)$ does not exceed 8. Therefore we can also say that the quantity $2h/\epsilon^2$ expresses the order of magnitude of the equilibrium time of the ideal cascade.

For a square cascade, H is found by replacing, in the integral of Eq. 4.120 the expression $N = N(S)$, which can be extracted from Eq. 4.78, or with simpler forms for the case of low concentrations. As for transport at entry (τ_{in}), the maximum value given by Eq. 4.120 is retained longer than in an ideal cascade. For an approximate evaluation of t_e, we can therefore use the initial transport, $\tau = \tau_{max}$. .

For a more detailed description of the transient times of a cascade in the infinitesimal case, we must return to the conservation equation

$$hL \frac{\partial N}{\partial t} = -\frac{\partial \tau}{\partial s} \qquad (4.126)$$

which is written with the assumption that there is no load transient, but only a concentration transient.

Calculating the derivative of Eq. 4.119 with respect to s and substituting Eq. 4.126, we have

$$hL\frac{\partial N}{\partial t} = \frac{\partial}{\partial s}\left[\frac{L}{2}\frac{\partial N}{\partial s} - \epsilon LN(1 - N) - PN\right] \qquad (4.127)$$

Analytical solutions of this transient equation have been found only for square cascades and for low concentrations or for concentrations close to 1, with which it becomes linear:

$$hL\frac{\partial N}{\partial t} = \frac{L}{2}\frac{\partial^2 N}{\partial s^2} - (\epsilon L + P)\frac{\partial N}{\partial s} \qquad (4.128)$$

The following boundary conditions may be fixed:

$$N = N_0 \quad \text{when } s \to \infty \text{ and } t \equiv (0,\infty) \qquad (4.129)$$

$$N = N_0 \quad \text{when } t = 0 \text{ and } s \equiv (0,S) \qquad (4.130)$$

$$\partial N/\partial s = 2\epsilon N \quad \text{when } s = S \text{ and } P = 0 \qquad (4.131)$$

Equation 4.129 is a mathematical artifice for getting an analytical solution, which cannot be obtained with the (physically sound) condition $N = N_0$ for $s = 0$ and all values of t. Furthermore, in the initial period the concentration gradient is confined to the high stages, and the situation does not change appreciably if the feed point, with its N_0 concentration, is shifted an infinite distance away.

The solution with the above-mentioned conditions, when $2\epsilon S \to \infty$ proves to be

$$\frac{N_S'}{N_0} = \left(1 + \frac{\Theta}{2}\right)\left[1 + \text{erf}\left(\frac{\Theta}{4}\right)\right]^{\frac{1}{2}} + \left(\frac{\Theta}{\pi}\right)^{\frac{1}{2}}\exp\left(-\frac{\Theta}{4}\right) \qquad (4.132)$$

where

$$\Theta = \frac{\epsilon^2}{8h}t \qquad (4.133)$$

is a (nondimensional) reduced time. From a more detailed analysis, we could see that the curve represented by Eq. 4.132 branches out for the various values of $2\epsilon S$, as shown in Fig. 4.18.

When $\Theta \gg 1$ and when $S \gg 1/2\epsilon$, we have

$$\frac{N_S'}{N_0} \simeq 2 + \Theta \qquad (4.134)$$

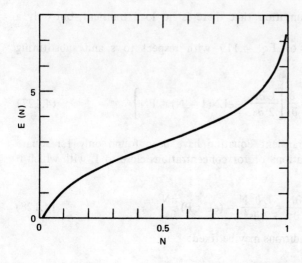

Fig. 4.17 Behavior of the E(N) function for uranium ($N_0 = 0.0071$) relative to the ideal cascade. (Based on K. Cohen, *The Theory of Isotope Separation*, p. 16, McGraw-Hill Book Company, Inc., New York, 1951.)

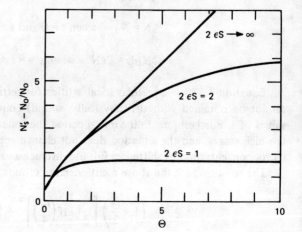

Fig. 4.18 Pattern of the enrichment of square cascades (P = 0) as a function of the reduced time Θ.

From Fig. 4.18, we infer, when $S \leqslant 1/2\epsilon$

$$t_e \lesssim \frac{N_P - N_0}{N_0} \frac{8h}{\epsilon^2} = (a-1) \frac{8h}{\epsilon^2} \tag{4.135}$$

From the foregoing conditions, we can see that the equilibrium time for a square cascade, when $S \leqslant 1/2\epsilon$, is higher by a factor of about $4(a-1)$ than the equilibrium time for an ideal cascade with equal enrichment.

Again, for the study of flow fluctuations and of the related control problems, we must consider the transient equations of the cascade, which, however, must be generalized for the case of $L = L(t)$.

THE IDEAL CASCADE AS A TERM FOR COMPARISON

The structure of the ideal cascade, with the complications brought in by the stage-to-stage flow variation, has never been followed to the letter. In practice, it is easier to approximate the ideal pattern with a squared-off cascade (pages 127-128), as shown in Fig. 4.19. To select the most economically suitable scheme among the many possible, we must make comparisons between the ideal cascade and a nonideal cascade (e.g., a square one) in the generic concentration interval (N_a, N_b).

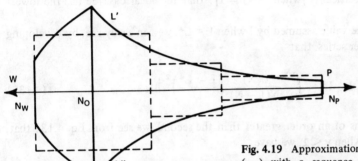

Fig. 4.19 Approximation of an ideal cascade (—) with a sequence of square cascades (– – –), called a "squared-off cascade."

The principal elements for comparison are the following:

$$\text{Total flow:} \qquad \int_{s_a}^{s_b} L \, ds = \int_{N_a}^{N_b} L(N) \frac{ds}{dN} \, dN$$

$$\text{Number of stages:} \qquad s_b - s_a = \int_{N_a}^{N_b} \frac{ds}{dN} \, dN$$

$$\text{Equilibrium time:} \qquad t_e$$

Recalling Eq. 4.53, we see that, for a typical cascade, the integral of any variable $\phi(N)$ proportional to L is given by

$$I = \int \phi(N) \, L \, ds = \int_{N_a}^{N_b} \frac{\phi(N)}{N(1-N)} \times \frac{L^2}{2L - L^*} \, dN \qquad (4.136)$$

in which

$$L^* = \frac{2P(N_P - N)}{N(1 - N)}$$

is the flow of the corresponding ideal cascade.

We have the lowest value of I when

$$\frac{d}{dL} \frac{L^2}{2L - L^*} = 0$$

that is, when

$$L = L^*$$

This shows, specifically [when $\phi(N) \equiv I$], that the ideal cascade has the lowest possible total flow.

If we call I^* the value assumed by I when $L = L^*$, we can easily see, by developing Eq. 4.136 in a power series, that

$$I - I^* = \int_{N_a}^{N_b} \frac{\phi(N)}{N(1 - N)} \left(\frac{L - L^*}{L}\right)^2 dN + \ldots \qquad (4.137)$$

Neglecting terms of an order greater than the second, we see from Eq. 4.137 that, if $|L - L^*| \leqslant yL^*$ when $y < 1$, we have

$$|I - I^*| \leqslant y^2 I^* \qquad (4.138)$$

This means that, if we are not more than 20% away from the ideal flows, there will be no more than 4% increase in the I integrals (specifically in the total flow).

The ideal cascade, since its concentration gradient is half the physically possible maximum, does not ensure the minimum number of stages, which we will get with $L \to \infty$.

The net holdup of isotope H (see Eq. 4.122) is one of the functions which is minimized in the ideal cascade. Consequently even the equilibrium time t_e derived from it is minimum by comparison with any other cascade.

OPTIMIZING THE SQUARE CASCADE

From Table 4.1 we see that the same production P at concentration N_P from an ideal cascade can be obtained from a number of square cascades. Among these cascades, Q-1 and Q-4 represent two extreme cases, whereas Q-2 and Q-3 equal the ideal cascade either in number of stages or in the feed flow.

The situation, also shown in Fig. 4.20, poses the general problem of optimizing the square cascade which can be stated in either of the following two ways: (1) If the number of stages S and the total enrichment a ($< \exp gS$) are fixed, what is the optimum yield? (2) If the total enrichment and the yield η are fixed, what is the optimum number of stages S?

Table 4.1

COMPARISON OF CORRESPONDING CASCADES

	Q-1	Q-2	Ideal	Q-3	Q-4
S	∞	525	525	343	262
L, mols hr^{-1}	244,000	280,000	488,000	488,000	∞
η	0.0062	0.0054	0.0031	0.0031	0
ρ	1	0.91	...	0.61	0
$\Sigma_i L_i$ mols hr^{-1}	∞	1.47×10^8	1.1×10^8	1.67×10^8	∞
$t_e(d)$	∞	...	$\lesssim 43$	300	∞

Common Features

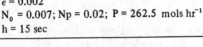

$\epsilon = 0.002$
$N_0 = 0.007;\ Np = 0.02;\ P = 262.5$ mols hr^{-1}
$h = 15$ sec

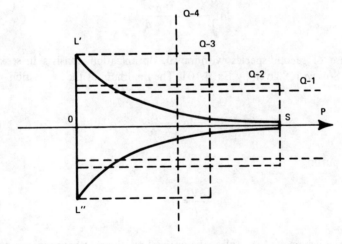

Fig. 4.20 Corresponding cascades for equal product (P,Np): ideal (———) and square Q-1 to Q-4 (– – –).

Let us limit our considerations to the infinitesimal case with low concentrations. Introducing the relative yield ρ, we see first that there is only one way to state the problem: Given enrichment a, what is the corresponding optimum relative yield?

Assume now that the total cost of separation is proportional to the total flow $\Sigma_i L_i = SL$, which is substantially what happens for irreversible processes.

In such a case the optimum operation will come when SL/PNp is minimum, or when $S/a\psi$ is minimum.

Using Eq. 4.80 for S, we now have to minimize the expression

$$\frac{1}{\psi(1 + \psi)} \ln \frac{a}{1 - \psi(a - 1)}$$

with respect to ψ or, recalling that $\rho = a\psi/(1 + \psi)$, the expression

$$\frac{(a - \rho)^2}{a\rho} \ln \frac{a - p}{1 - \rho}$$

with respect to ρ. In this way we obtain the optimum equation

$$\ln \frac{a - \rho}{1 - \rho} = \frac{\rho}{1 - \rho} \times \frac{a - 1}{a + \rho} \tag{4.139a}$$

When $\psi \ll 1$ or when we are dealing with very high enrichments or very small yields, we have $\rho \ll a$, and Eq. 4.139a becomes

$$\ln \frac{a}{1 - \rho} = \frac{\rho}{1 - \rho} \tag{4.139b}$$

In the case of second-species withdrawal, optimization consists in seeking the minimum for S/ρ, with S given by Eq. 4.101. The minimum of the expression

$$V = \frac{1}{\rho} \ln \frac{a - \rho}{1 - \rho} \tag{4.140}$$

obtainable by putting

$$\frac{\partial V}{\partial \rho} = 0 \tag{4.141}$$

leads to the establishment of the following optimal relationship between ρ and a:

$$\ln \frac{a - \rho}{1 - \rho} = \frac{\rho}{1 - \rho} \times \frac{a - 1}{a - \rho} \tag{4.142}$$

The solution to Eq. 4.142 is shown graphically in Fig. 4.21.
When $a - 1 \ll 1$, we find from Eq. 4.142

$$\rho \simeq \frac{1}{2} \left(1 - \frac{a - 1}{2}\right) \tag{4.143}$$

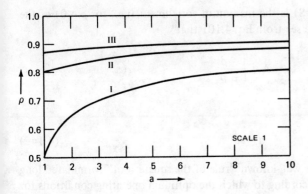

Fig. 4.21 Optimum relative yield ρ for a square cascade with second-species withdrawal, as a function of enrichment a. Scale II = scale I x 10; scale III = scale I x 100.

It is easy to show that this is equivalent to adopting for the square cascades with S stages the same enrichment obtainable with an ideal cascade having the same number of stages. For the latter, we find

$$S = \frac{2}{g}\ln a \tag{4.144}$$

which, when compared with Eq. 4.101, gives

$$a^2 = \frac{a - \rho}{1 - \rho} \tag{4.145}$$

or

$$\rho = \frac{a}{a + 1} \tag{4.146}$$

In the case of $a - 1 \ll 1$, developing Eq. 4.146 in series of powers of $a - 1$, we have Eq. 4.143 as our first approximation.

Equation 4.146 comes fairly close to the optimum ratio of Eq. 4.142, up to values of $a \sim 2$.

For higher values of a, a good analytical approximation of Eq. 4.142 is given by

$$\rho = \frac{a}{a + 1}\left(\frac{z}{1 + z} + \frac{1}{a}\right) \tag{4.147}$$

where

$$z = \ln[a(1 + \ln a)]$$

Remembering that $A = \exp(gS)$ is the maximum enrichment (i.e., for $\rho = 0$) of the square cascade with S stages, we see from Eq. 4.101 that

$$A = \frac{a - \rho}{1 - \rho}$$

and therefore for Eq. 4.145

$$a = A^{\frac{1}{2}} \qquad (4.148)$$

This equation expresses the well-known "rule of the square root" formulated long ago for distillation columns, according to which the optimum operating conditions for a column require an enrichment equal to the square root of the enrichment at total reflux. The rule, which has been demonstrated here only in the case of low concentrations, can also be demonstrated for any concentrations.[1a]

In the final analysis, Eq. 4.148 means that in the square cascade operating in optimum conditions with the enrichment a not too high ($< \sim 2$), the mean value of the dN/ds gradient is equal to half the maximum value and hence coincides with that of the corresponding ideal cascade.

For higher values of a, the conditions of minimum volume for the square cascade draw away from those of the corresponding ideal cascade, as shown in Table 4.2.

Table 4.2

RELATIVE OPTIMUM YIELDS CALCULATED BY MEANS OF DIFFERENT FORMULAS

a	ρ_{id}(4.146)	ρ(4.142)	ρ(4.147)
1	0.500	0.500	0.500
1.10	0.525	0.523	0.559
1.50	0.600	0.592	0.656
2	0.667	0.645	0.703
3	0.750	0.701	0.736
5	0.833	0.751	0.766
10	0.909	0.796	0.798
100	0.999	0.869	0.870
1000	~1	0.902	0.900

As a increases, the ρ_{id} values exceed the corresponding values for the minimum-volume conditions. If, however, the cascade is to be optimized, allowing not only for the SL factor proportional to the total flow but also for factors proportional to the flow L (e.g., in relation to the costs of the heat exchangers in a distillation system), the search for optimum conditions lies in determining the minimum with respect to ρ of functions of the type

$$\frac{1}{\rho}(Sc_1 + c_2) \tag{4.149}$$

in which c_1 and c_2 are suitable constants. This shifts the optimum yields ρ in the direction of higher values than those corresponding to minimum volume.

In many practical cases the values for ρ_{id}, given by Eq. 4.146, come satisfactorily close to the optimum values obtained by minimizing the expressions given by Eq. 4.149.

OPTIMIZING SQUARED-OFF CASCADES

To approximate an ideal cascade with a squared-off cascade that produces the same total enrichment a_T, we must first establish: (1) the number of steps and (2) the ith-step enrichment a_i and yield ρ_i of each step. Assume that we have arbitrarily set the number of steps at m. The simplest solution for the second point is to choose the same enrichment for the various steps

$$a = a_T^{1/m} \tag{4.150}$$

Limiting ourselves to the infinitesimal case with low concentrations, we can then correspondingly determine the relative yield by means of one or the other of the optimal relationships, such as Eq. 4.139a or Eq. 4.142, according to the type of withdrawal.

But the search for the optimum conditions for the entire cascade (not merely for the individual step) leads us to consider different ith-step enrichments a_i from step to step.

If the search for optimum conditions is based on the determination of the cascade with m steps having the smallest volume, as might be convenient in the case of substantially irreversible processes, we have to minimize the total flow

$$\sum_{i=1}^{m} L_i S_i$$

overall for the step cascade. In the case of second-species withdrawal, we have $L_i = 2\tau/g\rho_i N_i$ (in which N_i is the feed concentration of the ith step), and S_i is given by Eq. 4.101. By eliminating the constant factors, the total flow will accordingly become

$$V = \sum_{i=1}^{m} \frac{1}{N_i \rho_i} \ln \frac{a_i - \rho_i}{1 - \rho_i} \tag{4.151}$$

in which $a_i = N_{i+1}/N_i$.

The optimum conditions are obtained through

$$\begin{cases} \dfrac{\partial V}{\partial N_i} = 0 \qquad (i = 2, 3, \ldots m) \\[2mm] \displaystyle\prod_{i=1}^{m} a_i = a_T \end{cases} \qquad (4.152)$$

We now have

$$V'_{N_i} = \frac{\partial V}{\partial N_i} + V'_{a_i}\frac{\partial a_i}{\partial N_i} + V'_{a_{i-1}}\frac{\partial a_{i-1}}{\partial N_i} = 0$$

where V' represents the derivative of V with respect to the index, which is to say

$$V'_{a_i} = \frac{\partial V}{\partial a_i} + \frac{\partial V}{\partial \rho_i}\frac{d\rho_i}{da_i}$$

From the last two equations, we can readily see that the derivation for each step involves only two terms of the function V. Calculating the partial derivatives and remembering Eqs. 4.141 and 4.142, we have

$$\frac{1}{\rho_i}\frac{a_i^2}{a_i - \rho_i} = \frac{1}{\rho_{i+1}(1 - \rho_{i+1})} \qquad (i = 1, 2, \ldots, m - 1) \qquad (4.153)$$

This expression links the enrichment a_i of the ith step to enrichment a_{i+1} of the succeeding stage through ρ_{i+1}, which in turn is linked to a_{i+1} through Eq. 4.142.

Table 4.3 shows the data for this procedure applied to optimization of the total flux of a squared-off cascade that produces an overall enrichment $a_T = 300$ (in the case

Table 4.3

**OPTIMUM ENRICHMENTS AND YIELDS OF INDIVIDUAL STEPS
IN A CASCADE WITH TOTAL ENRICHMENT $a_T = 300$**

i	For m = 1, $a_1 = 300$ and $\rho_1 = 0.887$							
	m = 2		m = 3		m = 4		m = 5	
(steps)	a_i	ρ_i	a_i	ρ_i	a_i	ρ_i	a_i	ρ_i
1	5.15	0.755	2.66	0.685	2.06	0.650	1.85	0.635
2	58	0.855	4.50	0.740	2.52	0.680	2.02	0.650
3			25.4	0.830	3.90	0.730	2.40	0.675
4					15.0	0.815	3.45	0.717
5							9.7	0.798
For m → ∞, $a_i \to 1$ and $\rho_i \to \tfrac{1}{2}$								

of low concentrations). The number of steps m has been gradually increased from 1 to 5, and Table 4.3 also includes the extreme case $m \to \infty$, corresponding in practice to the ideal cascade.

The choice of m generally presupposes a detailed economic evaluation (at least insofar as costs of plant and energy consumption are concerned) of cascades having different values of m. Energy-consumption levels can favor an increase or decrease of m according to whether the process is substantially irreversible (such as gaseous diffusion) or reversible (such as a distillation column).

Furthermore, the advantages derived from standardization tend to decrease m and to group together the greatest possible number of stages S in each of the steps. That number S may in turn encounter such various technical limitations as pressure drops in diffusion cascades and distillation columns. In the specific case of columns, another technical limitation is the maximum height that is practically feasible.

Once m is fixed, these same considerations, together with other factors of a practical nature, can lead to the selection of equal enrichment factors for all the various steps on the basis of Eq. 4.150. That choice is made easier because the minimums of functions like Eq. 4.151 with respect to the enrichment levels are rather flat and therefore do not differ much from the optimum conditions, even using values for a_i quite different from the optimum ones. This is shown in Table 4.4, where the values of V for the optimum case (V_{opt}) and for the case (V_{const}) in which $a = \mathrm{const} = a_T^{1/m}$, with ρ fixed according to Eq. 4.142, are compared.

Table 4.4

COMPARISON BETWEEN SQUARED-OFF CASCADES WITH
MINIMUM TOTAL FLOW (V_{opt}) AND
CONSTANT ENRICHMENT (V_{const})

m	V_{opt}	V_{const}	a; ρ
1	59.300	59.300	300; 0.887
2	34.500	38.800	17.33; 0.820
3	30.260	32.920	6.69; 0.775
4	28.700	30.400	4.16; 0.735
5	27.970	29.150	3.129; 0.706

From the foregoing considerations it is easy to see that optimum conditions like those expressed in Eqs. 4.142 and 4.153 are useful primarily as terms for comparison and points of departure for more complex calculations of optimization. The calculations are often made on electronic computers.

For practical reasons it may be better to approximate the final part of a cascade (from concentration N_a to N_P) with a much longer step than the others. If in this step we use the same flow as is found in the ideal cascade with an input concentration N_A, we reduce the number of stages at the expense of flows in a zone of the cascade in which the flows are small.

One essential element in the evaluation of the feed concentration N_A of the final step is the equilibrium time, which is a rapidly growing function of the total flow.

OPTIMIZING THE STRIPPING SECTION

As we have already seen, the stripping section of a cascade allows a reduction, at the expense of a greater separative work factor, of the feed flow F. This is particularly important in processes in which the feed material is expensive. A typical case is uranium enrichment, in which the feed material is UF_6, which costs about $22.50 per kilogram of uranium.

The best waste concentration N_W is the one for which there is a balance between the cost of the separative work in the stripping section and the corresponding saving in feed material. There is no point in going below a certain value of N_W, because the cost of the separative work begins to exceed the saving, as can be seen (in qualitative terms) in Fig. 4.22.

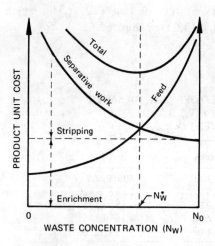

Fig. 4.22 Determination of the optimum waste concentration N_W^*.

The optimum value N_w^* is determined as follows. The cost C of the product PN_P is composed thus:

$$C = C_U \Delta U + C_F F$$

in which ΔU is the separative work necessary to produce PN_P, C_U is the corresponding unit cost (including capital costs and operating costs), and C_F is the unit cost of the feed.

The cost per unit of product C/P is

$$C_P = C_U \frac{\Delta U}{P} + C_F \frac{F}{P} \qquad (4.154)$$

From Eq. 4.112 we have

$$\frac{\Delta U}{P} = V'(N_P) + \frac{W}{P} V'(N_w) - \frac{F}{P} V'(N_0)$$

which, keeping in mind Eqs. 4.30 and 4.31 and abbreviating their notations, becomes

$$\frac{\Delta U}{P} = V'_P - V'_0 - (N_P - N_0) \frac{V'_0 - V'_W}{N_0 - N_W} \qquad (4.155)$$

Substituting Eqs. 4.155 and 4.30 in Eq. 4.154, we have

$$C_P = C_U \left[V'_P - V'_0 - (N_P - N_0) \frac{V'_0 - V'_W}{N_0 - N_W} \right] + C_F \frac{N_P - N_W}{N_0 - N_W} \qquad (4.156)$$

The optimum value N_W^* is the one for which $dC_P/dN_W = 0$, or

$$\frac{N_P - N_0}{N_0 - N_W} \left(\frac{dV'_W}{dN_W} - \frac{V'_0 - V'_W}{N_0 - N_W} \right) C_U + \frac{N_P - N_0}{N_0 - N_W} \times \frac{C_F}{N_0 - N_W} = 0$$

from which

$$\left[V'_0 - V'_W - (N_0 - N_W^*) \left(\frac{dV'}{dN} \right)_{N_W^*} \right] C_U = C_F \qquad (4.157)$$

Comparing Eq. 4.157 with Eq. 4.114, we see that the term which multiplies C_U represents the separative work required to produce a unit quantity of material at concentration N_0, starting from concentration N_W^* in an ideal cascade without a stripping section.

Hence the optimum value for N_W^* is the one for which the feed material at N_0 concentration can be obtained from N_W^* in an ideal cascade without a stripping section at the same unit cost C_F that is valid for an external feed.

Substituting Eq. 4.157 in Eq. 4.156, we have

$$C_P = C_U \left[V'_P - V'_{W*} - (N_P - N_W^*) \left(\frac{dV'}{dN} \right)_{N_W^*} \right] \qquad (4.158)$$

This means that the cost of the product in an ideal cascade with an optimized stripping section is equivalent to the cost in an ideal cascade without a stripping section and fed by material at the optimum concentration N_W^* that cost nothing.

Substituting V' through Eq. 4.110 in Eq. 4.157 and approximating for $N_W^* \ll 1$, we have

$$\left[\frac{N_0 - N_W^*}{N_W^*}(1 - N_W^*) - (1 - 2N_0)\ln\frac{R_0}{N_W^*}\right] = \frac{C_F}{C_U} \qquad (4.159)$$

Table 4.5 shows the values of N_W^* as a function of the C_F/C_U ratio for uranium separation, where we have $N_0 = 0.00715$.

Table 4.5

**OPTIMUM WASTE CONCENTRATIONS
IN THE CASE OF URANIUM**

N_W^*	C_F/C_U
0.00200	1.278
0.00225	1.030
0.00250	0.810
0.00275	0.645
0.00300	0.515

From the table we can see, for example, that with a unit cost for separative work of $32 per kilogram of uranium (the current cost in the United States in 1973), and with a feed cost of $22.50 per kilogram of uranium, the optimum waste concentration is close to 0.27%.

Using Eq. 4.158, and keeping in mind Eq. 4.110 while approximating for $N_W^* \ll 1$, we find for the unit cost of ^{235}U at N_P concentration the following expression:

$$\frac{C_P}{N_P} = \left[\frac{N_P - N_W^*}{N_W^*} \times \frac{1 - N_W^*}{N_P} - \frac{1 - 2N_P}{N_P}\ln\frac{R_P}{N_W^*}\right]C_U \qquad (4.160)$$

Figure 4.23 shows graphically the function $C_P/N_P C_U$ calculated using Eq. 4.160 and referring C_P to the gram and C_U to the kilogram. The function becomes zero when $N_P = N_W^* = 0.002$ and tends toward infinity when $N_P \rightarrow 1$, (but, when $N_P = 0.999$, then $C_P/N_P C_U$ is still only equal to 0.511) after a plateau in the 0.5 to 0.9 interval. This function enables us to calculate the cost per gram of ^{235}U at the various concentrations. (Given the slight relative difference in economic weights between ^{235}U and ^{238}U, it is permissible to use the concentrations in weight in place of the mol fractions.)

For example, taking $C_U = 32 per kilogram, for ^{235}U at natural concentration, we obtain a cost of $5.75 per gram; at 3% the cost is $12 per gram, whereas the cost in the high-concentration interval is about $16 per gram.

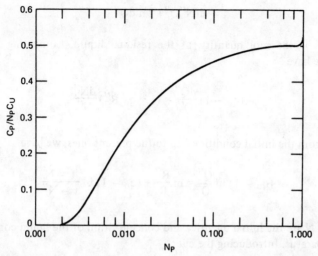

Fig. 4.23 Ratio between the cost per gram of ^{235}U and the cost per kilogram of separative work, at various concentrations.

DISCONTINUOUS PROCESSES

The treatment developed thus far has dealt with a separating element operating according to the law

$$R' = \alpha R \qquad R'' = \frac{1}{\beta} R \qquad (4.161)$$

with α and β constant. This type of separating element is very commonly used, but separating elements operating in a quite different way can also be conceived. A typical and extremely important case is that of Rayleigh's distillation process or, in general, of the "batch" processes.

Consider the distillation process as it progresses; at every instant the vapor (of mol fraction n) is coming from the liquid and is in equilibrium with the liquid (of mol fraction N'') remaining in the distilling container. The equilibrium equation, expressed in relative abundances, is

$$r = q_0 R'' \qquad (4.162)$$

The composition of the residual liquid changes continually during the distillation process since the vapor rising from it carries off the most volatile component by preference. The conservation of matter thus allows the following equation to be written:

$$d(N''Q'') = n \, dQ'' \qquad (4.163)$$

in which Q'' is the mol quantity of the residual liquid. Combining the last two equations, we have

$$(q_0 - 1) \frac{dQ''}{Q''} = (1 + q_0 \, R'') \frac{dN''}{N''} \qquad (4.164)$$

Integrating from the initial conditions up to the present ones, we have

$$(q_0 - 1) \ln \frac{Q''}{Q} = \ln \frac{R''}{R} + (q_0 - 1) \ln \frac{1 - N}{1 - N''} \qquad (4.165)$$

where Q and N are the initial quantity and concentration of the liquid contained in the distilling apparatus. Introducing the cut

$$\theta = \frac{Q'}{Q} = \frac{Q - Q''}{Q}$$

in which Q' is the quantity of the distillate. Since $q_0 - 1 = g_0$, we can write Eq. 4.165 as

$$\frac{R''}{R} \left(\frac{1 - N}{1 - N''} \right)^{g_0} = (1 - \theta)^{g_0} \qquad (4.166)$$

This equation represents a relation between R'' and R like the one given by Eq. 4.161. However, this equation is analytically completely different and represents a different type of separating element.

Assuming that g_0 is small, we obtain from Eq. 4.166

$$\frac{R''}{R} = \left[(1 - \theta) \frac{1 - N''}{1 - N} \right]^{g_0} = \exp \left[g_0 \ln (1 - \theta) \frac{1 - N''}{1 - N} \right] \qquad (4.167)$$

Expanding in series, neglecting terms of the second or higher order, and further considering that the ratio of $(1 - N'')$ to $(1 - N)$ is close to unity for low enrichments, we can express the ratio R''/R as

$$\frac{R''}{R} = 1 + g_0 \ln (1 - \theta) \qquad (4.168)$$

Analogously we can express the ratio R'/R, in which R' refers to the distillate, while remembering that, for the mol fractions involved, the equation for conservation of matter (Eq. 4.15) must still remain valid. Hence

$$\frac{R'}{R} = 1 + g_0 \frac{1-\theta}{\theta} \left(\ln \frac{1}{1-\theta} \right) \tag{4.169}$$

If the cut θ remains practically constant, Eqs. 4.168 and 4.169 assume a form totally analogous to that of the (4.161) equations already written. It is possible then to apply to the Rayleigh distillation and to the batch processes the cascade theory already developed for the infinitesimal case, introducing a constant enrichment factor $\alpha = 1 + \epsilon_0$, where

$$\epsilon_0 = g_0 \frac{1-\theta}{\theta} \left(\ln \frac{1}{1-\theta} \right) \tag{4.170}$$

Consider a distilling element which has an infinitesimal enrichment and the features studied above and which handles G mol sec^{-1} of feed material producing θG mol/sec of distillate and $(1-\theta)$G mol sec^{-1} of residue. According to Eq. 4.118, which gives the separative power of the element, and introducing the expression ϵ_0 given by Eq. 4.170, we have

$$\delta U = \frac{G}{2} g_0^2 \frac{1-\theta}{\theta} [\ln(1-\theta)]^2 \tag{4.171}$$

Table 4.6 tabulates both the separative power per unit of initial batch $\delta U/G$ and the separative power per unit of distillate, $\delta U/\theta G$. Both these quantities are normalized by dividing them by $g_0^2/2$.

Table 4.6

SEPARATIVE POWER IN RAYLEIGH DISTILLATION

θ	$\dfrac{2\delta U}{G(g_0)^2}$	$\dfrac{2\delta U}{\theta G(g_0)^2}$
0.0	0.000	1.000
0.1	0.0999	0.999
0.2	0.1992	0.996
0.3	0.2968	0.990
0.4	0.3914	0.979
0.5	0.480	0.961
0.6	0.559	0.932
0.7	0.622	0.888
0.8	0.647	0.809
0.9	0.589	0.655
0.95	0.473	0.497
1.0	0.000	0.000

By increasing the cut, we can concentrate the residue $(1 - \theta)G$ in the less volatile component at will. We see, however, that the separative power has a maximum when $\theta = 0.8$, beyond which the greater quantity of material separated no longer compensates for the remixing that occurs in the distillate to an increasing degree as the cut is increased.

This remixing makes the quantity $\delta U/\theta G$ decline monotonically as the cut increases, as is shown in the third column of Table 4.6.

The maximum separative power per unit of distillate is the extreme value when $\theta = 0$, which is $Gg_0^2/2$. It can be approximated by subdividing the distillate into a number of small portions successively rather than allowing it to remix. This is tantamount to subdividing the process into a sequence of operations in each of which the cut is very small.

REFERENCES

1. K. Cohen, *The Theory of Isotope Separation*, McGraw-Hill Book Company, Inc., New York, 1951.
1a. *Ibid.,* Chap. 2, Sec. 3.
2. E. Cerrai, M. Silvestri, and S. Villani, The Cascading Problem in a Water Distillation Plant for Heavy Water Production, *Z. Naturforsch.,* 11a: 694 (1956).
3. M. Benedict and T. H. Pigford, *Nuclear Chemical Engineering*, Chap. 10, McGraw-Hill Book Company, Inc., New York, 1957.
4. A. M. Rozen, Teoriya Razdeleniya Izotopov v Kolonnoi, Goskomitet A. E., Moscow, 1960.
5. H. London (Ed.), *Separation of Isotopes*, Sec. 1, Newnes Educational Publishing Co., Ltd., London, 1961.
6. K. K. Higashi, T. Saito, H. Doi, and J. Oishi, Optimization of Square and Squared-Off Cascades for Uranium Enrichment by Gaseous Diffusion Process, in *Problemi Della Separazione Isotopica dell'Uranio,* (Problems in the Isotopic Separation of Uranium), p. 11, Comitato Nazionale per l'Energia Nucleare, Rome, 1968.

UF$_6$ DIFFUSION PLANTS

GENERAL REMARKS

In gaseous diffusion plants the elementary separation effect described in Chap. 3 is exploited in separating elements consisting essentially of a chamber (the diffuser) divided into two regions by the porous barrier or barriers. Into one region, at a proper rate of flow and under the maximum pressure compatible with the average diameter of the pores, flows the gas to be enriched in the light component. In the other region the diffused gas is held at a much lower pressure than that on the other side of the barriers.

The elementary separation factor for molecular diffusion is calculated by assuming zero pressure downstream from the porous barrier (with respect to the direction of the diffused flow) and fairly low pressure upstream, so as to guarantee a pure Knudsen flow through the pores. The fact that these conditions do not occur in actuality, plus other causes of inefficiency, causes the separation factor for the stage to be lower than the elementary separation factor $q_0 = (M_2/M_1)^{1/2}$ defined in Chap. 3.

BARRIER EFFICIENCY

To calculate the separation factor for the stage, we first define the efficiency β_0 of the barrier as the ratio

$$\beta_0 = \frac{v - n''}{v - n^*} \tag{5.1}$$

in which n'' is the mol fraction upstream from the barrier, v is the corresponding mol fraction of the gas through the barrier pores, and $n*$ is the mol fraction the gas should have upstream to produce, by diffusing under ideal conditions (i.e., with a separation factor of q_0), a gas whose composition is v through the barrier pores. From the definition of the separation factor, we find

$$n* = \frac{v}{v + q_0(1 - v)} \tag{5.2}$$

thanks to which Eq. 5.1 becomes

$$\beta_0 = \frac{(v - n'')\,[v + q_0\,(1 - v)]}{(q_0 - 1)\,v\,(1 - v)} \tag{5.3}$$

Note that the definition of barrier efficiency given by Eq. 5.1 is analogous to the Murphree local efficiency in the plates of the distillation column (see Chap. 9).

The phenomena which, by reducing the separation caused by the Knudsen flow, determine the efficiency of the barrier are essentially four in number: (1) back diffusion of the low-pressure gas, (2) nonseparative laminar flow (Poiseuille flow), (3) nonseparative flow of ordinary diffusion, and (4) resistance to mass transfer in the gas upstream from the barrier.

The first three effects stem from the practical requirement of not using operating pressures that are too low in a diffusion plant, in which specific volumes of gas that are too high would not be tolerable. This would increase the dimensions of all plant components and of the barrier areas, thus canceling out the advantage of the smaller number of stages obtainable with a higher separation factor.

The efficiency of the barrier, considering only the effects of back diffusion and of laminar flow, can easily be assessed as a first approximation.

According to a pattern suggested by Present and Pollard,[5] in the interval of intermediate pressure between the region of molecular flow and that of laminar flow, the flow ϕ of gas through a porous barrier can be approximately expressed as a linear combination of a Knudsen flow and a Poiseuille flow:

$$\phi = \frac{c_1(p'' - p')}{M^{1/2}} + \frac{c_2(p''^2 - p'^2)}{\eta} \tag{5.4}$$

where M = molecular weight
    η = viscosity
    p'' = high pressure
    p' = low pressure

The constants, c_1 and c_2, characteristic of the barrier, can be found experimentally by measuring the flow as a function of p'' and p' and plotting $\phi/(p'' - p')$ as a function of the sum $p'' + p'$. In Eq. 5.4 the term relating to the Knudsen flow emerges as the difference of two flows in opposite directions. In this way we allow for the back diffusion of the gas at pressure p' toward the high-pressure area.

The flows of the two components of a binary gas mixture through the porous barriers can thus be expressed, with the usual notations (n'' and n' are the mol fractions of the gas on the high- and low-pressure sides of the barrier, respectively), in the following way:

$$\phi_1 = \frac{c_1}{(M_1)^{\frac{1}{2}}} (p''n'' - p'n') + \frac{c_2}{\eta} n'' (p''^2 - p'^2) \tag{5.5}$$

$$\phi_2 = \frac{c_1}{(M_2)^{\frac{1}{2}}} [p''(1 - n'') - p'(1 - n')] + \frac{c_2}{\eta} (1 - n'')(p''^2 - p'^2) \tag{5.6}$$

The mol fraction of the light component in the gas inside the pores then becomes $v = \phi_1/(\phi_1 + \phi_2)$, or

$$v = \frac{q_0(rn'' - n') + n''(r - 1)(p'' + p')/p_c}{(q_0 - 1)(rn'' - n') + (r - 1)[1 + (p'' + p')/p_c]} \tag{5.7}$$

in which r is the compression ratio $r = p''/p'$ and

$$p_c = \left(\frac{c_1}{c_2}\right) \frac{\eta}{(M_2)^{\frac{1}{2}}}$$

The quantity p_c is called the "characteristic pressure" since it expresses the order of magnitude of the pressure at which the mean free path (MFP) of the molecules in the gas equals the average diameter of the pores. Clearly the higher the characteristic pressure the better the barrier since it allows the plant to operate, with equal separation, at higher pressure and hence with better plant dimensions.

For cylindrical pores with a radius $\bar{r}$ (still using the approximation in which we assume the flow through the pores to be made up of a Knudsen flow and a Poiseuille flow),

$$p_c = \frac{16\eta\bar{v}_2}{3\bar{r}} = \frac{32(2RT)^{\frac{1}{2}}}{3\bar{r}(\pi)^{\frac{1}{2}}} \times \frac{\eta}{(M_2)^{\frac{1}{2}}} \tag{5.8a}$$

in which $\bar{v}_2$ is the mean velocity of the heavy molecules.

For example, at 65°C the viscosity of gaseous UF_6 at pressures of about 1 atm is approximately 1.90×10^{-4} P, and from Eq. 5.8a we obtain

$$p_c = \frac{14.3}{\bar{r}} \tag{5.8b}$$

with p_c in units of atmospheres and $\bar{r}$ in centimicrons.

Expanding n″ in Eq. 5.7 and substituting in Eq. 5.3, we have

$$\beta_0 = \left[1 - \frac{1}{r} \times \frac{q_0 n'(1-v) - v(1-n')}{(q_0-1)v(1-v)}\right]$$

$$\times \frac{1 + (q_0-1)(1-v)}{1 + (q_0-1)(1-v) + (1-1/r)(p''+p')/p_c} \qquad (5.9)$$

In this equation the first term expresses the effect of back diffusion and the second term expresses the effect of the nonseparative laminar flow. In the case of cross-flow diffusers (meaning that in the high-pressure region the gas flows in a direction perpendicular to that in the low-pressure region close to the barrier surface), $v = n'$, and therefore, when $q_0 - 1 \ll 1$, Eq. 5.9 becomes

$$\beta_0 = \frac{1 - 1/r}{1 + (1-1/r)(p''+p')/p_c} \qquad (5.10)$$

Although as a general rule the barrier's efficiency depends on the composition of the gas in the low-pressure region (n'), its dependency vanishes in the particular case of cross-flow operation.

The preceding discussion is an incomplete treatment of the question in that it does not allow for the effect of ordinary nonseparative diffusion deriving from collisions between light and heavy molecules inside the pores, with the light molecules moving faster than the heavy ones, on an average. These collisions cause a transfer of momentum from the light molecules to the heavy, with a consequent trend toward equalization of velocities and hence a drop in separation.

This fact leads to a lowering of the characteristic pressure with respect to the value given by Eq. 5.8; a detailed analysis of this phenomenon has been done by Present and Bethune,[6] who worked out a more precise equation than Eq. 5.10 for barrier efficiency.

Strictly speaking, such a treatment as that on pages 156 and 157 would not be justified, since it neglects the ordinary diffusion flow ϕ_D, while allowing for the laminar flow ϕ_η. In fact, according to Present and Bethune,[5] for isotopic mixtures we would have $\phi_D \simeq 6.5\phi_\eta$.

In any case, Present and Bethune[6] get over this contradiction in their analysis, which leads to the following expression for efficiency:

$$\beta_0 = \frac{\int_{\psi''}^{\psi'} \exp\left[(1+X)\psi + (X/2)\psi^2\right] d\psi}{\psi'' \exp\left[(1+X)\psi'' + (X/2)\psi''^2\right]} \qquad (5.11)$$

in which $\psi = p/p_c$ is a parameter that can be interpreted as a "reduced pressure," i.e., referred to the characteristic pressure p_c defined in Eq. 5.8, and X is a parameter dependent on the physical characteristics of the mixture to be separated; for an isotopic mixture of UF_6, X is equal to $64/3\pi$. The ψ' and ψ'' indices refer, respectively, to the regions upstream and downstream from the pore.

From Eq. 5.11 we obtain the value of ψ'' which, with downstream pressure zero ($\psi' = 0$), gives us $\beta_0 = 0.50$; that value is $\psi''_{0.5} = 0.1834$, and hence the corresponding pressure

$$p_{\frac{1}{2}} = 0.1834 p_c$$

which we shall call the "critical pressure" of the porous barrier. Recalling Eq. 5.8b, the critical pressure as a function of the mean radius of the pores, $\bar{r}$, turns out to be (at $65°C$)

$$p_{\frac{1}{2}} = \frac{2.6}{\bar{r}}$$

Introducing a new reduced pressure, $\pi = p/p_{\frac{1}{2}}$, which we shall call the "relative pressure," we can write Eq. 5.11 in this form:

$$\beta_0 = \frac{\int_{\pi''}^{\pi'} \exp(1.430\pi + 0.1142\pi^2)\,d\pi}{\pi'' \exp(1.430\pi'' + 0.1142\pi''^2)} \tag{5.12}$$

For $\pi'' \leqslant 2$ and $\pi' = 0$, Eq. 5.12 can be approximated with an error not in excess of 1% through the expression

$$\beta_0 = \frac{1}{1 + 0.662\pi'' + 0.338\pi''^2} = \frac{1}{f_1(\pi'')}$$

Now it is easy to see that Eq 5.12 can be written, for $\pi'' \lesssim 2$ and $\pi' \neq 0$, in the form

$$\beta_0 = \frac{1}{f_1(\pi'')} - \frac{1}{r} \times \frac{f_2(\pi')}{f_1(\pi')f_2(\pi'')} \tag{5.13}$$

where r is the compression ratio and

$$f_2 = \exp(1.43\pi + 0.1142\pi^2)$$

The behavior of β_0 as a function of π'' and r is shown in Fig. 5.1. Of course the real value of the critical pressure $p_{\frac{1}{2}}$ must be found experimentally through enrichment measurements since the value given by the equation $p_{\frac{1}{2}} = 2.6/\bar{r}$ or any other such relation is broadly indicative.

Next we consider the resistance to mass transfer in the gas upstream from the barrier, which gives rise to a depletion in light components in the gas layers closest to the porous barrier. The influence of this effect, however, is not easy to calculate under

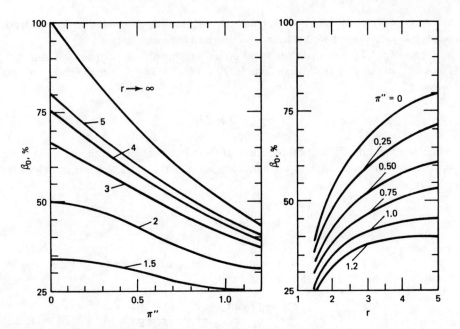

Fig. 5.1 Efficiency of the barrier β_0 as a function of the relative pressure π'' and the compression ratio r.

usual conditions since it varies radically according to the particular flow state of the gas in the high-pressure region of the diffuser. With laminar flow the supply of the light component to the layers closest to the porous barrier is entrusted solely to diffusion, which is a relatively slow process. In this case we have a very noticeable drop in efficiency, which may be reduced as much or more than 50%. The situation is better, however, in a decidedly turbulent flow with high Reynolds numbers. In this way there is a remixing of most of the flow, and the depletion is confined to the final layer, which will be thinner as the velocity of the gas flow increases. This means that it is best to take the highest possible Reynolds number compatible with pressure drop in the pipes. Often it is possible to contain the efficiency loss due to resistance to mass transfer to within 5%.

There have also been some studies as to the possible effect on barrier efficiency of the surface migration of the layer of gas adsorbed on the pore walls, but, under the conditions relevant to working separation plants, the effect, which declines with temperature, is not very important.

STAGE EFFICIENCY

The individual separating element, in practically feasible systems, displays internal remixing between portions of gases of different compositions, which reduce the separation factor of the element in comparison with the elementary separation factor q_0. Out of the separating element come the enriched and depleted portions, whose mol fractions are, respectively, N' and N'', giving a separation factor

$$q = \frac{N'(1 - N'')}{N''(1 - N')} \qquad (5.14)$$

whereas, if there were no internal remixing in the element, given the same composition of the enriched flow, the depleted flow would have a mol fraction N^*, given by the equation

$$q_0 = \frac{N'(1 - N^*)}{N^*(1 - N')} \qquad (5.15)$$

As we know, in the cases of $g = q - 1 \ll 1$ and $g_0 = q_0 - 1 \ll 1$, Eqs. 5.14 and 5.15 can be written, neglecting second-order terms with respect to g and g_0, in the following way:

$$g = \frac{N' - N''}{N'(1 - N')} \qquad (5.16)$$

$$g_0 = \frac{N' - N^*}{N'(1 - N')} \qquad (5.17)$$

If we define the efficiency β of the separating element as the ratio

$$\beta = \frac{N' - N''}{N' - N^*} \qquad (5.18)$$

then Eqs. 5.16 and 5.17 give us

$$g = \beta \times g_0 \qquad (5.19)$$

Now we shall see what relation there is between the efficiency β of the element and the efficiency β_0 of the porous barrier. For this purpose we will first distinguish between two basic categories of separating elements.

In the first category there are elements that bring about a complete remixing, both in the high-pressure region and in the low-pressure region. Here we have $n'' = N''$, and, in addition, we have $v = n' = N'$ (see Fig. 5.2). When Eq. 5.15 is compared with Eq. 5.2, we see that $n^* = N^*$ as well, and consequently, when Eq. 5.18 is compared with Eq. 5.1, we find that

$$\beta = \beta_0$$

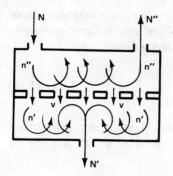

Fig. 5.2 Diffuser with mixing on both sides of the barrier.

or, in other words, that the efficiency of the separating element is equal to the efficiency of the porous barrier.

In the second category, however, we have the cross-flow separating elements, those in which there is no remixing in the high-pressure region in the direction of the flow (high Reynolds number), and in whose low-pressure region the gas is pumped out so that the fluid stream lines closest to the barrier are perpendicular to the direction of flow in the high-pressure region and do not give rise to remixing. In the low-pressure region, the remixing takes place at some distance from the porous barrier. The flow upstream from the barrier is gradually depleted in light components and the yield l gradually declines from L to $(1 - \theta)L$ (see Fig. 5.3).

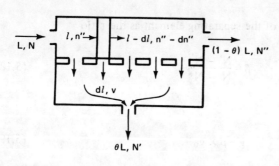

Fig. 5.3 Cross-flow diffuser.

The equation for isotope conservation in an infinitesimal segment of the high-pressure conduit in which the yield varies by the quantity dl, is written

$$ln'' - (l - dl)(n'' - dn'') = v\, dl \tag{5.20}$$

and so

$$l\frac{dn''}{dl} = v - n'' \tag{5.21}$$

Furthermore, from Eq. 5.3 it is shown that, for q very close to 1, we have (neglecting terms on the order of g_0^2)

$$v - n'' = \beta_0 g_0\, n''(1 - n'') \tag{5.22}$$

Combining Eqs. 5.21 and 5.22, we then have

$$l\frac{dn''}{dl} = \beta_0 g_0\, n''(1 - n'') \tag{5.23}$$

If we recall that β_0 is independent of the composition of the gas (see Eq. 5.10) and note that n'' varies very little with l, so that we can say that $n'' = \text{const} = N'$, by integrating Eq. 5.23 we obtain

$$N - N'' = \beta_0 g_0\, N'(1 - N') \ln \frac{1}{1 - \theta} \tag{5.24}$$

Combining this expression with the equation for conservation of the light component going through the separating element, which is

$$N - N'' = \theta(N' - N'') \tag{5.25}$$

we have

$$N' - N'' = \beta_0 g_0\, N'(1 - N') \frac{1}{\theta} \ln \frac{1}{1 - \theta} \tag{5.26}$$

Recalling the definition for the efficiency of the separating element (Eq. 5.18) and Eq. 5.17, we find that

$$\beta = \beta_0 \frac{1}{\theta} \ln \frac{1}{1 - \theta} \tag{5.27}$$

And so, with crossed flows, β will always be greater than β_0. In the particular case in which $\theta = \frac{1}{2}$, $\beta = 1.386\beta_0$. This is analogous to what happens in the distillation plates, where in the case of crossed flows the efficiency of the plate is higher than point efficiency.

Knowing the efficiency β of the stage, we can then calculate the number of stages needed to perform a given enrichment; for example, with $\beta = 0.72$, we have $g = \beta g_0 = 0.00357$.

CONNECTION IN CASCADE

The simplest way to connect a cascade of stages for a gaseous diffusion plant is shown in Fig. 5.4, which is a diagram for an ideal cascade in the part that includes the feed (F) input stage (stage 0) and the two flanking stages, respectively, in the enrichment section (stage 1) and in the stripping section (stage − 1).

The rectangles in Fig. 5.4 represent the diffusers, and the shading indicates the high-pressure regions, separated by barriers from the low-pressure regions. Each stage includes, in addition to the diffuser, the compressor C to recompress the diffused gas, followed by the heat exchanger S needed to return the heated gas to operating temperature, and the blower R (with a low compression ratio) to circulate the undiffused gas moving toward the lower concentration stages. In some cases, with proper regulation of pressures, the blowers R can be spaced to serve more than one stage, with the obvious economic advantage of thus reducing the number required.

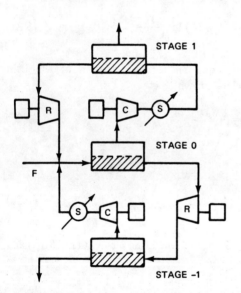

Fig. 5.4 Entrance to a diffusion cascade.

There are, however, other systems for recycling the undiffused gas, which make it possible to do away with the circulation blowers R altogether. There are three different methods to do this in practice:

The first method consists in using multistage compressors to compress the diffused gas and in sending the undiffused gas to the input of the final stages of the compressor of the preceding stage [see Fig. 5.5(a)]. This system has the drawback of requiring complex multistage compressors, which are rather expensive.

The second method uses a control valve in the undiffused gas to reduce it to low pressure, so that it can go to the compressor that feeds the preceding stage for recompression [Fig. 5.5(b)].

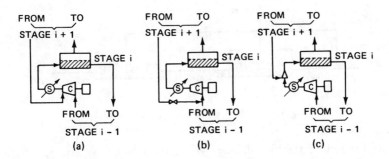

Fig. 5.5 Methods of recycling without circulation blowers. (a) System based on multistage compressors. (b) Recycling with throttling valves. (c) Recycling with ejectors.

The simplicity of this method runs into one major difficulty in the low-concentration stages. It requires a great increase in the pumping power and an increase, equally great, in the size of the compressors, which are already quite large. This solution can thus be used only for the high-concentration portion of the cascade, the part in which energy consumption is low and the stages are small in size.

The third method consists of using an ejector in which the gas coming from the feed compressor of one stage aspirates and recompresses the undiffused gas coming from the succeeding stage [Fig. 5.5(c)]. Compression with the ejector system is rather low in yield, but even so this yield calls for compression work which normally is less by an order of magnitude than the work done by the feed compressor and is often equal to only a few percentage points of that work. Thus the decline in overall efficiency is not very great, and in any case it can be offset by the simplicity of design and operation of the ejector, which requires little maintenance and is not subject to frequent breakdowns. The ejector system could thus find applications in low-concentration stages, where the dimensions of the equipment are large and the energy consumption is high.

STAGES WITH TWO OR MORE DIFFUSERS IN SERIES

The separating elements we have considered thus far consist of a single diffuser. It is possible, however, to build more complex separating elements, with two or more diffusers in series. In the two-diffuser element shown in Fig. 5.6, the gas that has not diffused in the first diffuser feeds the second.

The fraction that diffuses in the second diffuser is recycled to feed the first. So what we actually have is recycling of the gas inside the separating element.

We shall now calculate the efficiency, using for the flows and the mol fractions the symbols shown in Fig. 5.6. Note that we have called k the ratio between the diffused flow in the second diffuser and the diffused flow in the first. The term k thus also expresses the ratio between the areas of the porous barriers in the second and first diffusers, respectively.

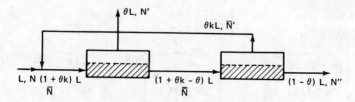

Fig. 5.6   Separating element with two diffusers.

Since for each of the two diffusers we can use an equation analogous to Eq. 5.24, we see

$$\overline{N} - \overline{\overline{N}} = \beta_0 g_0 \, \overline{\overline{N}}(1 - \overline{\overline{N}}) \ln \frac{1 + \theta k}{1 + \theta k - \theta} \tag{5.28}$$

$$\overline{\overline{N}} - N'' = \beta_0 g_0 \, \overline{\overline{N}}(1 - \overline{\overline{N}}) \ln \frac{1 + \theta k - \theta}{1 - \theta} \tag{5.29}$$

Further, for isotope conservation in the node ahead of the first diffuser, we have

$$N - \overline{N} = \theta k(\overline{N} - \overline{N}') \tag{5.30}$$

or

$$N - \overline{N} = \theta k(\overline{N} - \overline{\overline{N}}) + \theta k(\overline{\overline{N}} - \overline{N}') \tag{5.31}$$

Next we will introduce the equation for conservation of the isotope that goes through the second diffuser,

$$(1 + \theta k - \theta) \overline{\overline{N}} = (1 - \theta) N'' + \theta k \, \overline{N}' \tag{5.32}$$

and thus expressing through Eq. 5.32 the difference $\overline{\overline{N}} - \overline{N}'$, we can write Eq. 5.31 in the form

$$N - \overline{N} = \theta k \, (\overline{N} - \overline{\overline{N}}) - (1 - \theta)(\overline{\overline{N}} - N'') \tag{5.33}$$

Then, combining Eqs. 5.28 and 5.29 with Eq. 5.33, we have

$$N - \overline{N} = \beta_0 g_0 \, \overline{\overline{N}}(1 - \overline{\overline{N}}) \left[\theta k \ln \frac{1 + \theta k}{1 + \theta k - \theta} - (1 - \theta) \ln \frac{1 + \theta k - \theta}{1 - \theta} \right] \tag{5.34}$$

and finally, adding Eqs. 5.28, 5.29, and 5.34, we have

$$N - N'' = \beta_0 g_0 \, \overline{\overline{N}}(1 - \overline{\overline{N}}) \left[(1 + \theta k) \ln \frac{1 + \theta k}{1 + \theta k - \theta} + \theta \ln \frac{1 + \theta k - \theta}{1 - \theta} \right] \tag{5.35}$$

Now to express the difference $N' - N''$, we can use the equation for conservation of the light isotope going through the entire separating element, which is still equal to Eq. 5.25. And so we find

$$N' - N'' = \beta_0 g_0 \, \overline{\overline{N}}(1 - \overline{\overline{N}}) \left(\frac{1 + \theta k}{\theta} \ln \frac{1 + \theta k}{1 + \theta k - \theta} + \ln \frac{1 + \theta k - \theta}{1 - \theta} \right) \qquad (5.36)$$

Since $g_0 \, \overline{\overline{N}}(1 - \overline{\overline{N}}) \simeq g_0 \, N'(1 - N')$ except for small quantities on the order of g_0^2 or more, recalling Eqs. 5.17 and 5.18, we derive the following expression for the efficiency of the separating element with two diffusers:

$$\beta = \beta_0 \left(\frac{1 + \theta k}{\theta} \ln \frac{1 + \theta k}{1 + \theta k - \theta} + \ln \frac{1 + \theta k - \theta}{1 - \theta} \right) \qquad (5.37)$$

For $k = 1$ and $\theta = \frac{1}{2}$, we have $\beta = 1.9\beta_0$, while for the single-diffuser element β, we have $1.386\beta_0$. The approximately 37.5% increase in efficiency was obtained at the cost of a greater flow entering the element and a greater diffused flow; the feed flow is increased by 50%, whereas the diffused flow is doubled. Relative to the diffused gas, we find that the flow of undiffused gas recycled to the preceding stage is halved. In conclusion, when we compare a single-diffuser element with a double-diffuser element fed by an equal flow F, we find (in the infinitesimal case and with $k = 1$) that, while in the single-diffuser element both the diffused and undiffused portions are equal to $F/2$, in the double-diffuser element the diffused portion is $\frac{2}{3}F$ and the undiffused portion is $\frac{1}{3}F$.

By building a plant with double-diffuser elements instead of single diffusers, we would have a smaller number of stages, and furthermore, it would be more convenient to use ejectors for recycling the depleted gas. But there would also be some drawbacks to such a system, such as the greater total diffused flow (the ratio of the squares of g equals 1.89, whereas the ratio of the diffused fractions is 2) and the two-by-two connection of the stages. This means that the double-diffuser elements are better applied in the medium- and high-concentration section of a cascade, rather than in the low-concentration section where the diffused flows are already high and the stages are large in size.

The cascade arrangement of double-diffuser elements is shown in Fig. 5.7.

Hitherto we have been talking about double-diffuser elements with $k = 1$, but in the design of a plant, of course, the k parameter must be determined on the basis of economic considerations over the entire cascade.

As we mentioned earlier, it is possible to build separating elements with more than two diffusers. Figure 5.8 shows the diagram of a three-diffuser element.

In a cascade with three-diffuser elements per stage, the stages are arranged in groups of three. This disadvantage, which is most serious for maintenance purposes, plus the great complexity of connections, restricts the applicability of elements of this type to high concentrations. Actually in this zone, in which the stages are small and

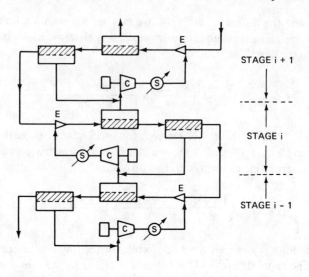

Fig. 5.7 Connection of double-diffuser elements in a cascade.

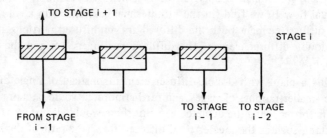

Fig. 5.8 Separating element with three diffusers.

numerous, the three-diffuser element is an attractive solution because, by markedly reducing the nondiffused fraction, it allows recycling with the throttling-valve system without excessively costly energy losses.

PHYSICOCHEMICAL AND CHEMICAL PROPERTIES OF UF$_6$

At ambient temperature and normal pressure, UF$_6$ is a colorless crystalline solid, with a symmetrical octahedral structure. At 25°C, its density is 5.060 g cm^{-3} and its vapor pressure is 108 torrs. Some of the principal thermodynamic properties of UF$_6$ are:

Sublimation at		
normal pressure	T = 56.5°C	p = 1 atm
Triple point	T = 64.05°C	p = 1.5 atm
Critical point	T ≃ 245°C	p ≃ 50 atm

The phase diagram for the UF$_6$ is shown in Fig. 5.9.

Under the triple point in the range 0 to 63.1°C, the vapor pressure of UF$_6$ in the solid state is calculable—to within a few percent—by means of the equation

$$\log p_{\text{sol.}} = 21.87103 - \frac{3123.479}{T} - 3.77962 \log T \qquad (5.38)$$

in which p is in torr and T is in °K. The vapor pressure in the liquid phase can be found to within less than 1% from the equation

$$\log p_{\text{liq.}} = 18.60033 - \frac{2065.679}{T} - 3.72662 \log T \qquad (5.39)$$

in the same units of measurement.

The density of the liquid at 65°C is 3.667 g cm^{-3}. The density of the gas can be calculated with good approximation from the equations for perfect gas. The viscosity

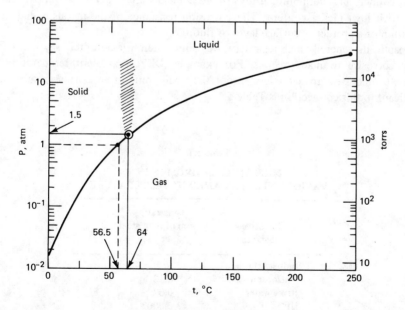

Fig. 5.9 Diagram of UF$_6$ state.

of gaseous UF$_6$ in the temperature interval 0 to 200°C can be calculated to within 2% by the equation

$$\eta \times 10^4 \text{ (poises)} = 1.67 + 0.0044 \, t \quad (t \text{ in } °C)$$

As for its chemical properties, UF$_6$ is remarkable for its high reactivity, a consequence of the fact that UF$_6$ breaks down according to the reaction UF$_6 \rightarrow$ UF$_4$ + F$_2$.

Almost all organic substances are rapidly attacked by UF$_6$, many of them even at ambient temperature, producing HF and carbon fluorides. The chlorine derivatives react to produce CCl$_2$F$_2$.

On the contrary, the fluoro compounds are particularly stable; specifically useful among these is the tetrafluoroethylene polymer (Teflon), which can find applications both in the fabrication of porous barriers and in various gaskets in diffusion plants.

The reaction of UF$_6$ with water is vigorous, forming HF and UO$_2$F$_2$. Its reaction with glass, however, is slow if the UF$_6$ is free of HF (or humidity, which causes formation of HF), and hence it can be kept for a long time in glass containers without any visible alteration.

From the preceding information it is quite obvious that UF$_6$ is a highly toxic substance.

Among inorganic substances, in addition to the fluoro compounds, the most stable are oxygen and nitrogen and, of course, dry air.

Among the metals considered highly resistant to corrosion are gold, platinum, nickel, copper, and aluminum. Alloys of these metals are also very good, particularly those with high nickel content. The corrosion resistance of the metals is due to the formation of a protective surface layer of fluoride.

Despite its generally high reactivity, we cannot therefore definitely say that UF$_6$ is highly corrosive to many metals. For example, UF$_6$ at ambient temperature will penetrate mild steel to a far less extent than will some other corrosive substances. Significant in this connection is Table 5.1.

Table 5.1

**MILD-STEEL CORROSION IN
VARIOUS MEDIA AT AMBIENT TEMPERATURE**

Corrosive substance	Penetration, mm of mild steel per year
Industrial urban atmosphere	0.12
River water	0.07
UF$_6$	0.0002

When comparing various metals and alloys to select those most compatible with UF$_6$, notice particularly the conditions under which they are to be used. If the conditions vary, a particular choice may no longer be the optimum one. This is shown in Fig. 5.10. Beyond 130°C, mild steel corrodes less than a stainless steel (Z3CN18-10). The stainless steel, however, is far more resistant than the mild steel at temperatures from 50 to 80°C.

Aside from the surface state, of which we shall have more to say later, corrosion is influenced by the crystalline structure of the metal. Corrosion is favored by crystalline disorientation, such as occurs in cold-worked metal, and in general structures with small grains or polyphase composition.

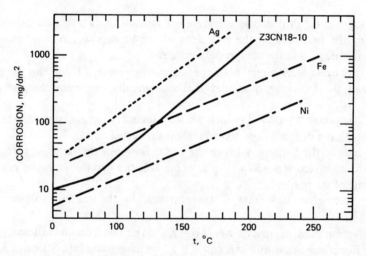

Fig. 5.10 Corrosion (gain in weight) of some metals as a function of temperature (Fe stands for mild steel, and Z3CN18-10 is a stainless steel).

Also harmful are the impurities in metals in the form of precipitates out of solid solution. Sulfides, silicates, and carbides are preferentially attacked by UF$_6$ and can cause perforation of the metallic wall.

Reacting with the surface of a metal, M, according to a total reaction of the following type,

$$UF_6 + M \rightarrow MF_x + UF_{6-x}$$

the hexafluoride is reduced, and there is abundant formation of solid UF$_4$. The same thing occurs when UF$_6$ attacks dirt and grease residues inevitably present in a plant, especially right after its construction.

In a diffusion plant a certain mass of gas comes into contact with a very large metallic surface. Even a very slight attack to the surface causes the deterioration of a considerable quantity of the circulating gas.

In the final analysis the corrosiveness of UF$_6$, at the relatively low temperatures used in the diffusion process, constitutes a problem related not so much to the integrity of the metallic components as to the following facts: (1) destruction of some of the circulating gas, (2) an increase in uranium holdup in the plant and the risk of criticality in the case of highly enriched uranium, and (3) buildup of solid UF$_4$ and scales of corroded metals with the danger of blockages (particularly in the porous barriers), erosion, and other mechanical damage (particularly to rotating components).

CHOICE OF OPERATING CONDITIONS

Assuming that the diffusion temperature will remain constant, consider the criteria for choosing the pressures on the two sides of the barriers, or, in other words, the upstream pressure p$''$ and the compression ratio r.

These two parameters affect both the separative power, δU, of the separating element, and the following quantities that substantially determine the cost of the process:

1. The compression power E (which we shall assume, as a first approximation, has to do only with the diffused flow $\frac{1}{2}$G and not the recycled flow).

2. The area of the barriers A [since the molar flow ϕ of the gas going through the unit of barrier surface is $\phi = K(p'' - p')$, where K is the permeability, the parameter characteristic of the barrier].

3. The volumetric flow rate C (proportional to the suction volume of the compressor).

The effect on the separative power $(\delta U = \frac{1}{4}g^2 G)$ derives from the efficiency of the barrier β_0. For crossed-flow diffusers and $\theta = \frac{1}{2}$, we have, using Eqs. 5.19 and 5.27,

$$\delta U = 4.5 \times 10^{-6}\ \beta_0^2\ G \tag{5.40}$$

which tends toward the limit value $4.5 \times 10^{-6} \times G$ when, simultaneously, $\pi'' \to 0$ and $r \to \infty$; then we have $\beta_0 \to 1$, according to either Eq. 5.10 or Eq. 5.13.

For the pressure dependence of the three quantities E, A, and C, we can write

$$E = \frac{1}{2}GRT \ln r \tag{5.41}$$

assuming the compression is isothermic;

$$A = \frac{1}{2}\ G/Kp_{\frac{1}{2}}\ \pi''(1 - 1/r) \tag{5.42}$$

and last

$$C = \frac{1}{2}GRT\ r/p_{\frac{1}{2}}\ \pi'' \tag{5.43}$$

Clearly the economy of the process is determined as a first approximation by the following equations:†

$$\xi_E = \frac{E}{\delta U} = 1.1 \times 10^5 \, RT \times \frac{\ln r}{\beta_0^2} \tag{5.44}$$

$$\zeta_A = \frac{A}{\delta U} = \frac{1.1 \times 10^5}{Kp_{1/2}} \times \frac{r}{\pi''(r-1)\beta_0^2} \tag{5.45}$$

$$\zeta_C = C/\delta U = \frac{1.1 \times 10^5 \, RT}{p_{1/2}} \times \frac{r}{\pi''\beta_0^2} \tag{5.46}$$

Figure 5.11 shows the behavior as a function of r (with π'' as a parameter) of the quantities $\xi_E' = \ln r/\beta_0^2$, $\zeta_A' = r/\pi''(r-1)\beta_0^2$, and $\zeta_C' = r/\pi''\beta_0^2$, in which for β_0 we have used the expression of Present and Bethune (Eq. 5.13).

Taking, for example,

$$T = 65°C$$

$$K = 0.5 \text{ kg UF}_6 \text{ m}^{-2} \text{ hr}^{-1} \text{ torr}^{-1}$$

$$p_{1/2} = 1.3 \text{ atm}$$

the above-mentioned equations can be written as follows:

$$\xi_E = 0.041 \, \xi_E' \text{ MW metric ton}^{-1} \text{ U year}^{-1}$$

$$\zeta_A = 37.5 \, \zeta_A' \text{ m}^2 \text{ metric ton}^{-1} \text{ U year}^{-1}$$

$$\zeta_C = 1120 \, \zeta_C' \, (\text{m}^3\text{hr}^{-1})/(\text{metric tons U year}^{-1})$$

The charts in Fig. 5.11 show that

$$\xi_E' \text{ min for } \pi'' = 0 \text{ and } r = 3.5$$

$$\zeta_A' \text{ min for } \pi'' = 1 \text{ and } r \to \infty$$

$$\zeta_C' \text{ min for } \pi'' = 1 \text{ and } r = 2.5$$

With the compression ratio constant, the increase in pressure π'' leads to greater energy consumption but lower capital costs.

---

†Energy consumption levels evaluated through the expression of ξ_E discussed above do not allow for the compression of undiffused gas, nor for the efficiency of real compression as opposed to isothermal compression. Allowance for both these factors must be made in more precise calculations.

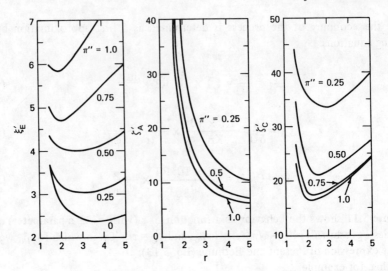

Fig. 5.11 Behavior of the functions ξ'_E, ζ'_A, and ζ'_C (E = energy consumption, A = barrier area, and C = volumetric suction flow rate) as a function of the compression ratio r and the relative pressure π''.

The choice of optimum conditions thus involves minimizing the functions obtained by combining and properly weighing (through unit costs) the parameters ξ_E, ζ_A, and ζ_C. Naturally other terms will have to be taken into consideration to obtain complete optimization.

It can be said, however, that a compromise between energy consumption and capital costs can be found in most cases in the region

$$0.25 \lesssim \pi'' \lesssim 0.50$$

$$2.5 \lesssim r \lesssim 4$$

Taking r = 3, we find at the extremes of the pressure range considered:

	$\pi'' = 0.25$	$\pi'' = 0.50$
ξ'_E/ξ'_E min	1.3	1.7
ζ'_C/ζ'_C min	3.4	2.2
ζ'_A/ζ'_A min	2.0	1.2

Figure 5.11 also shows that, as the relative pressure increases beyond $\pi'' = 0.50$, the reduction found in the terms ζ_A and ζ_C tend to disappear, whereas there is a corresponding rise in the energy factor. At $\pi'' = 0.75$, we already have $\xi'_E \simeq 2\xi'_E$ min.

Although it is unlikely that the optimum pressure will fall outside the range considered, the compression ratio r can be pushed to higher levels by the high specific costs of the porous barriers. The values r = 8 and r = 15, cited in connection with the development of UF_6 compressors in France (1958), are an example of this fact.

In the pressure interval considered, when r is varied from 3 to 6, β_0 shifts from 0.53 to 0.72.

From Eqs. 5.44 to 5.46, we see that, although ξ_E is not affected by the critical pressure, ζ_A and ζ_C are inversely proportional to it.

Hence through $p_{1/2}$ the mean radius $\bar{r}$ of the pores in the barriers directly affects capital costs. These costs, for equally permeable barriers, are found to be roughly proportional to $\bar{r}$.

From Eq. 5.42 we see that A depends on $Kp_{1/2}$. Since $p_{1/2}$ is inversely proportional to $\bar{r}$, clearly A does not change so long as the $K/\bar{r}$ ratio is constant. French estimates (1958) set the unit cost of production independent of the $K/\bar{r}$ ratio in the interval of $\bar{r}$ from 100 to 300 Å. This means that the cost of the barriers has a very considerable effect on the total cost of production.

With $\bar{r} = 2.5$ cμ it is $p_{1/2} = 1.04$ atm, therefore the limits of the pressure range considered are in absolute terms

$$p'' = 200 \text{ torrs } (\pi'' = 0.25); p'' = 400 \text{ torrs } (\pi'' = 0.5)$$

Recent developments in French technology suggest the possibility of operating at pressures considerably higher than 1 atm by using barriers with pore radii smaller than 100 Å. Apparently, however, these developments are not conclusive for purposes of industrial-scale processing.

To arrive at the choice of operating temperature and pressure (p''), we must first understand that the efficiency of porous barriers is determined, for a given mean pore radius, by the MFP of the molecules in the gas. The MFP is in turn determined by the molecular crowding, i.e., by the density of the gas, and is unchanged by variations in the absolute temperature and pressure if they are held in the same ratio.

At a given pressure the lower limit of the temperature is represented by the crystallization or liquefaction temperature, according to whether we are working below or above the critical point. For example, at 300 torrs, UF_6 crystallizes at 40°C.

When the temperature is increased, more work is required for compression (proportional to the absolute temperature). If the pressure is also increased by an equal amount, so as to hold the density constant, a saving is obtained in the area of the barriers since the rate of diffusion through the pores is proportional to the square root of the temperature. This translates into a saving in the cost of the diffusers which can roughly be taken as proportional to the area of the barriers. But assuming that the impact of the compression work and impact of the diffusers on the cost of production are fairly close together, there is no point in increasing the temperature, at least with the process we are considering, in which the gas is cooled after compression.

If we further consider that, as the temperature rises so does corrosion and dissipated heat, we see that in such a process it is best to keep the temperature as low as possible, allowing only a certain margin of safety to avoid a change of state and consequent plugging of the barrier pores. This is the solution adopted for the diffusion plant of the French Commisariat à l'Energie Atomique (CEA) in which the high pressure is set at 300 torrs and the operating temperature at 65°C, which is 25°C above the crystallization temperature.

An alternative to this situation was proposed by Perona.[2] He proposes the adoption of a higher temperature and pressure, cooling the gas, however, before compression instead of after. Since the gas is cooled at low pressure, a much lower temperature can be attained than in the other case. A decrease is thus attained in the compression work, in the barrier area, and in the compressor cross section. Moreover, the decrease of the operating temperature of the compressors decreases the corrosion effects. However, this alternative has the disadvantage of a higher cost of the low-pressure heat exchangers.

A comparison of the two systems that are shown in Fig. 5.12, as characterized by the following values of the temperature and pressure (referring to the points indicated in the figure),

	System a	System b	Difference b − a
T''	333°K 60°C)	383°K (110°C)	+15%
p''	240 torrs	276 torrs	+15%
T'	333°K (60°C)	303°K (30°C)	−9%
p'	30 torrs	34.5 torrs	+15%
r	8	8	0

yields the following variations in the process parameters:

	Difference b − a
Barrier area	−7.5%
Compression work	−9%
Compressor cross section	−24%

The differences in system capital and energy costs are roughly

	Difference b − a
Diffusers	−7.5%
Compressors	−12%
Energy consumption	−9%

These figures are obtained by assuming that the cost of the diffusers is proportional to their area and that the cost of the compressors is proportional to the square root of their cross section.

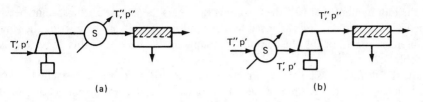

Fig. 5.12 (a) System with high-pressure heat exchanger. (b) System with low-pressure heat exchanger.

A study must then be made to determine whether or not the incidence on the production costs resulting from higher capital costs due to the low-pressure heat exchangers is compensated for by the lower energy consumption.

PLANT CONSTRUCTION FEATURES

The materials used in the construction of the various components that come into contact with UF_6 are chiefly alloys of aluminum, copper, and stainless steel. The French plants used primarily an 18/10 type of austenitic stainless steel with the addition of molybdenum and a very low carbon content and light alloys with a very high aluminum content. Particular care is required in preparation of the internal surfaces in contact with UF_6. For their plants, the French prescribe scouring with very fine-grained emery. For the gaskets and accessory parts, a good material is Teflon.

The diffuser is a component analogous in a way to a heat exchanger, in that its function is to enclose in an envelope of given volume the greatest possible diffusing surface. There are two basic designs for diffusers, one having flat barriers and the other tubular. The tubular design was adopted in the French CEA diffusion plant and also in an Italian project (1958).

The design for the Italian diffuser is shown schematically in Fig. 5.13, which also shows the system for connecting the diffusers in series by means of short cylindrical connections R. The gas under high pressure comes into the connecting cylinder to the left of the diffuser, part of it coming (the undiffused flow) from the diffuser on its left, and part of it coming (the diffused and recompressed flow) from the diffuser on its right. Passing into the porous tubes S (the figure shows only two of them), half the gas flow diffuses and is drawn off by a compressor through an opening (not shown on the figure) in the medial portion of the vessel.

The diameter of the tubes can be chosen within fairly broad limits, depending on the specifications of the porous material. However, if the tubes were too small, an excessive number of flange joints would be required, and, if the tubes were too big, the ratio between the diffuser cross section (and hence its volume) and the diffusing surface would be increased. In practice, diameters between 1 and 3 cm are most commonly used. The length of the tubes is determined, once the Reynolds number at the outlet is set (always higher than 4000 to reduce the effect of the boundary layer), by the requirement that half the incoming flow must be diffused. The spacing between the tubes has a lower limit imposed by the need to refrain from hampering the flow of diffused gas drawn off by the compressor. Some of the features of this design are listed in Table 5.2.

In the diffuser design shown in Fig. 5.13, the porous tubes are attached between the flange F and the counterflange CF through a metallic spring connection M. The tightness of the flange to the envelope is ensured by means of six tension cables T. The various sections of the porous tubes are connected by the metallic joints that are fixed to the perforated support disks D; the tubes thus form a bundle that can be lifted from the diffuser vessel in a single piece.

Table 5.2

DIFFUSER FEATURES IN THE ITALIAN DESIGN

Vessel length, m	2.40
Vessel diameter, m	1.00
Overall pipe length, m	2.00
Pipe diameter, cm	1.80
Length of each pipe section, cm	50
Number of pipe sections	600
Diffused UF$_6$ flow in the diffuser (with $\Delta p = 220$ torrs), metric tons hr^{-1}	2
Length of cylindrical connection, cm	19

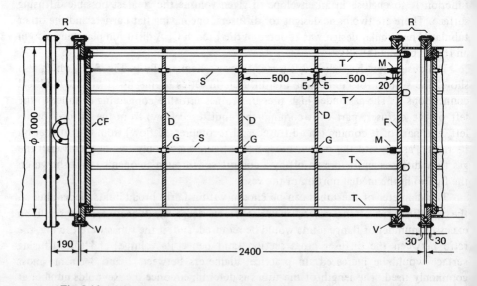

Fig. 5.13 Diffuser plan from the Italian design. (Dimensions are in millimeters.)

All the flanges are designed with a double seal to prevent air inleakage, and in the ring-shaped cavities V between the Teflon gasket, a pump induces a vacuum stronger than that in the low-pressure region of the diffuser.

To prevent air inleakage, the French use another method in their plant. They maintain a nitrogen atmosphere in the gap between the seal elements, at a pressure higher than the highest pressure in the plant. In this case, there must be purifiers to rid the UF_6 of nitrogen that has come into the plant. The purifying is generally done by liquefying the UF_6.

The diffuser shown in Fig. 5.13 can handle only very limited gas flows.

We have heard about diffusers, such as those in the low stages of American plants, with capacities almost 150 times greater, but we have no details on construction features. Some data on these plants are given on pages 195 to 200.

We shall see later that, even in plants of very large dimensions (e.g., $\Delta U = 6000$ metric tons U year^{-1}, $N_P = 3\%$, $N_o = 0.71\%$, and $N_W = 0.26\%$), a single diffuser—rather than several diffusers in parallel—can be used for each stage, even for the lower stages in the cascade.

As we have already seen, the porous barriers are identified by the mean radius $\bar{r}$ of their pores (which must be on the order of 100 Å) and by their permeability K. Generally, in a given fabrication process, any decrease of the pore radius will produce a decrease in the permeability. The quality of a barrier is thus determined by the ratio $K/\bar{r}$, but its durability and its mechanical strength must also be considered. The durability requirement imposes a lower limit on the pore radius (pores that are too small will quickly clog up), and the mechanical-strength requirement limits the thickness (thin barriers give great permeability but not much mechanical strength).

A principal distinction between the various types of barriers can be made by dividing them into simple barriers and compound barriers. The simple ones have a structure that is homogeneous throughout the thickness, whereas the compound barriers consist of a highly permeable nonseparating support combined with a thin layer of microporous material that provides the separating effect. Compound barriers must be so arranged that the separating layer faces the high-pressure part to avoid the effect of the boundary layer that would form on the support.

As for barrier-fabrication methods, we can classify them into two categories: (1) methods for producing barriers that are initially nonporous and (2) methods for producing barriers that are agglomerations of granules of very small diameter.

One of the type 1 methods is the chemical attack of a metallic alloy membrane. For example, by treating a sheet of solid 40% gold—60% silver solution with HNO_3 at 36°Bé, a barrier can be produced with a mean radius of around 300 Å and $K = 5$ mols of air m^{-2} hr^{-1} torr^{-1}.

In research work, permeability is usually expressed in units of air, since air is the medium used for standard comparative testing. If we go from air to another gas with a molecular weight M, the permeability factor must be adjusted according to the ratio $(M_{air}/M)^{1/2}$ in favor of the lighter gas.

Figure 5.14 shows the surface of a porous barrier obtained by attacking a 0.2-mm-thick sheet of silver—zinc alloy (2/1) with slightly dilute hot hydrochloric

Fig. 5.14 Surface of a porous barrier in silver−zinc alloy as seen under the electron microscope (Havliček, Institut J. Stefan, Lubiana)

acid. Satisfactory barriers were made by this method in the United States while the Manhattan Project was under way (early in the 1940s).

Chemical attack can also be performed electrolytically. Excellent results have been reported from the anodic oxidation of aluminum in a bath containing sulfuric or oxalic acid. Oxidation of the aluminum produces a large number of straight and evenly distributed pores, and the depth of these pores increases with the thickness of the oxidized layer.

Table 5.3 shows the characteristics of a barrier obtained by oxidizing an aluminum sheet in an electrolytic bath with 5% H_2SO_4 at 25°C. Since a completely oxidized sheet of aluminum is not very strong, the structure can be strengthened by oxidizing only isolated spots, separated by unaltered metal. This is done by using a suitable material to protect the areas of the surface that are not to be oxidized. Strips of aluminum with holes cut at regular intervals will serve the purpose.

Among the type 2 processes we cite, particularly, the sintering of very fine aluminum powder at 1150°C or of nickel powder at 650°C (a system much in use for tubular barriers) and the pressure bonding of precipitated Teflon emulsions to thin metallic meshes (for flat barriers). A system quite similar to the one just mentioned for flat barriers consists in sprinkling a fine, thin metallic mesh with powdered aluminum produced by an arc in a nitrogen flux. The powder is then forced into the mesh by a rolling mill or hydraulic press and finally sintered.

One of the main difficulties encountered in the fabrication of sintered barriers stems from the formation of the kind of lumps caused by the coagulation of grains whose dimensions are less than a micron. These lumps or clots are the equivalent of large grains and hence give rise to a loss of uniformity in pore radius.

Table 5.3

CHARACTERISTICS OF SOME
EXPERIMENTAL POROUS BARRIERS*

Material	Thickness, μ	K, mols m^{-2} hr^{-1} $torr^{-1}$	$\bar{r}$, $c\mu$
A. Perforated type			
Electro-oxidized aluminum	50	2.5	2.5
Electro-oxidized aluminum	...	3.6	1
B. Agglomerated type			
Aluminum powder (arc) sintered on grid	50	2.9	2
Sintered alumina	...	2.7	2.5
Sintered nickel	30	1.5	2
Teflon granules pressed into grid	...	1.5	1.5

*Permeability refers to tests with air.

Another difficulty lies in the growth of crystalline formations during heat treatment. This growth will depend both on the sintering conditions and on the purity of the materials used.

We should also cite the formation of microcracks caused by residual stresses. Barriers made by sintering metallic powders or ceramics are rather fragile; they will stand compression but not traction or impact. Usually they are designed in tubular form. Since permeability is roughly inversely proportional to thickness, barriers should be as thin as is compatible with the requirements for mechanical strength. In practice, we have thicknesses of a few tenths of a millimeter.

Table 5.3 also shows the characteristics for several experimental barriers obtained with various procedures.

The specific surface of porous barriers consists of several tens of square meters per gram and hence is of the same order of magnitude as the catalysts used in many chemical processes. Naturally this involves problems with corrosion and plugging up. A preliminary treatment of the barriers with fluorine and also with $CClF_3$ will improve barrier resistance to the corrosive action of UF_6.

We have no data on the barriers used in industrial plants, but these barriers are likely to be tubular because of easy assembly and installation. As materials, sintered nickel and alumina and Teflon may perhaps offer satisfactory solutions.

The following is a discussion of compressors suitable for use in diffusion plants:

1. **Reciprocating Compressors.** These can give almost any compression ratio, but they are big and costly if we consider the pressures at which we are working. These compressors can be considered only for very small stages (with flows up to a hundred or so kilograms per hour, for example.

2. **Multiwheel Centrifugal Compressors.** As a general rule, these require several wheels if we are to obtain the compression ratios that we need. This means that these compressors are complicated machines from the construction viewpoint.

3. **Single-Wheel Supersonic Compressors.** These offer a solution that is attractive because of their simplicity of construction. Machines of this type have been developed in France, with compression ratios of about 8; efficiency increases slightly as the compression ratio increases. Since it is desirable, for reasons of safety and economy (absence of gears and frequency controllers) for the compressors to turn at the grid frequency (which is 2900 rpm, allowing for slippage), their use is confined to high flows. For example, with a compression ratio of 8 and a low pressure of 40 torrs, the lower limit of the flows will be about 12 metric tons UF_6 hr^{-1} per unit.

4. **Axial Compressors.** These machines are fairly complicated to build, partly because they call for several buildup stages to reach the required compression ratios. This is compensated for, however, by their excellent efficiency. Their use is limited to very high flows (lower stages of the cascade). Axial compressors have been installed in the lower stages of the American diffusion plants.

In France (1972) work has been done on axial compressors having capacities of about 150 and 600 metric tons UF_6 hr^{-1}. The latter are suitable, for example, for feeding the larger stages of a plant which has a separative power of 6000 metric tons

UF_6 year^{-1} and which yields a product of 3% ^{235}U from natural uranium with 0.26% waste.

A very important problem, and one common to every type of compressor, is that of strict separation of the UF_6 from the bearing lubricant.

Figure 5.15 shows the solution adopted for the five-stage centrifugal compressor used in a French pilot plant. The UF_6 is kept away from the shaft bearings by means of a ring-shaped cavity filled with nitrogen under higher pressure than the highest pressure in the plant. Inleakage of nitrogen on the order of 10^{-4} g sec^{-1} is tolerated for each seal.

There are no special problems connected with the heat exchangers, except those of tightness. To obviate the danger of interaction with UF_6, Freon can be used instead of water as a cooling medium.

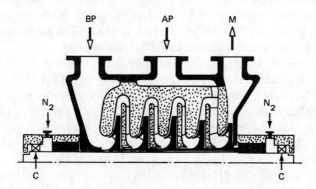

Fig. 5.15 Five-stage centrifuge compressor (C = bearings; BP = low-pressure intake; AP = high-pressure intake; and M = high-pressure delivery).

PRODUCTION, SUPPLY, AND EXTRACTION OF UF_6

Particularly important in the processes of producing nuclear fuel in its various forms (mainly as ceramic UO_2) is the chemistry of uranium relating to the $U(IV)^+$ and $U(VI)^+$ valences.

The following U(IV) compounds are important: the uranous oxide, UO_2 (brown oxide) and the tetrafluoride, UF_4 (green salts). The following U(VI) compounds are also important: uranic oxide, UO_3 (orange oxide); the uranyl radical, UO_2^{2+}, and its salts: and the uranate radical, UO_4^{2-}, and its salts (diuranate, $-O \cdot UO_2 \cdot O \cdot UO_2 \cdot O-$).

Uranium occurs with both these valences in its "black oxide," U_3O_8, which can be considered a combination through oxygen of two uranic oxide molecules with one molecule of uranous oxide: $UO_3 \cdot UO_2 \cdot UO_3$.

In nature, uranium is known to exist in more than 100 minerals. Among the most noteworthy of these are uraninite (containing UO_3 and UO_2 in varying proportions along with sundry impurities) and its variants of pitchblende and carnotite (containing vanadate of potassium and uranium: $K_2O \cdot 2UO_3 \cdot V_2O_5 \cdot nH_2O$). Deposits of uraninite are exploited in Europe (Czechoslovakia, France, and Spain), in Africa (Congo), and in America (United States and Canada). Carnotite is mined extensively in the United States (Colorado, Utah, and Arizona) and in the USSR (Siberia).

Aside from a few exceptions, uranium-bearing minerals are found mixed in with other minerals, so that the elemental-uranium content is often very low. It is economically feasible to work deposits with U_3O_8 content even lower than 1 kg per ton of rock. Particularly low assays are tolerable when the uranium is taken as a by-product, as it is from the South African gold mines. Sometimes, when the uranium-bearing mineral is widely scattered, mechanical means are used for its initial separation from the gangue.

The biggest producers of U_3O_8 in the Western world are the United States and Canada. In each of these countries, proven and economically profitable reserves in 1971 amounted to more than 200,000 metric tons of U_3O_8. The production process may be divided into two successive phases, extraction and refining.

Extraction is done in two stages. The first stage is the attack of the ore with an acid or an alkali. The second is the precipitation (with NH_3 or NaOH) of the diuranate [$(NH_4)_2U_2O_7$ or $Na_2U_2O_7$, respectively,] from the properly treated leach solution.

The diuranate thus obtained, which obviously contains a considerable percentage of impurities, is filtered and dried. It is called "yellow cake" because of its color. When it is calcined, it yields UO_3 or a mixture of UO_3 and diuranate. These products are generally called concentrates since they contain from 70 to 90% U_3O_8.

Uranium refining consists in: (1) elimination of impurities down to the low levels required to inhibit neutron absorption and (2) reduction of U(VI) to U(IV) in its various forms, usually UO_2 and UF_4.

Foregetting for the moment the elimination of impurities, we see that, among the various reduction procedures, the most commonly used reaction is

$$UO_3 + H_2 \rightarrow UO_2 + H_2O + 25 \text{ kcal mol}^{-1} \qquad (5.47)$$

in the temperature range of 540 to 575°C. This reaction is most commonly produced by using, in place of pure hydrogen, thermally dissociated ammonia. In addition, the following fluorination reactions are used:

$$UO_2 + 4HF \rightleftharpoons UF_4 + H_2O + 45 \text{ kcal mol}^{-1} \qquad (5.48)$$

at approximately 450°C and

$$UF_4 + F_2 \rightarrow UF_6 + 20 \text{ kcal mol}^{-1} \qquad (5.49)$$

in the temperature range of 350 to 450°C. Production of the hexafluoride is always done with UF_4 as an intermediate stage so as to cut down fluorine consumption. Inversely, the hexafluoride is reconverted to UF_4 via the reaction

$$UF_6 + H_2 \rightarrow UF_4 + Q \text{ kcal mol}^{-1} \tag{5.50}$$

or to UO_2 by hydrolyzing UF_6 as UO_2F_2 and precipitating a diurnate. The diuranate is then pyrolyzed with steam (to eliminate the fluorine) and reduced to UO_2.

There are two major industrial processes for refining uranium. These processes differ primarily in the method used to eliminate impurities.

In the first, which we shall call the conventional process, purification is done hydrometallurgically at the beginning of the process, before reduction. The concentrate, when treated with nitric acid, yields an aqueous solution of uranyl nitrate. With a suitable solvent (such as tributyl phosphate diluted in an inert hydrocarbon) the purified $UO_2(NO_3)_2$ is extracted and transformed by calcination into UO_3. Then come the fluorination reactions, customarily effected in vertical reactors.

In the second process, a more advanced method, the purification step occurs partly during reduction (Eq. 5.47) and during the fluoridation reactions (Eqs. 5.48 and 5.49), when many such impurities as hydrides and volatile fluorides are removed, and partly at the completion of the process, when the UF_6 is distilled at $75°C$ under 2 atm pressure. The reactions in Eqs. 5.47 to 5.49 are induced on fluidized beds, and the temperatures are the highest among those indicated. Better fluidization is obtained by mixing UF_6 with CaF_2 and diluting the fluoride with nitrogen.

In both processes, distilling the UF_6 also serves to eliminate the HF (less than 0.01% remains in the final product), whereas the fluorine is isolated in a previous condensation of the UF_6. In both processes the temperatures involved are fairly high, and therefore Monel metal is widely used in the reactors.

The most advanced process, developed at Argonne National Laboratory (USA), was used in the Allied Chemical Corporation plant at Metropolis, Ill. (capacity of 10,000 metric tons U year^{-1}).

The quantity of UF_6 required by a diffusion plant having $\Delta U = 6000$ metric tons U year^{-1}, $N_P = 3\%$, $N_F = 0.71\%$, and $N_W = 0.26\%$ is about 15,000 metric tons year^{-1}. Production of this much UF_6 requires two satellite plants for producing the HF (7500 metric tons year^{-1}) and the fluorine (2300 metric tons year^{-1}) needed in the process.

In the United States (Paducah, Oak Ridge, and Portsmouth) and France (Pierrelatte), UF_6 is produced next to the diffusion plants from UF_4 or even UO_3. Even reconversion after isotopic enrichment is done on the site. The Pierrelatte plant has a production capacity of 80 metric tons UF_6 year^{-1}, and UF_4 is obtained there by direct reduction of $UO_2(NO_3)_2$ in aqueous solution.

In Great Britain (Springfields) there is a UF_6 plant which has a capacity of 3000 metric tons year^{-1} and which uses the fluidized-bed process. Part of the product of this plant is sent to the Capenhurst diffusion plant.

The Pierrelatte and Springfields plants also produce UF_6 for toll enrichment in the American plants.

As for the price of UF_6, we could take as an indication (1972) a cost for conversion of refined U_3O_8 to UF_6 of about \$3 per kilogram of uranium. If we keep in mind that the conversion yield is usually 99.5%, and if we start with a price of

$18.50 per kilogram of uranium as U_3O_8 (which is about $7 per pound of U_3O_8), we arrive at a unit cost for UF_6 of about $22.50 per kilo of uranium.

The hexafluoride is delivered at the diffusion plant as salt, shipped in very large containers. These containers are then connected directly to the feed lines. Figure 5.16 shows this operation being carried out at the Capenhurst plant in Great Britain.

There are various ways of feeding the UF_6 into the plant. One is to introduce the hexafluoride into a pressurized tank where it is held in the liquid state at about 80°C; it is then vaporized and enters the circuit at low pressure through a throttling valve.

In medium-sized plants both the enriched product and the waste can be drawn off by cooling the hexafluoride to induce crystallization. The hexafluoride is removed from the cascade at the higher pressure; then the diffused flow in the final stage must be recompressed. Precooled in a first exchanger into which the coolant fluid flows at about 0°C, the gas enters the crystallizer, which is brought down to a temperature of −50 to −60°C by another cooling circuit. Since an increase in the thickness of crystallized hexafluoride on the cooling tubes increases the resistance to heat transfer, two crystallizers in parallel are used, each with a preliminary exchanger, and are alternately tied into the diffusion plant. While one of the units is operating to withdraw the hexafluoride from the end stage of the cascade, the other is liquefying the crystallized hexafluoride by passing a heating fluid at about 70 to 80°C through the crystallizer tubes. Given the impossibility of avoiding mixing of the coolant fluid and the heating fluid, they must be the same. Freon is particularly suitable, thanks to its low reactivity with UF_6. Once the hexafluoride is liquefied, it flows by gravity down from the crystallizer into a holding tank. At its crystallization temperature of −50 to −60°C, the vapor pressure of UF_6 is on the order of 10^{-1} torr, but the pressure in the crystallizer would tend to reach much higher levels, owing to the buildup of such volatile impurities as HF and nitrogen. The pressure in the crystallizer is kept low by drawing off the gases from it by means of a pump connected, as shown in Fig. 5.17, through a liquid-nitrogen trap and a purifying cartridge of activated alumina.

The pumps used for this purpose are of the membrane type, lubricated with fluorinated oil. Before the gas drawn off is vented into the atmosphere, it is passed through a counterflow of soda solution in a scrubbing column.

In large plants where the flows to be extracted would be too large for crystallizers to be practical, withdrawal can be done by compressing the gaseous hexafluoride to a level beyond the triple point pressure and then cooling it in an exchanger until it liquefies.

TECHNICAL AND OPERATING PROBLEMS: INSPECTION

One of the principal technical problems encountered in setting up a diffusion plant lies in the almost absolute elimination of inleakage of air (and of the humidity it carries) from any portion of the plant which will come in contact with low-pressure

Fig. 5.16 Capenhurst plant (Great Britian) hookup operation for a UF₆ container to the plant feed system.

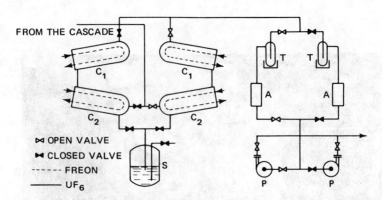

Fig. 5.17 Diagram for the UF$_6$ extraction system (C$_1$ = precooling heat-exchanger; C$_2$ = crystallizer; S = UF$_6$ holding tank; T = liquid nitrogen trap; A = activated alumina bed; and P = vacuum pump).

UF$_6$. To do this requires that vacuum seals of every component be tested and, once the components are in place, that whole plant sections be retested.

The operation is performed with the aid of special mass spectrometers as leak detectors. This is the way to obtain the high sensitivity needed to detect small leaks in large plant volumes.

There are various ways of applying the method. One way consists in first surrounding with a helium atmosphere the device whose leaktightness is to be tested and then analyzing with a mass spectrometer the gas drawn off from the device. The appearance of the helium line on the mass spectrum indicates inleakage of helium from outside (the concentration of helium in the air is very small, on the order of 10^{-4} to 10^{-5}); then by the intensity of the line—after a suitable calibration—we can measure the size of the leak. If the part to be tested is too large to be enclosed in a helium atmosphere, its outer surface can be inspected with a jet of helium. In this way the leak can be pinpointed to within a centimeter. Another variation consists in filling the portion to be tested with helium instead of emptying it. If this is done, the outer surface is inspected with a suction tube connected with the analyzing spectrometer. This procedure, however, is not quite so sensitive.

The method of using the helium spectrometer for detecting leaks was developed in the United States during the 1940s, specifically for the problem presented by UF$_6$ diffusion plants. Prior to that time the use of vacuum techniques on an industrial scale was limited—for comparable leaktightness requirements—to far smaller volumes than those involved in diffusion plants. The mercury-vapor rectifier with an overall volume of about 2 m^3, consisting of 15 distinct parts, was for a long time the biggest high-vacuum device in use on a commercial scale.

The leaktightness specifications set for American diffusion plants stipulate that the maximum inleakage of ambient air into the processing gas (UF$_6$) must not exceed 10^{-5} STP m^3 hr^{-1} for each cubic meter of plant volume, which is 10^{-5} STP m^3 air m^{-3}

hr^{-1}. With high vacuum in the plant, e.g., with a pressure of 1μ Hg (1 mtorr), there is a corresponding increase in pressure of about 8μ Hg hr^{-1}. The overall seal actually achieved led to a level that was actually lower, $2 \mu hr^{-1}$ for the entire plant.

The effects of air inleakage were cut down in the plant, by placing most of the components in an air-conditioned zone having a dew point of $4.5°C$.

Tightness measurements on a given component or group of components are taken by setting up a vacuum in them and then taking repeated readings of the increase in pressure of the gas (helium) seeping in from outside. Since this pressure is inversely proportional to the inner volume of the component being tested, the unit of tightness can be made independent from the internal volume, using as a measurement of tightness the product of that volume times the pressure increase per time unit. This gives rise to great numbers of different units of tightness (or better, of inleakage), such as m^3 atm hr^{-1}, $m^3 \mu Hg hr^{-1}$, cm^3 atm sec^{-1}; and $\ell\mu$ Hg sec^{-1}. This last unit is also referred to as a "lusec." Obviously, for every measurement of tightness, the gas, the differential pressure, and the temperature must be specified.

The increase in pressure due to an imperfect tightness in a block of components having the total volume V_{total} is thus obtained by dividing by V_{total} the sum of the inleakage measurements expressed in one of the above-mentioned units. This is equivalent to compounding the various increases in pressure and weighing them with respect to the corresponding volumes.

Table 5.4 is an example of the above-mentioned tightness measurements and relates to the tightness specifications for various components in an American diffusion plant. It can be seen from Table 5.4 that there is a noticeable margin between the specification of $0.44 \mu hr^{-1}$ relating to the sum of the components and that of $8 \mu hr^{-1}$ established for the entire finished plant.

Since, for obvious reasons, it is not possible to perform a thermal degassing of the plant's metallic surfaces, all of them are first put through careful washing and degreasing with various chemical ingredients prior to emplacement.

Table 5.4

TIGHTNESS SPECIFICATIONS FOR THE
VARIOUS COMPONENTS OF A PLANT

Components	Volume, (m^3), %	Spec. Δp, $\mu\ hr^{-1}$	Inleakage $(m^3 \mu\ hr^{-1})$, %
Diffusers	68.6	0.25	17.1
Compressors	2.2	0.50	1.1
Vessels	3.8	0.1–1.0	0.4
Valves and tubing	25.4	1.00	25.4
Instruments	<0.1	<1.00	<0.1
Total	100.0	0.44*	44.1

*Value found by weighing against volume.

A vacuum can be induced in the plant by the use of oil diffusion pumps and rotary or membrane preliminary pumps. The inleakage of oil into the plant must be reduced to a minimum, and it is also advisable to use highly halogenated oils that will not react with UF$_6$.

In a diffusion cascade, various factors can cause changes in flows and pressures which deviate from the norm, with consequent variations in concentrations. Among these factors are alterations in barrier permeability and variations in the suction speed by the compressors.

Furthermore, even as early as the planning stages, there is a shift away from the ideal cascade for practical reasons. Hence the squared-off cascade is adopted, although at the cost of a slight mixing. Slight variations in flow rate and pressure thus give rise to mixing effects that are superimposed upon the effects of the nonideality of the flows. The drops in yield which result from this are, however, as was shown in Chap. 4, of a lower order of magnitude than that of the disturbances which caused them. For example, the efficiency term that allows for back diffusion is equal to $1 - p'/p''$. If, with a compression ratio of 8, the low pressure varies by 10%, it is easy to see that the efficiency term will vary in the opposite direction by 1.4%. This same 1.4% variation is encountered again in the diffused flow if, with a compression ratio of 8 and the high pressure unchanged at p'', the low pressure varies by 10%. In fact the diffused flow is proportional to the difference $p'' - p'$. Of course, the effects of the variation in efficiency and of the variation in flow cumulate.

Control of a diffusion plant so as to hold the transport constant should require a constant difference between the flow of diffused gas from one stage and the nondiffused flow from the next stage (recycled flow). We are dealing here, of course, with flows that are quite similar (differing only from the flow P—or W—coming out of the plant), and so it is hard to measure the difference. It is therefore wise to control flows by maintaining constant pressures in certain points in the plant, such as the mean pressure in the high-pressure pipes. If the plant consists of single-diffuser stages with a compressor for circulating the high-pressure gas between each group of several diffusers in series, a valve with an adjustable aperture can be installed upstream of each compressor and can thus produce a marked pressure drop. In this way there is a quick damping of pressure waves (derived from transitional flows), and the outflow speed of the nondiffused gas coming from the group of diffusers upstream of the valve will no longer depend upon the suction speed of the compressor. The valve aperture is controlled by the mean pressure in the high-pressure pipe of the group of diffusers upstream, so that this pressure remains constant.

Any variations in the compressor suction speed will produce only a change in the pressure at the entrance to the compressor but no change in the valve aperture which would upset the pressure regime in the diffusers upstream. The various groups of diffusers, although subject to the constancy of the pressures, have their own system of regulation.

As for barrier permeability, a drop of 10% per stage is generally tolerable. If we assume that the decline in permeability of a barrier is 10% in τ years, replacing the barriers in one diffuser out of five will give the distribution of permeability (in percentages of the permeability K of the new barrier) shown in Table 5.5.

In this way the overall permeability of a stage will vary by 10% over a period of τ years, with a mean value of 0.75 K.

Table 5.5

PERMEABILITY DISTRIBUTION IN DIFFUSERS IN A PLANT

		% permeability for the indicated diffuser					Average, %
		No. 1	No. 2	No. 3	No. 4	No. 5	
t = 0		100	90	80	70	60	80
t = τ (years)	a*	90	80	70	60	50	70
	b†	90	80	70	60	100	80

*Before barrier replacement.
†After barrier replacement.

CALCULATIONS RELATING TO THE CASCADE

Next is the calculation of the separation gain g of a separating element which operates at pressures $p'' = 350$ torrs, with a compression ratio $r = 3.5$ ($p' = 100$ torrs) and at temperature $T = 65°C$. Let $p_{\frac{1}{2}} = 1.04$ atm be the critical pressure for the barriers, which means that $\pi'' = 0.34$.

Consider the single-diffuser stages, and disregard the effect of the boundary layer. From Fig. 5.1 we see that $\beta_0 = 0.60$. And so we have

$$g = 1.39 \times 0.60 g_0 = 0.83 \times g_0 = 0.00357$$

For a symmetrical ideal cascade, $\epsilon = 0.001785$. The separative power of a separation element is therefore

$$\frac{\delta U}{G} = \frac{1}{2}\epsilon^2 = 1.625 \times 10^{-6}$$

Let the ideal cascade have a total separative power ΔU of 6000 metric tons U year^{-1}. If we then wish to produce uranium at a concentration of $N_P = 2.98\%$, starting from the natural concentration $N_F = 0.715\%$ and discarding from the stripping section tailings whose content is $N_W = 0.26\%$, we have

$$F = P \frac{N_P - N_W}{N_F - N_W} = 5.87P$$

and therefore

$$W = F - P = 4.87P$$

Equation 4.112 can be written in the form

$$\Delta U = F(V'_W - V'_F) - P(V'_W - V'_P)$$

in which V'_W, V'_F, and V'_P represent the separative potential $(2N - 1) \ln R$ calculated, respectively, at points N_W, N_F, and N_W. And so we have

$$\Delta U/P = 5.87 (5.92 - 4.87) - (5.92 - 3.20) = 3.47$$

Therefore P = 6000/3.47 = 1740 metric tons U year^{-1} = 300 UF$_6$ hr^{-1}

F = 10,000 metric tons U year^{-1} = 1750 kg UF$_6$ hr^{-1}

W = 8260 metric tons U year^{-1} = 1450 kg UF$_6$ hr^{-1}

The ^{235}U contained in the product is PN_P = 52 metric tons ^{235}U year^{-1}. The total flow in the cascade is

$$\Sigma L = Gn = G\frac{\Delta U}{\delta U} = \frac{6000}{1.625 \times 10^{-6}} = 3.7 \times 10^9 \text{ metric tons U year}^{-1}$$

$$= 420,000 \text{ metric tons U hr}^{-1} = 625,000 \text{ metric tons UF}_6 \text{ hr}^{-1}$$

and the total diffused flow

$$\frac{1}{2}\Sigma L = 312,000 \text{ metric tons UF}_6 \text{ hr}^{-1}$$

The feed flow of the first stage is

$$L_0 = \frac{2P(N_P - N_F)}{\epsilon N_F(1 - N_F)} = 3620\, P = 6.3 \times 10^6 \text{ metric tons U year}^{-1} =$$

$$1060 \text{ metric tons UF}_6 \text{ hr}^{-1}$$

The number of stages in the enrichment and stripping sections is, respectively,

$$S + 1 = \frac{\ln (0.0298/0.00711)}{0.001785} = 820$$

$$B = \frac{\ln (0.00711/0.0026)}{0.001785} - = 570$$

$$\text{Total } S + 1 + B = 1390$$

The mean interstage flow in the cascade will thus be

$$\bar{L} = \frac{\Sigma L}{1390} = 2.67 \times 10^6 \text{ metric tons U year}^{-1} = 450 \text{ metric tons UF}_6 \text{ hr}^{-1}$$

In a real cascade of equal separative power, the mean flow $\bar{L}$ will certainly be higher since the total flow ΣL is greater. Also, squaring off the cascade will lower L_0.

Recall that $L_{min} = \frac{1}{2}L_{id}$. A square cascade with equal enrichment and an infinite number of stages would thus have a flow

$$L_{min} = 3.15 \times 10^6 \text{ metric tons U year}^{-1} = 530 \text{ metric tons UF}_6 \text{ hr}^{-1}$$

We now assume that we are building a squared-off cascade similar to the ideal cascade, and we will give the first step a flow of

$$L = 1.15 \, L_{min} = 3.6 \times 10^6 \text{ metric tons U year}^{-1} = 610 \text{ metric tons UF}_6 \text{ hr}^{-1}$$

If each of the low stages is to consist of a single separating element, it must be able to handle a flow $G = L$.

With at least two steps in each of the two sections of the plant, the enrichment in each step is less than 2; hence, under optimal conditions, each separating element functions as if it were in an ideal cascade, and its separative power is

$$\delta U = 3.68 \times 10^6 \times 1.625 \times 10^{-6} = 5.8 \text{ metric tons U year}^{-1}$$

However, allowing for losses of separative power due to the mixing that occurs in a real cascade, if we wish to obtain $\Delta U = 6000$ metric tons U year^{-1}, we shall have to increase G so as to have $\delta U = 6$ metric tons U year^{-1}.

The separating element must compress the diffused flow $\frac{1}{2}G$ in the ratio r. The isothermic compression power at 65°C is

$$2.21 \times \ln r \quad \text{kW/(metric ton UF}_6 \text{ hr}^{-1})$$

To reach a rough estimate of the power absorbed by the element, we shall apply to this power an overall efficiency factor η. This factor will obviously depend on the pressure and on r, but we will assume it to be constant, nevertheless, at $\eta = 65\%$.

Furthermore, the nondiffused flow, which is also $\frac{1}{2}G$, must be compressed according to a ratio r_0 remarkably lower than r. Let us assume that $r_0 = 1.5$, with an efficiency of 68%.

The values for the power absorbed by an element capable of processing $G = 650$ metric tons UF$_6$ hr^{-1} now turn out to be those shown in Table 5.6, as a function of the main compression ratio r.

Table 5.6

POWER ABSORBED BY A SEPARATING ELEMENT WITH
G = 650 METRIC TONS UF$_6$ HR^{-1} (TYPICAL VALUES)

	r = 3	r = 3.5	r = 4	r = 6	r = 8
Diffused	1200	1350	1500	2000	2300
Undiffused	400	400	400	400	400
Total power, kW	1600	1750	1900	2400	2700
Hp	2170	2400	2600	3200	2700

Note: r = main compression ratio.

For the separating element with r = 3.5 and $\delta U = 6$ metric tons U year^{-1} considered on pages 191-193, the specific power would be $E/\delta U = 1.75/6 = 0.29$ MW/(metric tons U year). For the complete plant, however, we must allow for the power absorbed by the auxiliary installations (including the coolant-water circulation system). To allow for this, we shall increase E by 20%, which gives us overall

$$\xi_E = 1.2E/\delta U = 0.35 \text{ MW/(metric ton U year}^{-1})$$

Thus the power absorbed by a plant with $\Delta U = 6000$ metric tons U year^{-1} comes to 2100 MW.

Current American plants have as their overall mean $\xi_E = 0.35$ MW/(metric ton U year^{-1}), but by improving the process there is hope to bring that down to $\xi_E = 0.25$ to 0.30 MW/(metric ton U year^{-1}).

In the American literature there is the expression PUI (power utilization index), which is the inverse of ξ_E. It is usually expressed in kilograms of uranium per megawatt-day. It is easy to see that PUI = 10 kg U MWd^{-1} is equivalent to $\xi_E = 0.27$ MW/(metric ton U year^{-1}).

Using one of the American plants as an example, we see that the 3% ^{235}U content in the product of the plant will therefore require an energy consumption of about 350 kWh/g ^{235}U.

An evaluation of the area of porous barriers will conclude these general remarks on the cascade. For this discussion we shall assume a permeability K equal to 0.54 kg UF$_6$ m^{-2} hr^{-1} torr^{-1}.

The separating element fed by G = 650 metric tons UF$_6$ hr^{-1} will have to contain barrier surface (recall Eq. 5.42) of

$$A = \frac{325,000}{0.54 (350-100)} = 2400 \text{ m}^2$$

Assuming that we have a diffusing surface in tubular elements whose diameter 3.5 cm and whose length is 5 m, the diffuser must contain 4350 tubes, meaning that the diameter of the diffuser could be about 4 to 4.5 m.

The specific area per unit of separative power for the case we are contemplating would be

$$\zeta_A = A/\delta U = 400 \text{ m}^2/(\text{metric ton U year}^{-1})$$

and the total area for the entire cascade of $\Delta U = 6000$ metric tons U year^{-1} would be $A_{total} = 2,400,000 \text{ m}^2$, or 240 ha (or 592.8 acres).

PRODUCTION PLANTS

Gaseous diffusion plants are in operation in the United States (Oak Ridge, Tennessee; Paducah, Kentucky; and Portsmouth, Ohio), Great Britain (Capenhurst), France (Pierrelatte), the Soviet Union, and China. All these plants were built to meet military requirements.

Particularly in the United States, the decline in military requirements has made considerable separative power available for civilian use. The only plants on which detailed published data are available are the American installations and the French plant at Pierrelatte.

Some data relating to the American plants are shown in Table 5.7. Of course the separating elements are not all the same size, since they belong to different steps in the cascade. Each plant consists of several structures built at different times. At Oak Ridge, two buildings (K-25 and K-27) were put into operation in 1945–1946, two more in 1951, and one in 1954. The Paducah plant consists of four buildings; two of these were completed in 1953, and two similar ones came on line in the following year. Operations began in the three buildings at Portsmouth, one building at a time, during 1955 and 1956. We are not, of course, taking into account the ancillary buildings; at Oak Ridge alone there are 70 of them.

It is understood that the costs indicated in Table 5.7 are not uniform with respect to the values of the currency.

At both Oak Ridge and Portsmouth, the separating elements constitute that many stages in the cascade. With about 4000 stages in series, they achieve a 97.65% concentration at the end. Now, however, a good share of the Oak Ridge separation elements (all those in the old K-25 and K-27 buildings, plus 586 stages in the other buildings) are on standby status, and the end concentration is limited to about 4%.

The Paducah plant, however, consists of two identical cascades in parallel, each of them having about 880 stages.

Some data relating to the main process buildings (excluding those presumably on standby) in the American plants are shown in Table 5.8. Aside from the old K-25 and K-27 buildings at Oak Ridge, all the others are two-story structures. The separating elements (diffusers, compressors, etc.) are installed on the upper floor, whereas the ground floor is used for auxiliary installations and services, holding areas, and control rooms.

Table 5.7

DATA ON AMERICAN DIFFUSION PLANTS

Plant	Separating elements	Area covered, ha	Cost, millions of dollars
Oak Ridge	4384	42.5	815
Paducah	1812	30.0	755
Portsmouth	4080	37.5	756
Total	10,276	110.0	2326

Table 5.8

DATA ON PROCESS BUILDINGS
IN U. S. PLANTS

Plant	Building	Stages	Surface, ha	Surface per stage, m^2
Oak Ridge	K-29	300	2.7	90
	K-31	600	6.9	115
	K-33	640	13.1	205
Paducah	C-331	400	4.7	117
	C-333	480	10.0	208
	C-335	400	4.7	117
	C-337	472	10.0	208
Portsmouth	X-326	2340	11.0	47
	X-330	1100	13.0	118
	X-333	640	13.3	208

The stages in each building are the same size. Blocks of stages connected in series form so many operating units, and the cascade is made up of a series of such units.

From official information, we know that the stages in the C-331 and C-333 buildings at Paducah are about equivalent to those of the K-31 and K-33 buildings at Oak Ridge. This can also be seen in Table 5.8 by a comparison of the surfaces per stage. Extending this comparison to the other plants (and putting aside for the moment K-29, which will be mentioned later), we could deduce that the separation elements are substantially of three different sizes, to be used, respectively, in the lower, middle, and high sections of the cascade. Consequently the cascade at Paducah would have four steps (two for the enrichment section and two for the stripping section), and the Portsmouth cascade would have six steps (three plus three).

The installed electric power in the three American plants and the available cooling-water supplies are shown in Table 5.9.

Table 5.9

INSTALLED ELECTRIC POWER (Π) AND
AVAILABLE COOLING WATER (Q) IN U. S. PLANTS

Plant	Π, MW	Q, m³ hr⁻¹
Oak Ridge	1,700	63,000
Paducah	2,550	79,000
Portsmouth	1,750	71,000
Total	6,000	213,000

The load factor in all three plants is practically 100%. At the moment, however, the plants are not operating at full capacity, inasmuch as the demand for enriched uranium, although it is rising, is still at a fairly low level.

The separative power of the plants as a function of load is shown in Fig. 5.18. At maximum potential, the separative power totals about $\Delta U = 17,000$ metric tons U year⁻¹. The Paducah plant alone has ΔU of 7250 metric tons U year⁻¹.

In 1969 all three plants were operating on an integrated system: Paducah operated as the basic plant, producing 0.96% enriched uranium to supply both Oak Ridge and Portsmouth. In turn, the 4% product from Oak Ridge was sent to Portsmouth, which carried on with concentration to 97.65%. Tailings from all three plants emerged at 0.2%. The feed material consisted of material that had been partially depleted in

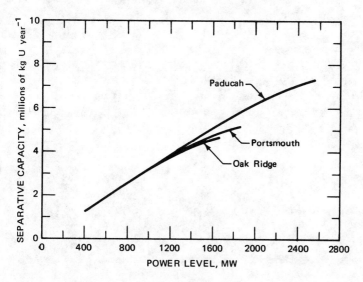

Fig. 5.18 Separative power of the American plants as a function of load.

earlier plant-operation cycles. Later (July 1, 1972) the tailing content level was raised to 0.3%, and the Oak Ridge–Portsmouth connection was abolished.

In American plants the stages are connected in series, as shown in Fig. 5.19. The diffuser incorporates the heat exchanger. The control valves on the high-pressure pipes are used to control the proper flow rate in the cascade.

Figure 5.20 is a view of some diffusers in the Oak Ridge K-33 building, showing them to be the biggest stages in the cascade. Also visible is the connecting tubing and the compressor for one stage. We have no data on the porous barriers, but from geometry we can deduce that they are tubular.

The compressors are axial and are driven by electric motors. The recycled flow from the stage downstream is introduced into an intermediate stage of the compressor.

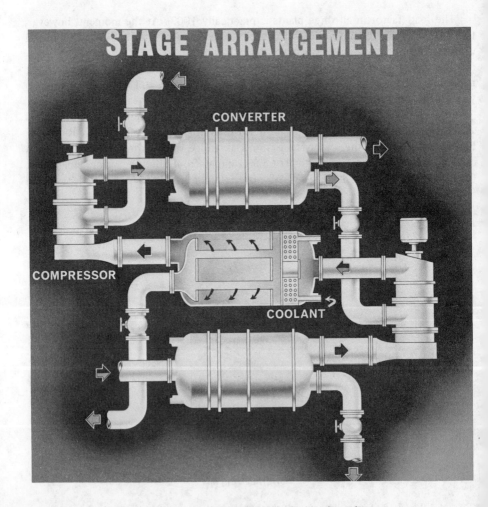

Fig. 5.19 Stages arranged in series in American plants.

Fig. 5.20 View of some stages in the Oak Ridge K-33 cascade.

The old Oak Ridge installations (K-25 and K-27) had centrifugal compressors, but after those were built it was proved that centrifugal compressors are better for the low stages, where flows are large. For this purpose the K-29 building was built (1951) to house the 300-stage prototype plant. No information has been published on the process parameters.

The French plant at Pierrelatte has a total separative power of about 400 metric tons U year^{-1} and consists of four sections: low, intermediate, high, and very high. Most of the low section operates as a stripping section, which consists of a single step. The very high section produces fully enriched material. Starting with the low section, the plant went into operation, section by section, during the years 1964 to 1966. The total surface occupied by the four processing buildings is about 11 ha, 5 ha of which are auxiliary to the low-section building, which also houses most of the auxiliary equipment.

We have no data on the number of stages or on the tailings concentration, which according to some indications would seem to run about 0.35%.

The compressors are centrifugal, operating in supersonic conditions, of the type referred to on page 182. The nitrogen-barrier seals have proved very effective, even in durability, since they have now been in use for more than 40,000 hr. As for the compression ratio, the values usually given for pilot units are about 7 or 8, but we do not know if these are the ones used at Pierrelatte.

The leak tightness specifications of the various plant components go as high as 10^{-2} lusecs m^{-3} [or 3.6 m^3 μ hr^{-1} (%)], which means that the specifications are comparable with those of some components in American plants, as shown in Table 5.4.

We have already mentioned the British Capenhurst hexafluoride production plant (capacity, 80 metric tons UF$_6$ year^{-1}) on page 185.

At Pierrelatte, there are pilot plants for the development of components for civilian plants. They have tested axial compressors with 800 kW of power for a flow rate of about 150 metric tons UF$_6$ hr^{-1}, as well as compressors rated at about 3000 kW and 600 metric tons UF$_6$ hr^{-1}. These components could be used for the high and low sections of a plant with a ΔU of 6000 to 10,000 metric tons of U year^{-1}.

ECONOMIC CONSIDERATIONS

Let us now discuss the economic conditions of the production of the three American installations, assuming that they operate at capacity [6000 MW(e)] with a separative power ΔU of 17,000 metric tons U year^{-1}.

On the basis of the data in Table 5.7, the specific investment comes to

$$\zeta = 2.3 \times 10^9 / 1.7 \times 10^7 = \$135 \text{ per kilogram of uranium per year}$$

We have already seen that $\xi_E = 0.35$ kW/(kg U year^{-1}), which is $\xi_E = 3080$ kWh/kg U. With a unit cost for electrical energy of $C_E = \$0.004$ per kilowatt-hour, the portion of the cost of separation relative to energy consumption will be

$$\xi = C_E \xi_E = \$12.32 \text{ per kilogram of uranium}$$

The total cost of a kilogram of separative work C_U can be found, obviously, by adding the operating and capital costs and adding a certain quota for contingency and miscellaneous costs. The cost of energy represents practically three-fourths of the out-of-pocket expenses and hence an even greater portion of the total operating costs.

From 1967 to the beginning of 1971, the C_U cost was assessed by the U. S. Atomic Energy Commission (AEC) at $26 per kilogram of uranium. The cost is analyzed as shown in Table 5.10. The "process cost" item in the table is made out of 90% ξ. It is shown that the $6.58 capital cost represents less than 5% of the specific investment ζ and is thus a very low figure.

The incidence of manpower on the cost of production is slight. In all three plants, a total of 4300 persons are employed, about 3000 of them in actual production.

Table 5.10

UNIT COST ANALYSIS OF SEPARATIVE WORK C_U FOR
THE UNITED STATES UNTIL 1971

Unit costs per kilogram of uranium	
Process costs	$13.90
Amortization (straight line with 34 years of compounded plant life)	3.65
Interest	
5% per year on average plant investment (one-half of the initial investment); 5% per year on working capital	2.93
Other costs (process development, administration, infrastructure)	0.87
Minimum overall cost	$21.35
Interest at 5% per year on the preproduction separation component	1.15
Contingency	3.50
Average overall cost	$26.00

More recent assessments of the C_U have yielded higher levels, such as $27.80 as of Feb. 22, 1971, $32.00 as of Sept. 6, 1971, and $36.00 (or $38.50) as of Aug. 14, 1973. This last figure, which is expected to rise at the rate of 1% every six months for the next few years, was heavily affected by the increase in preproduction costs, which came to only $1.15 when the total was $26. Also contributing to the increase was a 9% rise in the unit cost of electricity. The earlier increases in the C_U had been justified on the basis of rising overall operating costs.

Assuming that our unit cost C_U = $38.50 per kilogram of uranium and that the C_F = $22.50 per kilogram of uranium (using natural UF_6 as feed material), we see that the cost C_P of a kilogram of uranium produced at 3% with tailings of 0.26% (see Eq. 4.154 and pages 191 to 193) is

$$C_P = \$38.50 \times 3.47 + \$22.50 \times 5.87 = \$262 \text{ per kilogram of uranium}$$

This corresponds to $8.73 per gram of ^{235}U contained.

In 1972 the AEC published economic data (see Ref. 35) forecasts for new diffusion plants in two different versions: "1970 technology" and "advanced technology." The two sizes covered are 8750 and 17,500 metric tons U year^{-1}.

An 8750 metric ton U year^{-1} plant with 1970 technology, producing 4% material with natural feed and 0.25% tailings, would have 1180 stages arranged in three sectors (six steps). The biggest stage would be rated at 4150 hp (about 3000 kW). In Table 5.11 are some of the cost data for such a plant. An analysis of capital costs is given in Table 5.12.

Table 5.11

ECONOMIC DATA ON AN 8750-METRIC TON U YEAR^{-1}
PLANT WITH "1970 TECHNOLOGY"

Invested capital, millions of dollars	$1200
Specific investment (ζ), $/(kg U year^{-1})	137
Electric power, MW	2430
Specific power (ξ_E), kW/(kg U year^{-1})	0.278
Specific operating cost (exclusive of power), $/(kg U year^{-1})	2.08
Manpower, no. of people	900

Table 5.12

PERCENTAGE ANALYSIS OF CAPITAL COSTS
FOR AN 8750-METRIC TON U YEAR^{-1} PLANT
WITH "1970 TECHNOLOGY"

	%
Diffusers	8.9
Compressors	12.5
Compressor motors	7.6
Electrical system	13.1
Cooling system	4.4
Buildings and premises	7.1
Tubing and valves	7.9
Instrumentation	2.3
Miscellaneous systems	2.9
Startup and auxiliaries	0.9
Auxiliaries	8.0
Total equipment	75.6
Engineering, 4.5%	3.4
	79.0
Contingency, 15%	11.8
	90.8
Interest during construction	9.2
Total	100.0

Assuming a capital costs of 13% per year, an average cost of manpower at $10,000 per person, and a cost of electricity at $0.005 per kilowatt-hour, we calculate that the $C_{U \; min.}$ = $33.06 kilogram of uranium, as compared with the $21.35 per kilogram of uranium in Table 5.10.

If the size of the plant is increased, or if it is kept the same size but advanced technology is applied, investments and consumption will vary as shown in Table 5.13.

A preliminaty evaluation made in France (1971) for a 6000-metric ton U year^{-1} European plant, based on the French technology, showed $\zeta = \$101$ per kilogram of uranium per year and $\xi = 0.285$. However, the French estimates for operating cost (excluding power) and maintenance are almost double the American figures ($\$3$ per kilogram of uranium), which offsets the advantage derived from the lower ζ. Therefore, given equal economic parameters, the $C_{U\ min.}$ is very close to that calculated for the 8750-metric ton U year^{-1} American plant built with 1970 technology.

From the preceding discussion we can see how important the economy of generating electricity is to gaseous diffusion.

Table 5.13

PREDICTED INVESTMENTS AND
SPECIFIC CONSUMPTION FOR NEW U. S. PLANTS

ΔU, metric tons U year^{-1}; Technology:	8750 "1970"	17,500 "1970"	8750 "Advanced"
ζ, $ kg^{-1} U year^{-1}	137	109	120
ξ, kW kg^{-1} U year^{-1}	0.278	0.270	0.234

The construction of new gaseous diffusion plants also involves the building of new power plants, which means planning a number of years ahead. This also means the need for additional investment in power plants. Assuming that this capital is $\$180$ per electrical kilowatt and that $\xi_E = 0.3$ kW/(kg U year^{-1}), we have an investment figure for electric-power plants of $\$54$ per kilogram of uranium per year, which is about one-half of ζ.

One of several ideas suggested for getting cheaper electricity is that of assuming a lower load factor for the diffusion plant, lowering the load or actually stopping the plant during peak demand periods on the power grid. In this way the rate per kilowatt-hour would be lower.

Another proposal (see Ref. 29) actually suggests replacing the electric motors for the compressors with steam or gas turbines, in the case of a plant built in an area rich in fossil fuels. We should note here that most of the stages of a power plant with $\Delta U = 6000$ metric tons U year^{-1} with a product at 3 to 4% would have power stages no lower than about 2500 hp each.

The existing American plants, according to current forecasts, will gradually be restored to total power of about 6100 MW by 1978, which will enable them to meet the domestic and foreign demand for separative work up to a few years beyond 1980.

Meanwhile, these plants are to be beefed up with the implementation of two programs: the CIP (Cascade Improvement Program) and the CUP (Cascade Uprating

Program). The CIP consists in installing better porous barriers in the diffusers, and increasing the compressor efficiency. The CUP consists in increasing the power ratings of the plants from 6100 to 7400 MW, which will require rewinding the compressor motors and expanding the cooling systems. With CIP and CUP implemented, the plants will be able to operate at higher pressure and with bigger interstage flows.

With CIP, which will require an investment of $500 to $600 million, an increment of ΔU = 4800 metric tons U year^{-1} will be obtained. The specific power will decline from the current level, ξ_E = 0.35 kW/(kg U year^{-1}) to ξ_E = 0.28 kW/(kg U year^{-1}).

CUP will necessitate further investment of $200 to $300 million and will produce, by comparison with CIP, another increment of ΔU = 4500 tons U year^{-1} Given the greater power absorption, ξ_E will increase with respect to the level obtained with CIP. The marginal costs per kilogram of uranium in separation obtainable with CIP and CUP will be far lower than costs forecast for newly built plants.

If the American plants improve their previous capacity in this way (E = 7400 MW, and ΔU = 26,000 metric tons year^{-1}), they will be able to meet the demand until beyond 1980. Further demand, which is predicted to be in the range of an additional 5000 metric tons year^{-1} for the Western world in the 1980–1985 period, will therefore require timely construction of new plants.

REFERENCES

Reviews and General Works

1. C. Fréjaques et al., Principal Results Obtained in France in Studies of the Separation of Uranium Isotopes by Gaseous Diffusion, in *Proceedings of the Second United Nations International Conference on the Peaceful Uses of Atomic Energy, Geneva, 1958*, Vol. 4, p. 418, United Nations, New York, 1958.
2. G. Perona, *Plant for the Isotopic Separation of Uranium by Gaseous Diffusion*, Polytechnic Publication, Milan, 1959.
3. P. Caldirola and R. Fiocchi, *Isotopic Separation of Uranium*, Comitato Nazionale per l'Energia Nucleare, Rome, 1967.
4. C. Leduc, P. Plurien, and J. Volvey, French Know-How in the Separation of Isotopes, in *Proceedings of the Fourth International Conference on the Peaceful Uses of Atomic Energy, Geneva, 1971*, Vol. 9, p. 15, United Nations, New York, 1972.

Efficiency of Porous Barriers: Theory

5. R. D. Present and W. G. Pollard, *Phys. Rev.*, 73: 762 (1948).
6. R. D. Present and A. J. de Bethune, *Phys. Rev.*, 75: 1050 (1949).
7. D. Massignon, On the Theory of Separation of Constituents of a Gaseous Mixture of Isotopes by Diffusion Through a Porous Barrier, *Isotope Separation*, Symposium Proceedings, p. 524, North-Holland Publishing Company, Amsterdam, 1958.
8. A. S. Berman, Effects of Porous Boundaries on the Flow of Fluids in Systems with Various Geometries, in *Proceedings of the Second United Nations International Conference on the Peaceful Uses of Atomic Energy, Geneva, 1958*, Vol. 4, p. 351, New York, 1958.

9. A. S. Berman and L. M. Lund, Deviations from Classical Kinetic Theory in the Low-Pressure Transport of Gases Through Porous Media, *ibid.*, p. 359.

10. D. Massignon, Characteristics of Barriers That Can Be Used for Isotope Separation by Gaseous Diffusion, *ibid.*, p. 388.

11. J. P. Breton, Theory of Isotope Separation by Gaseous Diffusion Through a Membrane. Effect of the Internal Structure of the Membrane, in *Proceedings of the Turin Symposium, 1968*, p. 21, Comitato Nazionale per l'Energia Nucleare, Rome, 1968.

12. R. Fiocchi, Surface Diffusion Effect in Gaseous Diffusion, *ibid.*, p. 73.

Efficiency of Porous Barriers: Experimentation

13. J. Charpin, P. Plurien, and S. Mommejac, Application of General Methods of Study of Porous Bodies to the Determination of the Characteristics of Barriers, in *Proceedings of the Second United Nations International Conference on the Peaceful Uses of Atomic Energy, Geneva 1958*, Vol. 4, p. 380, New York, 1958.

14. O. Bilous and G. Courras, Determination of the Separation Factor of the Uranium Isotopes Produced by Gaseous Diffusion, *ibid.*, p. 405.

15. M. Mårtensson et al., Some Types of Membranes for Isotope Separation by Gaseous Diffusion, *ibid.*, p. 395.

16. M. Mårtensson, Determination of the Separation Properties of Gaseous Diffusion Barriers Using Nonisotopic Gas Mixtures, in *Proceedings of the Turin Symposium, 1968*, p. 145, Comitato Nazionale per l'Energia Nucleare, Rome, 1968.

17. J. C. Martin et al., Description of an Experimental Installation for Measuring the Characteristics of Gaseous Diffusion Barriers, *ibid.*, p. 173.

Experimental Plants

18. H. Albert, Design of a Gaseous Diffusion Uranium Hexafluoride Isotopic Concentration Experimental Line, in *Proceedings of the Second United Nations International Conference on the Peaceful Uses of Atomic Energy, Geneva, 1958*, Vol. 4, p. 412, New York, 1958.

Properties, Production, and Technology of UF_6

19. J. J. Katz and E. Rabinowitch, *The Chemistry of Uranium*, Part I: The Element, Its Binary and Related Compounds, Chap. 13, p. 398, McGraw-Hill Book Company, Inc., New York, 1951. [Reprint, Peter Smith Publisher, Inc. (clothbound), and Dover Publications, Inc. (paperback).]

20. J. Dixmier et al., Corrosion of Metallic Materials in the Gaseous Diffusion Process, in *Proceedings of the Turin Symposium, 1968*, p. 197, Comitato Nazionale per l'Energia Nucleare, Rome, 1968.

21. S. Lawroski et al., Production of Refined UF_6 from Ore Concentrates by Fluidization and Fractional Distillation Techniques, in *Proceedings of the Second United Nations International Conference on the Peaceful Uses of Atomic Energy, 1958*, Vol. 4, p. 44, New York, 1958.

22. S. H. Smiley and D. C. Brater, The Development of High Capacity, Continuous Process for the Preparation of UF_6 from Uranium Oxides and Ore Concentrates, *ibid.*, p. 153.

23. C. A. Powell, Current Manufacturing Processes Used in the United States for Mass Production of UF_6 from Purified UO_3, *ibid.*, p. 165.

24. M. Donato, Reflections on Plants for Conversion of Enriched UF_6 to UO_2, etc., in *Proceedings of the Turin Symposium, 1968*, p. 183, Comitato Nazionale per l'Energia Nucleare, Rome, 1968.

25. N. Benedict and C. Williams, *Engineering Developments in the Gaseous Diffusion Process*, McGraw-Hill Book Company, Inc., New York, 1949.

26. G. Roubeix, R. Dore, and Y. Coche, Application of Conventional Techniques in the Construction of a Pilot Plant for the Isotopic Separation of Uranium by Gaseous Diffusion, in *Proceedings of the Second United Nations International Conference on the Peaceful Uses of Atomic Energy, Geneva, 1958*, Vol. 4, p. 375, New York, 1958.

Economics of the Process

27. O. Bilous, Study of the Economics of a Plant for the Separation of Uranium Isotopes by Gaseous Diffusion, *ibid.*, p. 422.
28. C. Fréjacques and R. Galley, Lessons Learned from French Studies and Achievements in the Separation of Uranium Isotopes, in *Proceedings of the Third International Conference on the Peaceful Uses of Atomic Energy, Geneva, 1964*, Vol. 12, p. 329, United Nations, New York, 1965.
29. J. O'Donnel and G. H. Dyer, Uranium Enrichment Problems as Seen by the Engineer-Constructor, in *Proceedings of the Turin Symposium, 1968*, p. 9, Comitato Nazionale per l'Energia Nucleare, Rome, 1968.
30. S. A. Levin, Power Optimization for Gaseous Diffusion Plants, *ibid.*, p. 129.
31. Selected Background Information on Uranium Enriching, USAEC Report ORO-668, March 1969.
32. W. E. Johnson and S. R. Sapirie, Uranium Isotope Enrichment, in *Proceedings of the Fourth International Conference on the Peaceful Uses of Atomic Energy, Geneva, 1971*, Vol. 9, p. 31, New York, 1972.

Industrial Plants

33. *Pierrelatte, Uranium Isotope Separation Plant*, Commissariat à l'Énergie Atomique, Paris, 1967.
34. AEC Gaseous Diffusion Plant Operations, USAEC Report ORO-684, January 1972.
35. AEC Data on New Gaseous Diffusion Plants, USAEC Report ORO-685, April 1972.

CENTRIFUGATION

TYPES OF CENTRIFUGES

For isotope separation by means of centrifugation, the principles of which are explained in Chap. 3, three different types of centrifuges have been conceived: (1) evaporation, (2) cocurrent, and (3) countercurrent.

The three types of centrifuges are shown schematically in Fig. 6.1. Under ideal conditions the evaporation and cocurrent types will give, at the most, the elementary separation factor but are used only as laboratory equipment. With the countercurrent centrifuge, however, it is possible to multiply considerably the elementary separation effect in the single rotor. Therefore the countercurrent centrifuge is the object of intensive development work at present, and it could become an interesting possible alternative to gaseous diffusion for uranium-isotope separation on an industrial scale.

In the evaporation centrifuge, which was originally designed by R. S. Mulliken (American chemist), a discontinuous (batch) process is set up. The hollow rotor of the centrifuge [see Fig. 6.1(a)], which has first been emptied, is partially filled with a liquid compound containing the element to be separated into isotopes. When the rotor reaches its operating angular velocity, the layer of liquid around the outside of the rotor is evaporated by transmitting to it the evaporation heat. The vapor diffuses from the periphery to the center, in the direction opposite to that of the centrifugal field and is there extracted through the hollow shaft. The vapor removed is richer in the light component, whereas the heavy component tends to remain mostly in the liquid.

If the extraction is done slowly, so that the process occurs practically in equilibrium conditions, the ratio between the relative abundance of the enriched and

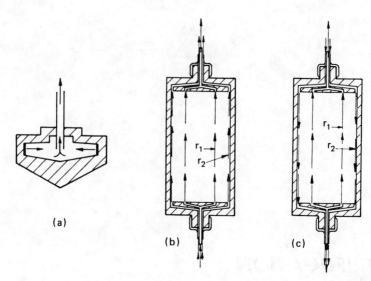

Fig. 6.1   The three basic types of centrifuges: (a) evaporation; (b) cocurrent; (c) countercurrent.

depleted fractions will coincide with the separation factor q_0, which we found in Chap. 3. Of course, as the process continues, the concentration of the light isotope in the liquid residue gradually diminishes, and consequently it also diminishes in the fraction drawn off. The equations describing the behavior of the concentrations are the general equations for discontinuous processes (see Chap. 4, pages 151 to 154).

Beams[1] conducted successful experiments using an evaporation centrifuge to separate ^{235}U by centrifuging UF_6. For these experiments Beams used a centrifuge with a Duralumin rotor having an outside radius of 5.04 cm, an inside radius of 4.12 cm, and a usable height of 0.72 cm. The flexible hollow shaft was made of stainless steel.

The second type of centrifuge referred to is the one-way cocurrent centrifuge. Inside the rotor [see Fig. 6.1(b)] are two concentric flows of gas, one flow at distance r_1 from the axis and the other flow at distance r_2, close to the wall. The gas flows are introduced into the rotor through the hollow shaft and the annular region between it and a concentric conduit. Extraction is done in the same way.

Thanks to the centrifugal field, a transport of each component occurs between the inner flow and the peripheral flow, countered by diffusion in the opposite direction. Gradually, as it moves from one end of the rotor to the other, the inner flow is enriched in the light component, whereas the peripheral flow is depleted. It is clear, however, that the separation produced by increasing as much as possible the distance traveled by the two cocurrent flows is that corresponding to the equilibrium conditions described in Chap. 3. Hence, between the relative abundances of the enriched and depleted streams, we have a maximum separation equal to the separation factor q_0. This process, too, since it does not achieve any multiplication of the elementary separation factor, is of use mainly for experimental purposes, like the evaporation centrifuge.

A cocurrent centrifuge with an aluminum rotor whose inside diameter was 16.6 cm and whose inside height was 84.14 cm was used by Beams to study the separation of $^{235}UF_6$. Most of the experiment was conducted at an angular velocity of 450 rps which, with the diameter given, corresponds to a peripheral velocity of about 235 m sec^{-1}.

In the countercurrent centrifuge, designed by H. C. Urey, the rotor has substantially the same structure as that of the cocurrent centrifuge, except that the two streams of gas are made to run in opposite directions to each other. In this way, as in any countercurrent process, we can achieve multiplication of the elementary separation factor. Provided we have a rotor high enough, we can achieve any separation factor whatever between the two ends of the rotor. The high separation factor of the individual unit makes it possible to build cascades with a considerably smaller number of stages (broad, short cascades in place of narrow, long ones), thus simplifying a number of operating problems.

The various types of centrifuges have several problems in common, and the problem that we cite first is the choice of a suitable material for the rotor, which must withstand very high tensile stresses derived from the centrifugal acceleration. This problem will be dealt with later.

In addition, the rotor must be enclosed in a container under a vacuum (10^{-1} to 10^{-3} torrs or even less, according to the velocity) because, by eliminating friction with air and the convection currents set up by it, we can obtain two desirable results: (1) less energy consumption and (2) no irregularities in temperature that could induce remixing of the gas inside the rotor.

For these same reasons, vibrations and irregularities in movement in the rotor must be kept to a minimum, and therefore good balancing of the rotor is required. Also required are some advanced solutions for the couplings between the rotating parts, particularly for the rotor shaft bearings. It should be remembered that the vessel containing the rotor also serves as protective containment in case of explosion.

Tightness problems involve not only penetration of air into the vacuum vessel but also gas leaks (UF_6) from the rotor into the vessel.

The centrifugal field sets up a strong radial pressure gradient in the gas inside the rotor. The peripheral pressure p'' is given by

$$p'' = p'C = p' \exp\left(\frac{M}{2RT} v^2\right)$$

in which p' is the axial pressure.

Working with UF_6 at ambient temperature (300°K), we find, at different peripheral velocities v, the values of the compression ratio C shown in Table 6.1.

Since at 300°K UF_6 desublimes at pressures greater than ~130 torrs, taking this figure as the extreme value for peripheral pressure, we obtain—at the various peripheral velocities—the maximum values for axial pressure shown in Table 6.1.

Table 6.1

COMPRESSION RATIO AND AXIAL
PRESSURE FOR VARIOUS
PERIPHERAL VELOCITIES

v, m sec^{-1}	$C = p''/p'$	p'_{lim}, torrs
200	16.4	8
250	84	1.5
300	550	0.24
350	5200	0.025

Even considering that the extraction ducts are at some distance from the axis, which means that the removal of the gas occurs at pressures higher than those shown in Table 6.1, nevertheless the extraction of gas from the axial zone of the centrifuge and thus the interstage flow in the cascade take place in practice at very low pressures, as low as a few torrs or even fractions of a torr.

Energy consumption in the process is governed by the following factors:

1. Mechanical losses of the rotating parts (electric motor, rotor).
2. Electrical losses.
3. Losses due to aerodynamic friction of the rotor.
4. Losses connected with the extraction of gas from the rotor.
5. Energy absorbed by the auxiliary equipment.

When Beams developed the evaporation centrifuge (1937), he used an air turbine rotating on an air cushion, but electric motors are used at present for the countercurrent centrifuge.

ROTOR MATERIALS

Among the construction problems posed by centrifuges, we cite first the choice of rotor material, whose mechanical resistance to tensile stress governs the maximum peripheral velocity the rotor can tolerate. Let us consider the equilibrium of the forces acting on a section of the rotor wall subtended by a small angle ϕ [see Fig. 6.2(a)].

From the vector diagram of the forces as shown in Fig. 6.2(b), we infer the following equation:

$$\rho r\phi \, dS \, \omega^2 \, r = 2\sigma \, dS \sin\frac{\phi}{2} \simeq \sigma \, dS \, \phi \qquad (6.1)$$

hence

$$\omega^2 \, r^2 = v^2 = \frac{\sigma}{\rho} \qquad (6.2)$$

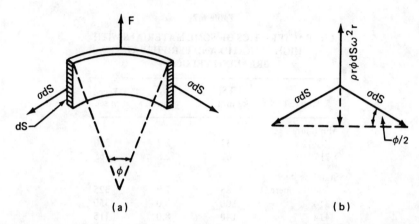

Fig. 6.2 Stresses in the thin wall of a rotating cylinder: (a) stresses in a sector of wall; (b) diagram of the equilibrium of forces.

where ω = angular velocity
    r = radius
    σ = stress
    ρ = density

Therefore rotors must be built of light materials that have a high ultimate tensile stress (UTS). These requirements are generally met by light aluminum alloys, by steel, by titanium, and even by composite materials (plastic and fiber glass or carbon).

In practice UTS may not be the limiting factor for the choice of the rotor material. The choice could be dictated by an acceptable creep strain over the design life.

By way of comparison, Table 6.2 shows the data for several particularly strong materials in current use for various industrial requirements. They have also developed some titanium alloys with a UTS about 30% higher than that for alloy A-155 shown in the table.

Table 6.2 also shows the peripheral velocities corresponding to the UTS in a rotor with thin walls. The safety factors used in design ensure that the velocities which can be reached in actual operation are well below v_{UTS} (see Table 6.2).

In selecting a composite material for making a rotor, we must pay careful attention to the uniformity of the material.

If an extruded material is chosen for the rotor cylinder, it must be machined to bring it to specified dimensions (diameter, differences in diameter at different axial positions, ovality, and thickness) called for in the design. Of course this is expensive. A more economic solution is the use of a drawn material, if one can be found that meets the design specifications.

From the point of view of material strength, it makes no difference whether we are working with a rotor of large or small radius, since the stress depends only on the

Table 6.2

CHARACTERISTICS OF SOME MATERIALS WITH
HIGH σ/ρ RATIO AND PERIPHERAL
BREAKING VELOCITY

Material	UTS, kg mm^{-2}	ρ, g cm^{-3}	v_{UTS}, m sec^{-1}
Aluminum			
ZG 42A	37	2.7	370
7178*	62	2.8	465
Stainless steel			
304 (tempered)	85	7.9	325
314	100	8.0	350
414	140	8.0	415
Titanium			
RC-130-B	92	4.6	440
A-155	110	4.6	485
Fiber glass Werkspoor, Amsterdam	50	1.8	520

*Metals Handbook, American Society for Metals,
1961.

peripheral velocity v. For that matter, there is an advantage in choosing large radii because the angular velocity ω can be correspondingly reduced, and thus the rotational speed of the bearings, which obviously lightens the load on them.

Another tie between velocity, dimensions, and mechanical properties of the material is imposed by the resonance frequencies (or critical frequencies) of the rotor. These occur when the rotation frequencies coincide with the rotor's own frequencies.

The basic axial vibration frequency can be considered as essentially proportional to $(E/\rho)^{1/2}$, where E is the modulus of elasticity and roughly proportional to D/L^2, where D is the diameter and L is the length of the rotor.

A centrifuge is said to be operating in subcritical or supercritical regions according to whether the rotor, as it is accelerated, stays below or goes beyond the angular resonance velocity (or a multiple of that value).

Figure 6.3 shows the dependence on L of the angular resonance velocity for a rotor having walls of thin aluminum and a diameter D of 20 cm.

We can see immediately that to turn the rotor at a peripheral velocity of 350 to 370 m sec^{-1} will require a maximum possible length of about 120 cm for subcritical operation. For supercritical operation the rotor length must be set at levels not too close to the points of resonance, and possible values are those which are indicated by the vertical lines marked 0, 1, and 2 in Fig. 6.3.

Supercritical operation naturally involves greater difficulties than does subcritical. These difficulties are partially surmounted by very accurate balancing of the rotor and by the use of a fairly powerful motor that permits very swift transition through the resonance zone; thus the buildup of oversevere stresses in the rotor and bearings is prevented.

With rotors of light aluminum alloys, velocities of as much as about 350 m sec^{-1} have actually been reached. With high-strength stainless steels, it is possible to reach and exceed 400 m sec^{-1}; but these steels are relatively expensive.

Titanium and its alloys make it possible to go as high as 450 m sec^{-1}. However, titanium metallurgy is still not highly developed, and titanium alloys are costly and are notoriously subject to corrosion. Corrosion protection is no easy matter, although some success has been achieved with electrolytic nickel plating.

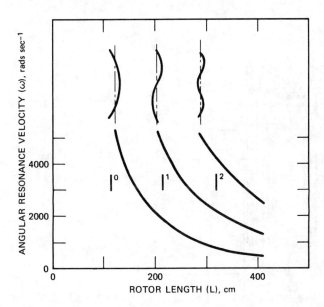

Fig. 6.3 Dependence of the angular resonance velocity on the length of the rotor (thin aluminum walls, diameter 20 cm).

Among the composite materials currently under development are polyesters reinforced with fiber glass (350 to 450 m sec^{-1}) and, more recently, plastic materials reinforced with carbon fibers (about 600 m sec^{-1}). For these composite materials, the problem of achieving a level of homogeneity comparable with that of the metallic materials now appears to have been satisfactorily solved.

In choosing the material for the rotor, we must consider, in addition to the σ/ρ and E/ρ ratios, its aging properties, its creep behavior, and its resistance to fatigue.

BEYERLE AND GROTH'S COUNTERCURRENT CENTRIFUGES

Countercurrent centrifuges with tubular rotors have been brought to a remarkable stage of development by Beyerle and Groth.[2] The principal construction features of these centrifuges will be described here.

Figure 6.4 shows the vertical section of the ZG3 centrifuge. The cylindrical vessel C, containing a vacuum (or hydrogen at low pressure), stands on two reinforced concrete pillars P. Inside it is the safety shield E, which has double walls and is attached to a thermostat to maintain the proper temperature around the rotor R, which turns inside the shield. The distance between the safety shield and the rotor is 4 mm, but this distance can be cut back to about $\frac{1}{10}$ mm.

The top of the vessel is closed by the body of the motor M, on top of which is fastened the gas-seal lock G. The bottom of the vessel is closed by the cover T, in the center of which is a socket to house the bearings for the tubular shaft, which is capped

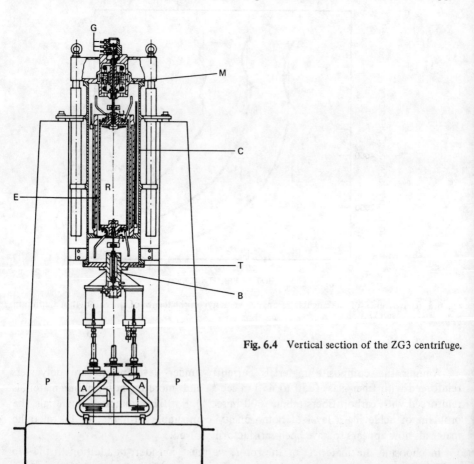

Fig. 6.4 Vertical section of the ZG3 centrifuge.

with the sealing device B. Around the base of the apparatus are arranged the shock absorbers A.

The countercurrent of gas within the rotor is not accomplished according to the diagram in Fig. 6.1(c) but is done by causing the gas to circulate by means of a vertical thermal gradient, as will be shown in detail later.

Centrifuges of the ZG3 type can operate either with a rotor whose internal length is 66.5 cm or with a 113-cm rotor, both having an internal diameter of 18.5 cm. The peripheral velocity achieved with either of these dimensions is about 300 m sec^{-1}.

Figure 6.5 shows three ZG3 centrifigues. The centrifuge in the foregouund has the rotor raised. With equipment like this, Beyerle and Groth successfully experimented with ^{235}U separation. These researchers have also tested centrifuges of more advanced designs (ZG6 and ZG7) having rotors with an internal length of 240 and 316 cm, respectively, and an inside diameter of 40 and 45 cm, respectively. The rotors were made by rolling sheets of aluminum alloy, which should yield peripheral velocities near 350 m sec^{-1}.

Too rigid a mechanical coupling between the rotor and the bearings at either end of the rotating system would transfer to the bearings any vibrations due to possible imbalance in the rotor and would thus cause the bearings to wear out more quickly. That possibility has been avoided by the development of very elastic tubular shafts through which gas can be introduced or drawn off. These shafts have a considerable aperture (as much as 10 mm); the thickness of the tube that constitutes the shaft is only 0.5 mm.

The bearings are of a special type designed to come reasonably close to satisfying two conflicting requirements: prevent any possible precession of the rotor and yet not set up too much resistance to a shift—due to unbalancing—of the rotor's longitudinal axis when it drifts away from the geometrical axis. This special type of bearing is shown schematically in Fig. 6.6. The tubular axis A passes through a mobile horizontal seat S, that is connected to the circular outer wall P by means of four telescoping legs G. The ring P is covered on both sides by two flat covers laterally screwed into place. This arrangement provides four separate chambers C into which the oil is introduced. Through the nozzle R, which is installed at the top of a four-branched system of pipes, a certain quantity of oil is fed into the chambers C and flows out through the tiny gaps between the seat S and the covers. Since the nozzle R is connected with an oil circuit under high pressure (9 to 12 atm), the flow of oil feeding the chamber is practically constant and unaffected by variations in the relatively low counterpressure in the chamber.

Inbalance in the rotor will transmit pressure vibrations to the oil in the chambers, causing it to flow out more swiftly through the gaps until small cavitations are set up allowing the seat S to vibrate almost freely. This prevents transmission of fast vibrations to the bearing.

Furthermore, a simultaneous slow precession motion by the rotor must push a certain amount of oil from one chamber into the next through the outside pipes, and that motion is thus damped, whether or not there are vibrations due to imbalance.

Fig. 6.5 Beyerle and Groth's type ZG3 centrifuge.

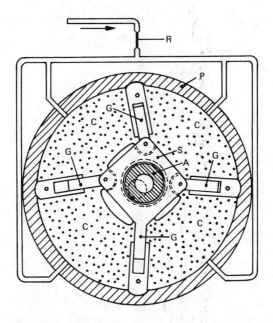

Fig. 6.6 Diagram of bearing for ZG centrifuges.

The gas countercurrent in the ZG3 centrifuge is obtained by means of convective currents generated by a vertical thermal gradient.

As is shown in Fig. 6.7, gas circulation is obtained by withdrawing, through the lower cover Z of the rotor, the compression heat of the gas and releasing the heat of expansion to the upper cover O. This is achieved in two ways: (1) through the hollow-ring cooling chamber C and (2) through the electromagnet E, which generates induction currents in the aluminum ring of the upper cover and thus heats it.

To control the convection currents so as to hold the system at optimum condition requires that the temperature of the two rotor covers be monitored. For this monitoring, two metallic rings M, which do not turn, are set into annular grooves in the lids so as to be in very close proximity to their surfaces. Thermal contact is provided by hydrogen at low pressure which fills the container R, and temperature monitoring is done by means of the thermocouples T fastened to the rings M.

Experiments performed by Groth et al.[3] on a centrifuge having a 63.5-cm rotor and two different peripheral velocities ($\omega_r = 252$ and 280 m sec^{-1}) allowed them to determine the temperature difference ΔT which yields maximum enrichment with zero product withdrawal; ΔT was found to be $18 \pm 5°C$, with a mean temperature of about $310°K$.

The gas feed F is provided through the hollow axis A, which is drilled halfway between the two covers. The light and heavy fractions are drawn off through pipes L and P, respectively.

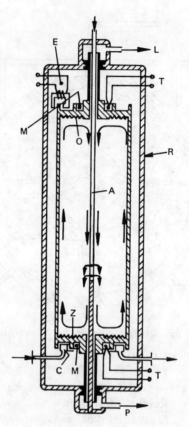

Fig. 6.7 Diagram of gas circulation in the ZG3 centrifuge.

In this way, the part of the centrifuge that lies below the gas-feed introduction point acts as the enriching section, and the upper part acts as the stripping section.

ZIPPE COUNTERCURRENT CENTRIFUGE

In the Soviet Union during the years 1946 to 1954, some work was done on the development of a long-rotor countercurrent centrifuge. The rotor consisted of a series of short tubular modules connected with one another by elastic joints so as to form a tube 3 m long with a 50-to-1 length/diameter ratio.

In 1953 and 1954 a group of German researchers worked on this project. Among them was Zippe,[4] who did additional work of that type in 1956 to 1960 at the University of Virginia, in the United States; there the work was on the development of a short-rotor countercurrent centrifuge with a rotor length up to about 50 cm and a length/diameter ratio of 5 to 1.

The main feature of the Zippe centrifuge is that the lower end of the rotor shaft rests on a socket seat, whereas the upper end is held in place by a magnetic coupling. The electric motor is at the bottom.

In the Beyerle and Groth[2] centrifuge, the shaft is centered by bearings at either end of the rotor and the electric motor is at the top.

The schematic design of the Zippe centrifuge is shown in Fig. 6.8. The rotor R, enclosed in the vessel V under a vacuum, is all one piece with the lower shaft A, into which the flexible needle P is inserted. The point of the needle P has been greatly hardened by heat treatment and rests on the concave seat hollowed out of a metal block S, which has also been highly tempered.

The block S fits into the footing T, which rests on three steel balls and can thus move laterally. Its lateral shifts are cushioned, however, by the surrounding oil, which also serves to lubricate the rotating parts.

The footing T is held in place by the attraction of the two magnets B and C. As for axial vibrations, they are cushioned both by a spring coupling S with C and by the friction of the oil.

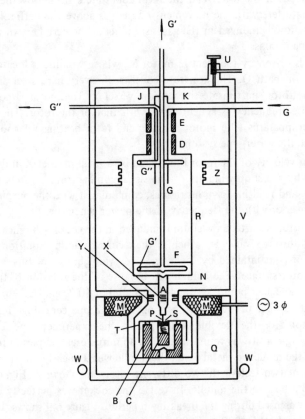

Fig. 6.8 Construction diagram of the Zippe centrifuge.

The upper bearing consists of a magnetic coupling between the permanent magnet D, attached to the upper cover of the rotor and the magnet E. The magnet E is hung from the upper cover of the vessel V by means of three steel wires J, whereas many flexible straps K of plastic material connect E with V and act as shock absorbers. The magnet D remains in fixed position in relation to magnet E, although there is no mechanical contact when there is no rotating movement.

Gas is supplied to the rotor, and the enriched and depleted fractions are drawn off through a system of fixed pipes. The feed flow G enters the rotor through a pipe which penetrates the rotor along its axis down to a certain level. This pipe at the rotor axis contains two smaller pipes, used for the removal of the enriched and depleted streams G' and G'', respectively. Extraction is done by picking up the gas in the peripheral zone of the rotor through hook-shaped Pitot tubes arranged on two planes perpendicular to the rotation axis and close to the top and bottom covers. The flow of outcoming gas from the Pitot tubes is caused by the impact pressure of the gas at the periphery of the rotor.

The Pitot tubes at the upper end of the rotor locally cut down the angular velocity of the gas, whereas at the lower end the Pitot tubes are screened by the baffle F and hence do not interfere with the movement of the gas above the baffle. In this way a countercurrent flow is induced in the gas, ascending at the periphery of the rotor and descending along its axis.

The rotor is driven by the electric motor M, whose winding is located below the vessel V in an oil bath Q. The armature consists of a very hard steel disk N, rigidly attached to the rotor shaft inside the vacuum vessel V. The motor is powered by an alternator whose frequency is synchronous with that of the rotor. The entire lower portion of the apparatus (the motor winding and rotor bearings) is cooled by water flowing through the water-pipe system W.

The angular velocity of the rotor is detected by a small magnet X in the rotor shaft A, surrounded by a pickup winding Y. The signal coming from Y can be sent through an oscilloscope and read in Lissajous figures, combining it with the output signal from a sample oscillator or with the frequency of the power generator.

Before the rotor is started, a vacuum is induced in the vessel V by means of a pump attached to it through valve U, which is then closed. During rotation the vacuum around the rotor is maintained by the cylinder Z, which has screw-type grooves in the wall near the rotor surface. The cylinder Z, because of the rotation of the rotor, acts like a Holweck molecular pump, setting up a vacuum of 10^{-6} mm Hg.

One delicate aspect of the lower bearing of the Zippe centrifuge has to do with wear to the point of the flexible needle P. In the experiments performed at the University of Virginia, it was found that, after an initial break-in period for the needle in its socket in the hardened metal plate, the needle wears linearly but slowly.

The results of two tests with two different rotors are shown in Fig. 6.9. In test A the socket had a boss in the middle. In test B the socket was perfectly concave, and lubricating oil was used during the breaking-in period. Figure 6.9 shows that the initial breaking-in period lasted 4000 to 7000 hr, after which time the wear continued at the

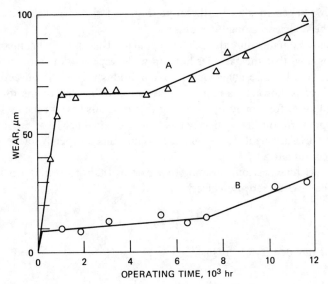

Fig. 6.9 Wear sustained by rotor support needle (in μm) in a Zippe centrifuge as a function of operation time (abscissa).

rate of 2.5 μm/1000 hr. The seat, or socket of the needle, however, was practically unaffected by wear.

The design features of one of the centrifuges tested experimentally by Zippe at the University of Virginia are the following:

Length of rotor section in which there is countercurrent flow (Z), 30.5 cm
Inside diameter of rotor (D), 7.41 cm
Ratio (Z/D), 4:1
Angular velocity (ω), 1500 rps
Peripheral velocity (v) 350 m sec^{-1}
Rotor weight, $\frac{1}{2}$ kg

Extraction of gas from the rotor by means of a Pitot tube was about 5 mg UF$_6$ sec^{-1}.

Energy consumption is determined not only by wear on the needle as it turns in its socket but also by the friction and impact pressure of the Pitot tubes. With the above-mentioned rotor turning at 1500 rps, the energy drain ascribed to the Pitot tube has been estimated at about 2.5 W mm^{-1} Hg.

THEORY OF THE COUNTERCURRENT CENTRIFUGE

The countercurrent centrifuge can be considered essentially as a square cascade in which the downward flow L' crosses the central region of the cross section of the rotor and the upward flow L'' crosses the peripheral region. In Fig. 6.10 the lines of flow are shown schematically. Furthermore, Fig. 6.11 shows a qualitative diagram of the field of the velocity v along the radius r.

The velocity contains only the axial component. The azimuthal component is zero because we assume that the gas does not slip with respect to the rotor, and the radial component is zero because under operating conditions the radial convection currents disappear. There is, however, a radial component at either end of the rotor, and this fact can be allowed for simply by assuming that it occurs beyond the useful height Z, which therefore turns out to be slightly less than the actual height of the rotor.

Within the useful height Z, we can also assume that v depends solely on r and not on the axial coordinate z.

For the enriching section, meaning that part of the rotor which lies beneath the feed point, the flow conservation gives†

$$L' - L'' = 2\pi \int_0^{r''} \rho v \, r dr = P \tag{6.3}$$

where ρ is the mol density of the gas:

$$\rho = \frac{p}{RT} = \frac{p'}{RT} \exp \frac{M\omega^2}{2RT} r''^2 \tag{6.4}$$

We shall also set

$$L' + L'' = 2\pi \int_0^{r''} \rho |v| \, r dr = L \tag{6.5}$$

Inside the rotor the flow ϕ of the desired component (expressed in moles per square centimeter per second) has a radial component ϕ_r and an axial component ϕ_z. We have

$$\phi_r = -D\rho \left[2\Omega^2 \, N \, (1 - N)r + \frac{\partial N}{\partial r} \right] \tag{6.6}$$

as the difference between the separative flow (first term) and the radial back-diffusion flow (second term < 0). In Eq. 6.6 we said

$$\Omega^2 = \frac{(M_2 - M_1)\omega^2}{2RT} \tag{6.7a}$$

and so

$$g = \Omega^2 \, r''^2 \tag{6.7b}$$

---

†For simplicity's sake we shall let r vary in the interval $0 \leqslant r \leqslant r''$ rather than $r' \leqslant r \leqslant r''$ (with $r' > 0$). For this second case, which is closer to reality, the equations to be developed can be adapted by inserting $r'' - r'$; $r''^2 - r'^2$, etc., in place of r''; r''^2, etc.

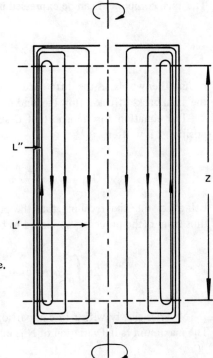

Fig. 6.10 Flow lines in a countercurrent centrifuge.

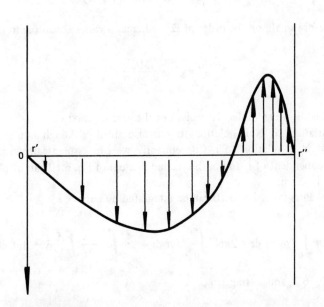

Fig. 6.11 Velocity field of the gas in a countercurrent centrifuge.

The axial component can be expressed in the form

$$\phi_z = \rho vN - D\rho \frac{\partial N}{\partial z} \qquad (6.8)$$

or, in other words, as the difference between the axial convection flow (first term) and the axial back-diffusion flow (second term). Note that the axis z is directed downward.

The equation for transport of desired isotope in the axial direction at the axial position z is written

$$2\pi \int_0^{r''} \phi_z r \, dr = PN_P \qquad (6.9)$$

Using Eq. 6.8 and recalling that the product $(D\rho)$ is independent from pressure and thus from r (the process is supposed to be isothermal), we obtain

$$2\pi \int_0^{r''} \rho vNr \, dr - 2\pi(D\rho)\int_0^{r''} \frac{\partial N}{\partial z}r \, dr = PN_P \qquad (6.10)$$

N varies slowly with r in comparison with the corresponding variation of ρ and v. The maximum radial variation of N is in fact

$$N' - N'' = \Omega^2 \, r''^2 \, N(1 - N)$$

and is therefore small, on the order of Ω^2, whereas ρ varies according to the law

$$\rho'' = \rho' \exp\frac{M\omega^2}{2RT} r''^2$$

in which M is the mean molecular weight of the gaseous mixture.

The variation of N in relation to z is also small, although not as small as the variation of N in relation to r. Consequently we can assume fairly accurately that $\partial N/\partial z$ is independent of r and in the second integral of Eq. 6.10 can be placed outside the integration sign.

The first integral of Eq. 6.10 can be integrated by parts:

$$2\pi \int_0^{r''} \rho vNr \, dr = 2\pi N'' \int_0^{r''} \rho vr \, dr - 2\pi \int_0^{r''} \frac{\partial N}{\partial r} \int_0^r \rho vr^* \, dr^* \cdot dr$$

Recalling Eq. 6.3, and setting

$$f(r) = \int_0^r \rho vr \, dr \qquad (6.11)$$

Eq. 6.10 becomes

$$-2\pi \int_0^{r''} \frac{\partial N}{\partial r} f(r) dr - \pi(D\rho) \, r''^2 \frac{\partial N}{\partial z} = P(N_P - N) \tag{6.12}$$

In Eq. 6.12 we have set N in the place of N'', which is quite allowable, given the slight difference with respect to N_P. Equation 6.12 thus expresses the balance of the desired isotope along the length of the rotor from z to bottom.

To find the enrichment equation for the centrifuge, namely the relationship between the axial concentration gradient and the transverse gradient (the latter determined by the elementary separative effect), we develop the equation for conservation of the desired isotope

$$\text{div} \, \vec{\phi} = 0 \tag{6.13}$$

In cylindrical coordinates this is written

$$\frac{1}{r} \frac{\partial(r\phi_r)}{\partial r} + \frac{\partial\phi_z}{\partial z} = 0 \tag{6.14}$$

Combining Eqs. 6.6, 6.8, and 6.14, we have

$$-\frac{(D\rho)}{r} \frac{\partial}{\partial r}\left[2\Omega^2 N(1-N)r^2 + r\frac{\partial N}{\partial r}\right] + \rho v \frac{\partial N}{\partial z} - (D\rho)\frac{\partial^2 N}{\partial z^2} = 0$$

This last equation can be simplified by disregarding $\partial^2 N/\partial z^2$, which is a very small term by comparison with the others since—as we have already seen—concentration varies slowly as a function of z. And so we have

$$\frac{\partial}{\partial r}\left[2\Omega^2 N(1-N)r^2 + r\frac{\partial N}{\partial r}\right] = \frac{\rho v r}{(D\rho)} \frac{\partial N}{\partial z} \tag{6.15}$$

which we can integrate with respect to r over the interval from 0 to r.

Since, for r = 0, the quantity within brackets cancels out (it would cancel out even if we had taken $r = r'$ as our lower limit because it is proportional to the radial flow), we have

$$\frac{\partial N}{\partial r} = -2\Omega^2 N(1-N)r + \frac{1}{(D\rho)r} \frac{\partial N}{\partial z} f(r) \tag{6.16}$$

The derivative $\partial N/\partial z$ was taken out of the integral sign because, as we said, it can be considered constant with respect to r. Equation 6.16 constitutes the enrichment equation for which we were looking.

To calculate the enrichment obtainable along the entire length Z of the enrichment section, we must integrate, with respect to z, an equation in $\partial N/\partial z$, such as Eq. 6.16, in which $\partial N/\partial r$ has already been evaluated. This can be done by using the value of $\partial N/\partial r$ given in Eq. 6.16 in the equation for the balance of the desired isotope, Eq. 6.12.

Assuming as usual that N varies slowly over the radius, we have

$$2\pi \times 2\Omega^2 N(1-N) \int_0^{r''} rf(r)\, dr - \frac{2\pi}{D\rho} \frac{\partial N}{\partial z} \int_0^{r''} \frac{f^2(r)}{r}\, dr$$

$$- \pi D\rho\, r''^2\, \frac{\partial N}{\partial z} = P(N_P - N) \quad (6.17)$$

Setting

$$\frac{1}{2} hL = \frac{2\pi}{D\rho} \int_0^{r''} \frac{f^2(r)}{r}\, dr + \pi D\rho\, r''^2 \quad (6.18)$$

and

$$\frac{1}{2} \bar{g} L = 2\pi \times 2\Omega^2 \int_0^{r''} rf(r)\, dr \quad (6.19)$$

Eq. 6.17 can be written

$$h\frac{dN}{dz} = \bar{g}N(1-N) - \frac{2P}{L}(N_p - N) \quad (6.20)$$

If we set $z/h = s$, Eq. 6.20 is identified as the equation (4.77) for the square cascade.

Integration of Eq. 6.20 thus leads, in the case of low concentrations and by analogy with Eq. 4.81, to the following expression for the enrichment $a = N_P/N_0$:

$$a = \frac{(1+\psi)\exp(\bar{g}/h)\,Z(1+\psi)}{1+\psi\exp(\bar{g}/h)\,Z(1+\psi)} \quad (6.21)$$

with

$$\psi = \frac{2P}{\bar{g}L}$$

The product withdrawal P is controlled from the outside of the rotor by means of a suitable valve in the withdrawal line.

The flow L, however, is determined by the conditions of internal recirculation, e.g., by the difference in temperature between the two ends of the rotor.

The corresponding value of the nondimensional parameter ψ (standardized production) can therefore be determined.

As we shall see later, the parameter $\bar{g}$ depends solely on the radial profile of the flow but not on the value of L, whereas h depends on both.

The quantity h depends on the efficiency of the mass transfer between the upward flow L'' and the downward flow L'. As shown in Eq. 6.18, h is the sum of two terms

$$h = \frac{4\pi}{D\rho} L r''^4 \int_0^1 \frac{f^2(\zeta)}{L^2} \frac{d\zeta}{\zeta} + \frac{2\pi(D\rho)r''^2}{L} \tag{6.22}$$

where we have set $\zeta = r/r''$. The two terms of which h is composed are called h_r and h_a:

$$h = h_r + ha \tag{6.23}$$

The two terms express the resistance to mass transfer in the radial direction (h_r) and in the axial direction (h_a), respectively.

As is shown in more detail later on when distillation is discussed, h takes the name of "transfer-unit height." This magnitude expresses the height of the portion of the column along which the difference in flow concentration (for example) moving upward is equal to the mean difference between real concentration and equilibrium concentration.

Since $f(r) = \int_0^r \rho\, vr\, dr$, it is easy to see that $f(r)/L$ does not depend on L but solely on the radial profile of the flow.

Hence, of the two terms that make up h, the first (h_r), is proportional to L and the second (h_a) is inversely proportional to L, which we should have expected, given the physical significance of these two terms.

Therefore h can be written in the form

$$h = \chi_r L + \frac{\chi_a}{L} \tag{6.24}$$

in which χ_r and χ_a are quantities independent from L.

As for $\bar{g}$, Eq. 6.19 gives us

$$\bar{g} = 4\pi \times 2\Omega^2 r''^4 \int_0^1 \frac{f(\zeta)}{L} \zeta d\zeta \tag{6.25}$$

or, indeed

$$\bar{g} = g \times 8\pi r''^2 \int_0^1 \frac{f(\zeta)}{L} \zeta d\zeta = \gamma g \tag{6.26}$$

in which γ is a factor of efficiency depending on the flow profile but not on L.

The dependency on L of the $\bar{g}/h$ ratio that appears in the enrichment expression, Eq. 6.21, is therefore

$$\frac{\bar{g}}{h} = \frac{\gamma g L}{\chi_r L^2 + \chi_a} \tag{6.27}$$

With Z and ψ fixed, enrichment will thus be maximum when $\bar{g}/h$ is maximum, or in other terms, when

$$L = L_0 = (\chi_a/\chi_r)^{\frac{1}{2}} \tag{6.28}$$

The existence of a maximum is readily understandable. In fact, by increasing L we reduce the axial back diffusion, but beyond a certain limit the increased resistance to radial mass transfer causes a decrease in the axial concentration gradient.

Substituting Eq. 6.28 into Eq. 6.24, we have

$$h = h_0 = 2 (\chi_r \chi_a)^{\frac{1}{2}} \tag{6.29}$$

and hence

$$h_{r_0} = h_{a_0} = (\chi_r \chi_a)^{\frac{1}{2}} \tag{6.30}$$

i.e., the two terms, radial and axial, which make up h are equal when the circulation rate is optimum.

Under such conditions, Eq. 6.27 becomes

$$\frac{\bar{g}}{h_0} = \frac{\gamma g}{2(\chi_r \chi_a)^{\frac{1}{2}}} \tag{6.31a}$$

By replacing the expressions of γ, χ_r, and χ_a, it is easy to see that Eq. 6.31a can be written

$$\frac{\bar{g}}{h_0} = \frac{g}{r''} \times \frac{\displaystyle\int_0^1 \frac{f(\zeta)}{L} \zeta d\zeta}{\left[\displaystyle\int_0^1 \frac{f^2(\zeta)}{L^2} \frac{d\zeta}{\zeta}\right]^{\frac{1}{2}}} = \beta \frac{g}{r''} \tag{6.31b}$$

in which $\beta = \gamma r''/h_0$ is a factor dependent on the profile of the internal flow.

Introducing the standardized circulation rate

$$m = \frac{L}{L_0} \tag{6.32}$$

and keeping in mind Eq. 6.28, we obtain the following expression for Eq. 6.27:

$$\frac{\bar{g}}{h} = \frac{\bar{g}}{h_0} \times \frac{2m}{1 + m^2} \tag{6.33}$$

and hence the enrichment a, given in Eq. 6.21 can be written in the form

$$a = \frac{(1 + \psi) \exp\left[\frac{\bar{g}}{h_0} Z(1 + \psi) \frac{2m}{1 + m^2}\right]}{1 + \psi \exp\left[\frac{\bar{g}}{h_0} Z(1 + \psi) \frac{2m}{1 + m^2}\right]} \tag{6.34}$$

As we have seen in Fig. 4.12, enrichment is a diminishing function with the increase of standardized production, ψ. For $\psi = 0$ we have

$$a = A = \exp\left[\frac{\bar{g}}{h_0} Z \frac{2m}{1 + m^2}\right] \tag{6.35}$$

whose maximum, for the above-mentioned reasons, is found when m = 1 and Eq. 6.35 is accordingly written

$$A_0 = \exp\frac{\bar{g}}{h_0} Z \tag{6.36}$$

The product withdrawal P can also be expressed as a function of the dimensionless parameters m and ψ. By the very definition of ψ we find

$$P = \frac{1}{2}\bar{g}L\psi = \frac{1}{2}\bar{g}L_0 m\psi \tag{6.37a}$$

Setting

$$P_0 = \frac{1}{2}\bar{g}L_0 = \frac{1}{2} g\gamma \left(\frac{X_a}{X_r}\right)^{\frac{1}{2}}$$

Eq. 6.37a is written

$$P = m\psi P_0 \tag{6.37b}$$

The calculation for finding the enrichment factor in the stripping section is in every way analogous to what was done for the enriching section. Consequently the feed input point is determined in such a way that there will be no mixing. Calling the enriching section and stripping section enrichment factors a_P and a_W, respectively, the centrifuge separation factor is

$$q = a_P \, a_W \tag{6.38}$$

The withdrawal rates at either end of the centrifuge are

$$P = \theta G \quad \text{and} \quad W = (1 - \theta)G \tag{6.39}$$

in which G is the feed rate and θ is the cut. Both a_P and a_W are functions of θ. In fact, if we call ψ_P and ψ_W the standardized production in the two sections of the rotor, we have

$$\psi_P = \frac{2P}{gL} - \frac{2\theta G}{\gamma gL} = \theta \psi, \text{ with } \psi = \frac{2G}{\gamma gL}$$

and

$$|\psi_W| = \frac{2W}{gL} = \frac{2(1 - \theta)G}{\theta gL} = (1 - \theta)\psi$$

The other parameters being equal, if we increase θ, we increase ψ_P and decrease $|\psi_W|$. Correspondingly, we have a decrease in a_P and an increase in a_W, according to Eq. 6.34 and the corresponding equation for the stripping section. Vice versa, by decreasing θ, we increase a_P and decrease a_W. Consequently the separation factor q is a function $q = q[(\bar{g}/h_0), Z_p, Z_W, m, \psi, \theta]$. Operating with $\theta = \frac{1}{2}$ and with equal enrichment

$$a_P = a_W = a$$

in the two sections of the rotor, we obviously have $q = a^2$.

Next is the calculation of the maximum separative power that a centrifuge could theoretically achieve if every element of its volume were operating at optimum condition. Such conditions are achieved, as we know, when both the net transport and the concentration gradient are equal to half the respective maximum values.

Suppose that there is no axial convection in the rotor, which produces enrichment in the axial direction at the expense of lower separation efficiency. Let us further suppose that the shift from equilibrium is due to the removal of a small amount along the axis and of an equal amount from the peripheral zone, replacing the withdrawals with a feed introduced at the suitable point (no mixing) and in a uniform manner so as not to cause any appreciable disturbance in the gas flow regime.

In this case the concentration gradient has a radial direction, and so does the transport τ of the desired isotope across the cylindrical surface $2\pi r Z$ inside the rotor and concentric with it:

$$\tau = -D\rho \left[2\Omega^2 r \, N(1 - N) + \frac{dN}{dr} \right] \times 2\pi r Z \tag{6.40}$$

Recalling Eq. 4.87 and neglecting P × N with respect to τ, the separative power dU of the volume of the rotor lying between the cylinders of radii r and r + dr is written

$$dU = \frac{-\rho D\left[2\Omega^2 r\, N(1-N) + \dfrac{dN}{dr}\right]\dfrac{dN}{dr}}{[N(1-N)]^2} \times 2\pi Zr\, dr \qquad (6.41)$$

Under optimum conditions we find of necessity that

$$\frac{dN}{dr} = -\Omega^2 r\, N(1-N)$$

and so Eq. 6.41 becomes

$$dU_{max.} = D\rho\,[\omega^2 r]^2 \times 2\pi\, Zr\, dr \qquad (6.42)$$

which, once integrated, gives

$$\delta U_{max.} = D\rho\Omega^4\, r''^4 \frac{\pi}{2} Z \qquad (6.43a)$$

or, recalling Eq. 6.7b:

$$\delta U_{max.} = \frac{\pi}{2} D\rho\, g^2 \times Z \qquad (6.43b)$$

Hence separative power is proportional to the fourth power of the peripheral velocity and also to the height of the rotor.

For UF_6 at ambient temperature, we have $D\rho = 2.35 \times 10^{-4}$ P, and hence

$$\delta U_{max.} = 3.7 \times 10^{-4} g^2 Z \qquad g\, UF_6\, sec^{-1} \qquad (6.43c)$$

Table 6.3 shows the values for $\delta U_{max.}$ corresponding to different peripheral velocities and referred to 1 m of rotor length (with T = 300°K).

In the case of axial enrichment not much greater than 1, the separative power of the centrifuge under optimum conditions, $\delta U_{opt.}$, is obtained when every element of the rotor of height dz functions with a concentration gradient half the possible maximum.

In fact, for each rotor element we have

$$\delta U_{opt.} = \frac{1}{8} \bar{g}^2\, L\, \frac{dz}{h} \qquad (6.44)$$

and, under the above-stated conditions, the mixing that occurs when the elements of height dz are arranged in a square cascade is negligible, which means that integrating along z and setting $L = mL_0$ we have

$$\delta U_{opt.} = \frac{1}{8} \bar{g}^2 \, L_0 \, m \frac{Z}{h} \tag{6.45}$$

Taking the expression $\bar{g}/h$ from Eq. 6.33 and recalling both Eqs. 6.28 and 6.29, Eq. 6.45 can be written

$$\delta U_{opt.} = \frac{1}{8} \frac{\gamma^2}{\chi_r} \times g^2 Z \frac{m^2}{1 + m^2} \tag{6.46}$$

Table 6.3

MAXIMUM SEPARATIVE POWER AT VARIOUS
PERIPHERAL VELOCITIES

	280 m sec⁻¹	300 m sec⁻¹	350 m sec⁻¹	400 m sec⁻¹	450 m sec⁻¹
$\delta U_{max.}/Z$					
g* hr⁻ m⁻¹	0.29	0.39	0.45	1.22	1.92
kg* year⁻¹ m⁻¹	2.6	3.4	4.0	10.7	16.8

*The weight refers to UF_6.

Since γ and χ_r do not depend on L, it is

$$\delta U_{opt.} = \lambda \times \delta U_{max.} \times \frac{m^2}{1 + m^2} \tag{6.47}$$

in which λ is an efficiency factor connected with the particular velocity field in the rotor.

Equation 6.47 was arrived at by assuming that the useful length Z that appears in Eq. 6.45 coincides with the length of the rotor, which is approximately true only for $Z \gg r''$. Hence, in actuality, λ must also incorporate an efficiency factor that decreases as the r''/Z ratio rises. This is, therefore, an incentive to the adoption of long rotors with small diameter, insofar as is compatible with the mechanical limitations already mentioned (critical frequencies and speeds relative to bearings).

From Eq. 6.47, we also see that the greater m is (with which there is a drop in the axial concentration gradient) the closer $\delta U_{opt.}$ comes to $\delta U_{max.}$. For m = 2, however, we can already arrive at 80% of the limit value, whereas with m = 3, we are at 90% of the limit value.

EXPERIMENTAL FINDINGS

Beyerle and Groth have made experimental enrichment of ^{235}U with countercurrent centrifuges of the UZ III B and ZG3 types. The rotor dimensions are the following:

Type	$2r''$, cm	Z, cm
UZ III B	13.4	63.5
ZG3	20	75 and 120

The experiments with the UZ III B centrifuge run with optimum circulation rate L, cut $\theta = \frac{1}{2}$, and enrichment $a_P = a_W = a$ (so that $q = a^2$) made it possible to determine the dependence of q on the feed rate G. This dependence agrees with the behavior of the curves for $a = a(\psi)$, where $\psi = G/\bar{g}L$, which was shown in Fig. 4.12.

The separation factor $Q_0 = A_0^2$ for zero production ($\psi = 0$) yielded the values shown in Table 6.4.

Table 6.4

SEPARATION PARAMETERS OBTAINED
UNDER OPTIMUM CONDITIONS (UZ III B)

Peripheral velocity (v), m sec^{-1}	Q_0	g	K
252	1.188	0.037	4.65
280	1.225	0.046	4.45

Table 6.4 also shows the multiplication factor $K = \ln Q_0/g$. Using Eq. 6.36, we see that $K = 2\bar{g}Z/g\,h_0$ and expressing $\bar{g}/h_0$ by means of Eq. 6.31b

$$K = 2\beta \frac{Z}{r''}$$

we can thus find that $K \cong Z/2r''$.

The separation factor with $v = 252$ m sec^{-1} was found to decrease from $Q_0 = 1.188$ to $q = 1.162$, moving from $G = 0$ to $G = 25$ g hr^{-1}.

The separative power, obeying Eq. 4.116, can be written

$$\delta U = G \frac{(q)^{\frac{1}{2}} - 1)\ln q}{2[(q)^{\frac{1}{2}} + 1]} \tag{6.48}$$

From the experimental values q = q(G), obtained from the UZ III B centrifuge, the δU expressed by Eq. 6.48 was determined. This is shown graphically in Fig. 6.12.

For v = 280 m sec^{-1} the maximum value is $\delta U \simeq 0.132$ g hr^{-1} UF$_6$, feeding at G $\simeq$ 50 g hr^{-1}. The corresponding separation factor is about q = 1.08.

With the same rotor length Z = 63.5 cm, the theoretical maximum separative power is $\delta U_{max.}$ = 0.18 (i.e., under the above-cited conditions, an efficiency of about 71% was achieved).

Zippe experimented with ^{235}U separation, using the centrifuge with Pitot tubes for gas extraction described on page 218. Here again are the principal design features: Z = 30.5 cm, r$''$ = 3.7 cm, and v = 350 m sec^{-1}.

The temperature difference between the upper lid (42 to 50°C) and the lower lid (35 to 47°) was not very great. Given the high peripheral velocity, the pressure of the gas along the axis was very low: 1 to 10 μm Hg.

Figure 6.13 shows the behavior of q = q(G) and of the corresponding separative power in a typical experiment. Because the cut was not exactly symmetrical, the enrichments a$_P$ and a$_W$ in the two sections of the rotor were not equal, and the δU was calculated either through the equation

$$\delta U = G\theta \, (1 - \theta) \frac{(q - 1) \ln q}{q + 1} \tag{6.49}$$

or by means of the value function. The maximum value in the experiment shown is $\delta U = 0.0456$ g UF$_6$ hr^{-1}, feeding at G $\simeq$ 18 g hr^{-1}. Accordingly we have q = 1.125.

With a rotor of equal useful length (Z = 30.5 cm) and at a temperature of 316°K, we have $\delta U_{max.}$ = 0.141 g hr^{-1}, which means that in this experiment the efficiency achieved was about 32%.

In a further test, with some modifications to the apparatus, Zippe achieved $\delta U = 0.065$ g hr^{-1} (or $\delta U = 0.0665$ g hr^{-1}, according to the value function) corresponding to q = 1.180.

ECONOMICS OF THE PROCESS

The power supplied to the UZ III B centrifuge was Π = 1.5 kW, hence the energy consumption per unit of separative work is: $\xi = \Pi/\delta U = (1.5/0.132) \times 10^3 = 11,350$ kWh/kg UF$_6$ = 16,800 kWh/kg U.

With the peripheral velocity of 300 m sec^{-1} attained by the ZG3 centrifuge, and introducing a few structural improvements that brought consumption down to 700 W per unit, we have

$$\xi = 6800 \text{ kWh/kg U}$$

In the Zippe experiments referred to earlier, the power absorbed in the first case ($\delta U = 0.0456$ g hr^{-1}) was 8.9 W, and in the second ($\delta U = 0.0665$ g hr^{-1}) the power was

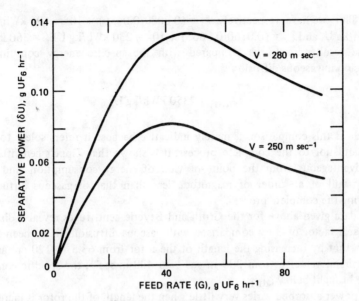

Fig. 6.12 Separative power of a type UZ III B centrifuge as a function of the feed rate G, with a constant cut.

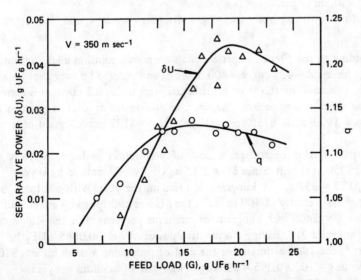

Fig. 6.13 Separative power δU and separation factor q of a Zippe centrifuge as a function of the feed rate G with a constant asymmetrical cut.

16.0 W. Thus we have, respectively, $\xi_1 = (0.0089/0.0456) \times 10^3 = 195$ kWh/kg $UF_6 =$ 290 kWh/kg U, and $\xi_2 = (0.0160/0.0665) \times 10^3 = 230$ kWh/kg $UF_6 = 360$ kWh/kg U.

These results are to be compared with the specific energy consumption for compression in gaseous diffusion

$$\xi_{diff.} = 2350 \text{ kWh/kg U}$$

Inasmuch as this comparison is merely indicative because it refers solely to the basic process and not to the complete process, it is shown that Zippe's centrifuge proved quite advantageous from the point of view of energy consumption and that it is probably still of an order of magnitude less than that of gaseous diffusion, even considering the complete process.

The data given above for the Groth and Beyerle centrifuges reveal a disadvantage by almost a factor of 3 by comparison with gaseous diffusion. It has been estimated, however, that by increasing the length of the rotor from 63.5 to 120 cm and upping the peripheral velocity from 300 m sec^{-1} to 400 m sec^{-1}, the specific consumption could be brought below $\xi_{diff.}$.

The power absorbed varies very little when the length of the rotor is increased. The fact is that power at nominal operating levels is, in practice, absorbed only by the shock-absorbing, thrust, and friction bearings.

In France an analysis of energy consumption made with rotors of length $Z = 125$ cm and velocity $v =$ m sec^{-1} yielded the results shown in Table 6.5. Reference is made to two different classes of motors:

1. Motors with friction bearings and hydrostatic or hydrodynamic shock adsorbers, operating with oil or gas.

2. Motors with hydrodynamic gas friction bearings and ball-bearing shock absorbers.

According to the French experience, an economic solution might be found with a centrifuge having $Z = 125$ cm, $v = 400$ m sec^{-1}, and absorbed power about 1 kW.

Again, to assess the status of centrifugation as to capital costs, it is convenient to use as the term of comparison the specific investment typical of gaseous diffusion (technology 1970, scale 8750 tons ΔU $year^{-1}$: $\zeta = \$137$ per kilogram of uranium per year.

For the UZ III B centrifuge, a cost of production in large lots was set at an estimated \$2500 per unit. Since $\delta U = 1.15$ kg UF_6 $year^{-1}$ or 0.78 kg U $year^{-1}$, we have $\zeta = 2500/0.78 = \$3200$ per kilogram of uranium per year. With a rotor 120 cm high and a peripheral velocity of 400 m sec^{-1}, the δU was multiplied by a factor of 8, which would give $\zeta = \$400$ per kilogram of uranium per year. For the Zippe centrifuge described on page 218, having a separative power of $\delta U = 0.0665$ g UF_6 $hr^{-1} = 0.395$ kg U $year^{-1}$, the 1960 estimate for the cost of producing a small lot was \$1000. This would give us $\zeta = 1000/0.395 = \$2540$ per kilogram of uranium per year.

It has been estimated that a Zippe centrifuge with a useful height of 46.5 cm and velocity of 400 m sec^{-1} could be built in mass production for \$235 per unit. Assuming

Table 6.5

ANALYSIS OF ENERGY CONSUMPTION
WITH FRENCH-BUILT
CENTRIFUGES

Category	A, W	B, W
Mechanical losses	1800	160
Electrical losses	250	250
Aerodynamic friction of the rotor	250	250
Gas extraction from the rotor	150	150
Total	2450	810

that the efficiency (actually low in the above-described experiment) could be doubled, we should have $\delta U = 2.042$ kg U year^{-1}, and hence the specific investment would be $\zeta = \$235/2.042 = \$115$ per kilogram of uranium per year. This sum, however, does not take into account auxiliary equipment.

According to 1968 French assessments, an economically advantageous solution would be to build a centrifuge for $2000 that would turn at 500 m sec^{-1}.

For an English–German–Dutch demonstration plant, with a separative-power rating of 300 metric tons U year^{-1} (start of operations, 1976), the estimated specific investment is $\zeta = \$150$ to $200 per kilogram of uranium per year. For larger plants (1500 metric tons U year^{-1}), the estimate is $\xi = 300$ kWh/kg U, and $\zeta = \$144$ per kilogram of uranium per year. It follows that the low energy consumption could make centrifugation competitive with gaseous diffusion even if the specific investment remains higher. In particular, it might be competitive even on a more modest scale than that of the present American installations, e.g., for plants of about 1000 metric tons U year^{-1} in separative power.

In such evaluations the δU must allow for the actual on-stream efficiency of the centrifuges, which can be evaluated only through the experience of operating a statistically representative number of machines.

EXAMPLE OF AN IDEAL CASCADE

We will calculate the principal parameters of an ideal cascade, having a total separative power

$$\Delta U = 6000 \text{ metric tons U year}^{-1}$$

made up of centrifuges with the following parameters: $v = 400$ m sec^{-1}; $Z = 120$ cm; $q = 1.5$, $a = (q)^{1/2} = 1.23$; $G = 50$ g UF$_6$ hr^{-1}; and $\delta U = 1.065$ g UF$_6$ hr^{-1} = 9.35 kg UF$_6$

year^{-1} = 6.31 kg U year^{-1}. Hence the number of centrifuges in operation in the cascade is

$$n = \frac{\Delta U}{\delta U} = \frac{6}{6.31} \times 10^6 = 950{,}000$$

Of course the number of machines installed must be greater; assuming an on-stream efficiency of 85%, there will be n/0.85 $\simeq$ 1,120,000.

The total flow of the cascade is

$$\Sigma L = nG = 50 \text{ metric tons UF}_6 \text{ hr}^{-1}$$

Assumint that the power absorbed is 1 kW per machine, the total absorbed power of the cascade will be

$$\Pi = 950 \text{ MW}$$

Adopting the following external parameters

$$N_P = 0.0298$$
$$N_F = 0.00715$$
$$N_W = 0.00260$$

we find F/P = $(N_p - N_W / N_F - N_W)$ = 5.87. Furthermore, as was seen in the discussion of gaseous diffusion (see page 197).

$$\Delta U / P = 3.47$$

The product, feed, and waste rates are: P = 6000/3.47 = 1740 metric tons U year^{-1} = 300 kg UF$_6$ hr^{-1}; F = 5.87 P = 10,000 metric tons U year^{-1} = 1750 kg UF$_6$ hr^{-1}; and W = 4.87 P = 8260 metric tons U year^{-1} = 1450 kg UF$_6$ hr^{-1}. Recall also that the ^{235}U contained in the product is PN$_P$ = 52 tons ^{235}U year^{-1}.

The number of centrifuge stages is thus

$$S + 1 = \frac{\ln(3/0.72)}{\ln 1.23} = 7 \text{ in the enrichment section}$$

$$B = \frac{\ln(0.72/0.26)}{\ln 1.23} - 1 = 4 \text{ in the stripping section}$$

Using Eq. 4.63 to calculate concentrations and Eq. 4.61 for the flow rates, we found the data shown in Table 6.6, which also shows the distribution of the centrifuges $n_s = L_s/G$ along the cascade.

From the foregoing we can see that cascades of centrifuges for uranium-isotope separation are characterized by a number of stages very much smaller than those in gaseous diffusion, by a factor of more than 100, external parameters being equal. With

Table 6.6

NUMBER OF CENTRIFUGES n_S IN THE
VARIOUS STAGES OF AN IDEAL CASCADE

s	N_S, mol %	L_S, metric tons UF_6 hr^{-1}	n_S
6	0.0245	0.65	12,000
5	0.0199	1.45	28,000
4	0.0163	2.4	45,000
3	0.0133	3.5	70,000
2	0.0108	5.0	98,000
1	0.00879	6.7	130,000
0	0.00715	9.0	175,000
Total, enrichment section		28.7	558,000
−1	0.00581	7.7	150,000
−2	0.00475	6.4	122,000
−3	0.00386	4.7	90,000
−4	0.00313	2.5	30,000
Total, stripping section		21.3	392,000
Total cascade		$\Sigma L = 50.0$	950,000

centrifugation, in brief, we are dealing with relatively "short and wide" cascades. Thus they are suitable, within certain limits, to be subdivided in several autonomous cascades in parallel.

PILOT AND DEMONSTRATION PLANTS

Experimental centrifuges for separation of ^{235}U have been built and operated in the following countries: United States, Germany, the Soviet Union, Holland, Great Britain, France, Italy, and Japan.

It has been announced that, in Great Britain, Holland, and Germany, a total of about 700 centrifuges in cascades have been in operation. Figure 6.14 shows a group of centrifuges arranged in cascade which were installed in Great Britain in 1972. Three metal tubes project from the upper part of each vessel. These tubes are probably used for feed and for extraction of the head and tail. The plastic tubes shown, on the other hand, probably carry water for cooling.

At Capenhurst in Great Britain, construction began in 1972 on a pilot plant rated at a ΔU of 15 metric tons U $year^{-1}$, capable of enriching ^{235}U as much as 2.5% with a waste concentration of 0.3%. This plant is to be expanded up to a ΔU of about 50 metric tons U $year^{-1}$.

At Almelo in Holland, construction began in 1972 on two pilot plants, one Dutch, rated at a ΔU of 25 metric tons U $year^{-1}$ (N_P = 2.5 − 4% ^{235}U; N_W = 0.2%), and one German plant of equal ΔU (N_P = 2.2 − 3.2% ^{235}U; N_W = 0.2%). The German plant is

Fig. 6.14 View of a group of experimental centrifuges arranged in a cascade (Great Britain).

divided into two parts ($\frac{1}{3}$ and $\frac{2}{3}$ ΔU) to allow for experimenting with various types of centrifuges. It was scheduled to go into operation gradually during 1973 and 1974.

Sometime in 1976, operations are scheduled to begin at an English–German–Dutch demonstration plant of about 300 metric tons year^{-1} of separative power. Some of the economic projections for this plant are given on pages 236 and 237. Certainly one of the most important points to be checked out in this plant is the reliability factor. As of now, we have heard of one single machine that has had more than $6\frac{1}{2}$ years in operation, but obviously such data must be averaged out over a great many mass-produced machines.

REFERENCES

Experimental Work

1. J. W. Beams, *Rev. Mod. Phys.*, **10**: 245 (1938).
2. K. Beyerle and W. Groth, Uranium Isotope Enrichment by Gas Centrifugation, in *Proceedings of the International Symposium on Isotope Separation*, p. 667 North-Holland Publishing Company, Amsterdam, 1958.
3. W. E. Groth et al., Enrichment of Uranium Isotopes by the Gascentrifuge Method, in *Proceedings of the Second United Nations International Conference on the Peaceful Uses of Atomic Energy, Geneva, 1958*, Vol. 4, p. 439, New York, 1958.
4. G. Zippe, The Development of Short Bowl Ultracentrifuges, Final Report, June 15, 1960, USAEC Report ORO-315, Nov. 1, 1960.

Theory

6. E. Cohen, *The Theory of Isotope Separation*, Chap. 6, McGraw-Hill Book Company, Inc., New York, 1951.
7. J. Los and E. Kistemaker, On the Influence of Temperature Distribution Inside a Gas Centrifuge, in *Proceedings of the International Symposium on Isotope Separation*, p. 695, North-Holland Publishing Company, Amsterdam, 1958.
8. A. M. Rozen, *Teoriya Razdeleniya Izotopov v Kolonnokh*, Chap. 6.1, Goskomitet, Moscow, 1960.
9. C. Ouwerkerk and J. Los, The Separative Power of Short Countercurrent Centrifuges, in *Proceedings of the Third International Conference on the Peaceful Uses of Atomic Energy, Geneva, 1964*, Vol. 12, p. 367, United Nations, New York, 1965.
10. D. R. Olander, *Technical Basis of Gas Centrifuge: Advances in Nuclear Science and Technology*, Vol. 6, p. 105, Academic Press, Inc., New York, 1972.

Economics and Plants

11. M. L. Bourgain, J. LeManach, and R. Berthoumioux, Gas Ultracentrifuges for Uranium Isotope Separation, in *Proceedings of the Turin Symposium, 1968*, Comitato Nazionale per l'Energia Nucleare, Rome, 1968.
12. M. Bogaardt, E. Einfeld, and J. Tatlock, Objectives and Progress in the Centrifuge Enrichment Plant Industry, in *Proceedings of the Fourth International Conference on the Peaceful Uses of Atomic Energy, Geneva, 1971*, Vol. 9, p. 63 New York, 1972.
13. H. Morhauer, Status of Uranium Enrichment in Europe, in *Hamburg Reactor Conference, 1972, Atomwirt., Atomtech.*, **17**: 300 (1972).

7 MASS DIFFUSION

As was shown in Chap. 3, mass diffusion for isotope separation makes use of the different diffusion coefficients of the various components of the isotopic mixture in a third component called the separating agent. The isotope with the lowest diffusion coefficient tends to be concentrated in the direction of flow of the separating agent, which flows irreversibly through the mixture.

Mass diffusion was originally developed by Hertz,[6] who applied it to the separation of helium from neon and also to separate the isotopes of neon. In 1939 Maier conducted an extensive experimental study of mass diffusion, building a cascade with particularly simple stages.

VARIOUS TYPES OF SEPARATING ELEMENTS

Figure 7.1 describes schematically the diffusion stage used by Maier. It is cylindrical in section and is divided internally into two annular chambers by means of a cylindrical porous screen. The gas to be separated is introduced from the upper end of the inner chamber by means of a suitable conduit, and then the gas drops toward the bottom. Part of the mixture diffuses beyond the porous screen into the outer chamber where the separating agent flows. The lighter isotope, with the higher diffusion coefficient, tends to diffuse preferentially and thus gives rise to a depletion of the light isotope in the current of gas that flows in the inner chamber and to an

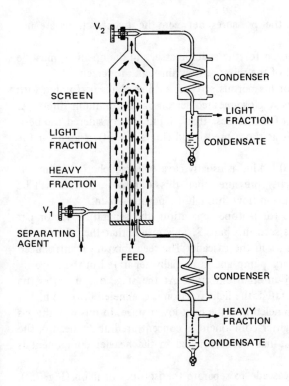

Fig. 7.1 Maier's mass-diffusion stage.

enrichment in the current of gas diffused beyond the porous screen and flowing toward the upper end of the stage. In this way a separation of the feed mixture into two currents is achieved; one current comes out of the upper end of the stage and is enriched in the light isotope, and the other comes out of the lower end of the stage and is enriched in the heavier isotope. Of course, both currents contain some of the separating agent. The currents are then passed through a cooling coil in which the separating agent, which is usually chosen so as to be less volatile than the components of the mixture, is condensed. The light and heavy fractions thus purified are then sent along to the adjacent stages in the cascade.

Note that the separation effect is not due to the presence of the porous screen, as happens in gaseous diffusion. The screen in mass diffusion offers fairly large openings into which the gases flow in a nonmolecular flux and hence with nonselective diffusion. The separation effect is due essentially to the presence of the separating agent, which facilitates the diffusion of the light molecules. The screen's function is to keep apart from each other the light and heavy fractions.

The stage is completed by several valves to control the flows circulating through the stage; suitable setting of the V_2 valve enables the operator to vary the pressure in the outer chamber of the stage and thus to control the flow of mixture diffusing through the porous screen. Separation can take place either with the light fraction at a higher pressure than the heavy fraction or vice versa. In any case the best conditions for separation are reached when the pressures between the two fractions are not excessively different.

The porous screen must be chosen for the specific case, and the openings must be small enough to allow tight control of the mixture flow through the screen.

Maier used various materials for his porous screens, such as plates perforated with holes about 0.4 mm in diameter, very close-meshed screens, and aluminum filters. As a rule, openings with a diameter of a little less than 10 μm are considered the best. Thin plates of porous metal, such as those used in oil filters, are often used for the purpose.

The pressure inside a stage of this kind is usually close to atmospheric pressure. It is also possible to work with higher pressures than this, but more trouble will be encountered in controlling the diffusion flow through the porous screen.

In all mass-diffusion processes for isotope separation, the separation factor per stage is very close to unity, as was seen in Chap. 3. This means that there is in most cases a need for a good many stages in the cascade. The feed mixture is introduced into each stage by means of a rotary pump and is partially separated in the stage by the steam that is introduced in countercurrent flow. At the stage output, after the steam has been condensed and separated, the light fraction is channeled into the higher stage, and the heavy fraction is channeled into the next lower stage. In this way the gas that has been enriched with the lighter component is concentrated at the head of the cascade, whereas the fraction that has been enriched in the heavier component is gathered at the tail of the cascade.

Hertz built a special type of cascade to separate the isotopes of neon (Fig. 7.2). Each stage in the cascade is made up of mercury-vapor diffusion pumps. The diffusion pump maintains the gas circulation in each stage and provides a vapor jet through which the pumped gas is diffused into the stage. This mercury-vapor jet is used to separate the isotope mixture.

In the cascade designed by Hertz, the vapor jet comes out of the inner tube of the pump, is condensed on the chilled outer surface, and drops back again to the base of the pump, where a heater keeps the jet rising back to the top. The gas to be pumped enters the mercury jet, is carried along with it, and is separated from it in the process of condensation of the mercury vapor on the wall.

During this process, however, the gas is diffused in a direction perpendicular to the lines of flow, partially penetrating the innermost layers of the vapor jet. This penetration is more efficient the higher the gas diffusion coefficient, and, in the case of an isotopic mixture, the lighter and faster moving component is concentrated inside the vapor jet. In the Hertz pump the mercury-vapor jet is deflected in such a way that part of it forms a countercurrent to the mixture to be separated. The lighter fraction is pumped to the upper stage by the undeflected mercury-vapor jet, whereas the heavy fraction falls down to the lower stage.

The degree of enrichment depends on the velocity of the jet, the diffusion coefficients, and the geometry of the apparatus. Very special attention must be paid to the geometrical construction of the pump so that only the innermost vapor jet is used for pumping.

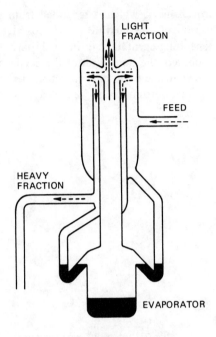

Fig. 7.2 Hertz type mass-diffusion stage.

The advantage of the Hertz apparatus is that only one component, the diffusion pump, allows production of the separating agent, separation of the feed mixture, and forwarding of the two separated fractions to the adjacent stages. To construct the cascade requires that the connecting tubes be scaled between one stage and the next so as to regulate the suction velocity of the pumps in such a way that they do not drain the lower stages in the cascade.

The separation factor calculated for a stage of this Hertz design is usually somewhat higher than the one obtained for a stage of the Maier type described earlier. The operating pressure in the Hertz design is, however, somewhat lower (it is only a few millimeters of mercury).

With a cascade of 12 pumps, Hertz obtained 50% ^{22}Ne; the system achieved equilibrium in about 45 min. The same system has been applied by others to separation of ^{18}O, ^{35}Ar, ^{15}N, and ^{13}C.

A later development in the techniques of mass-diffusion separation consists of the mass-diffusion column invented by Benedict.[7] This column (Fig. 7.3), with a generally cylindrical section, consists of four concentric chambers. The separating agent produced in an evaporator flows into the innermost chamber, which consists of a tube with holes in it. From this chamber it is diffused through the holes into the second chamber, where it meets the mixture enriched in the light isotope flowing toward the top of the column. In the third chamber, which is separated from the second by a porous screen, the heavy fraction of the mixture to be separated is flowing downward to meet in turn the separating agent that diffuses through the screen. The separating agent ultimately encounters the inner wall of the condenser, which is chilled by a stream of water that flows to the outermost chamber. Here the vapor condenses, and the liquid drops to the bottom to be recycled into the evaporator.

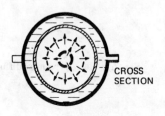

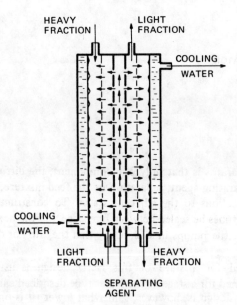

Fig. 7.3 Mass-diffusion column.

The separative effect is due to the radial flow of the separating agent which pushes the gas toward the condenser. This sets up a concentration gradient of gas in the vapor and a back diffusion of the gas toward the axis of the column. The diffusion coefficient of the light isotope is slightly higher than that of the gas as a whole; the contrary occurs for the heavier isotope. The result is that the gas ascending in the second chamber is enriched in the light isotope, whereas the descending flow in the third chamber is depleted.

The essential advantage of the mass-diffusion column over the Maier stage is that the separating agent is diffused uniformly in the light fraction of the mixture over the entire length of the column. Optimum conditions can be maintained at every point. The same is true of the condensation of the separating agent, which occurs uniformly along the chilled wall. The mass-diffusion column makes it possible to multiply, by means of a countercurrent process, the elementary separation factor. The main drawback is that its construction is rather complicated.

Diffusion-column operation requires that consideration be given to the effect of parasitic convection currents, which can lead to the mixing of gases of differing isotopic concentrations. In addition to asymmetrical effects, such currents can occur as a result of free convection of mixtures of gases and vapors of varying densities within the chambers or as a result of gas molecules captured by the liquid film running down along the condenser. In some separation cases the gas may actually go into solution in the liquid. All these effects can generally be reduced by lowering the operating pressure. For this reason the separation factor, independent from the pressure below 200 mm Hg, tends to drop markedly for higher pressure levels.

Among the various types of mass-diffusion separating elements, we should cite a diffusion column with three concentric chambers in which there is no porous screen separating the rising light fraction and the descending heavy fraction. The column consists of a cylindrical tube made of porous material surrounded by a cylindrical cooling chamber (Fig. 7.4). The vapor, as in a regular diffusion column, is diffused radially from the porous tube, condenses on the chilled surface, runs down the wall, and is then recycled.

The vapor may be generated by a boiler at the bottom of the column and introduced into the tube, or directly generated by the porous surface, forcing the liquid through the pores and evaporating it from the electrically heated surface. The separation process takes place in the usual way: the isotopic molecules are driven toward the condenser and back diffused at differing speeds in the vapor toward the central tube. The elementary separation factor for this effect has been calculated theoretically and is given by the following expression:

$$\ln q_0 = \frac{RT\,\phi_0}{p}\left(\frac{1}{D_{01}} - \frac{1}{D_{02}}\right) r_a \ln \frac{r_a}{r_b}$$

where   R = constant of the gases
   T = absolute mean temperature
   p = pressure
   r_a = radius of the porous tube
   r_b = radius of the condenser
   ϕ_0 = flow of the separating agent
D_{01}, D_{02} = diffusion coefficients

The elementary separation factor thus increases (1) with an increase in ϕ_0, (2) with an increase in r_a if the space $r_b - r_a$ between the two tubes is held constant, (3) with an increase in $r_a - r_b$ if the r_a/r_b ratio is held constant, and (4) with an increase in $[(1/D_{01}) - (1/D_{02})]$. This last effect can be achieved by increasing the molecular

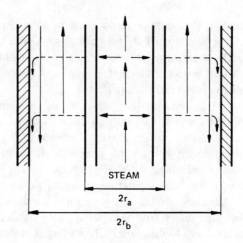

Fig. 7.4 Operating principle of a mass-diffusion column without a screen.

weight of the separating agent. The q_0 factor increases with the decline in temperature since T/D behaves much like $T^{-\frac{1}{2}}$. However, the influence of pressure is slight since, within certain limits, the product pD (pressure times diffusion coefficient) is constant.

Under the pull of gravity and given the difference in density between the two separated fractions, ascending and descending flows are set up, and therefore the log of the total separation factor for the column becomes proportional to the height of the column when no product is removed.

The total separation factor for the column increases as the elementary separation factor and as the length of the column increases and passes through a maximum as a function of $r_b - r_a$, of p, and of ϕ_0. This last result is obvious since the increase of ϕ_0 increases the elementary separation factor as is shown above. But this effect is offset by the decline in the vertical convection currents as the percentage of vapor in the column increases.

These results can be modified by the effect of parasitic flows and by secondary effects in the column, the most important of which is gas going into solution in the descending liquid phase of the separating agent. The above-mentioned column was designed and built by Cichelli, Weatherford, and Bowman.[8]

SCREEN PERFORMANCE

The theory of mass diffusion is based on the theory of diffusion for mixtures with several components. This theory can be obtained as an extension of the simple case of diffusion in a binary mixture.

In a two-component mixture at rest, the introduction of a gradient in the mol fraction of one of the components, dN_1/dr, induces a diffusive flow of ϕ_1 mol cm^{-2}

sec^{-1} of that component in a direction opposite to the gradient. Since we have assumed that the mixture as a whole is in a stationary state, the diffusive flow of the second component ϕ_2 will be equal to ϕ_1 and flowing in the opposite direction. As stated in Fick's law of diffusion, these diffusion flows are proportional to the concentration gradient:

$$\phi_1 = -\phi_2 = -\rho D_{12} \frac{dN_1}{dr} \tag{7.1}$$

in which ρ is the mol density expressed in mols per unit of volume and D_{12} is the diffusion coefficient of the binary mixture.

If the mixture as a whole is moving in the direction of the concentration gradient with a flow of ϕ, the flow of the index 1 component is changed, by reason of the convection flow, by a quantity ϕN_1, so that

$$\phi_1 = \phi N_1 - \rho D_{12} \frac{dN_1}{dr} \tag{7.2}$$

and keeping in mind that

$$N_1 + N_2 = 1 \tag{7.3}$$

and

$$\phi_1 + \phi_2 = \phi \tag{7.4}$$

we find that

$$\frac{\phi_2 N_1 - \phi_1 N_2}{\rho D_{12}} = \frac{dN_1}{dr} \tag{7.5}$$

For a mixture with n components, Eq. 7.5 can be generalized and becomes

$$\sum_{i=1}^{n} \frac{\phi_i N_j - \phi_j N_i}{\rho D_{ij}} = \frac{dN_j}{dr} \ (j = 1, 2, \ldots, n) \tag{7.6}$$

Only $(n - 1)$ out of these equations is independent, since the concentrations are governed by the equation

$$\sum_{j=1}^{n} \frac{dN_j}{dr} = 0 \tag{7.7}$$

To determine all the individual flows as a function of the diffusion coefficients of the various components of the mixture, we must add another condition. A helpful one is often the total flow of the mixture

$$\phi = \sum_{i=1}^{n} \phi_i \tag{7.8}$$

Quite important in the development of the theory and in designing the separation installations is the knowledge of the diffusion coefficients, which were dealt with in Chap. 3, pages 71-75. We must remember that the diffusion coefficient for a gaseous mixture at a pressure less than several atmospheres is inversely proportional to the pressure and increases with absolute temperature T as T^b, in which b is an exponent lying between 1.5 and 2 and is practically independent of the concentration ratio. In calculating such coefficients, we are therefore permitted to use the expression

$$D = \frac{D_0 (T/T_0)^{\overline{b}}}{p} \tag{7.9}$$

in which T is the absolute temperature in degrees Kelvin, p is the pressure, and D_0 is the diffusion coefficient at 273.2°K and unitary pressure. Consequently ρD_{12} is independent of pressure and increases as temperature.

In the Maier stage and in the diffusion column, the construction and quality of the porous screens are very important. The pore dimensions must be considerably larger than the mean free path of the gas and the vapor. At the same time the screen must have considerable hydrodynamic resistance to the flow of the gas—vapor mixture going through it since it is the drop in pressure across the screen that determines the possibility of controlling the flows through the screen.

We can now introduce two typical quantities for the porous screen of a mass-diffusion plant: the diffusivity C_D and the permeability to the mass flow K.

Diffusivity is a quantity proportional to the flow of gas through the screen and must be maximized to reduce the membrane surface required for a given separation operation. Permeability is proportional to the overall flow of gas and separating agent through the screen and must be minimized to facilitate flow control through the screen.

In dealing with the properties of screens and the operating characteristics of the mass-diffusion stage, we shall use the terminology shown in Table 7.1 for the mol fractions and flows of the three components of the mixture—separating agent and light and heavy components of the gas. The performance of the screen is illustrated in Fig. 7.5.

With these definitions, diffusivity is defined as the ratio between the masses of gas diffusing in the separating agent through the screen per unit of area per unit of time and the difference in mol fraction of gas between the flows moving along the opposite sides of the screen in conditions of equilibrium:

$$C_D = \frac{\phi_1 + \phi_2}{n'' - n'} \tag{7.10}$$

The flow through the diffusion screen is governed by Fick's law as expressed in Eq. 7.1. In finite form we find that, recalling Eq. 7.10,

$$C_D = \frac{\rho D}{\delta_L + \delta_H + \delta_S} \tag{7.11}$$

where we have written in the denominator of Eq. 7.11 the actual diffusion lengths of the conduits that carry the light and heavy fractions and of the screen itself. The sum of these three quantities represents a total diffusion length along which is maintained that concentration gradient which allows the gas to diffuse through the screen into the separating agent. The smaller these diffusion lengths, the greater will be the diffusivity, i.e., greater by as much as the resistance to diffusion of the gas is lessened.

Table 7.1

TERMINOLOGY FOR THE MASS-DIFFUSION STAGE

	Light fraction	Heavy fraction
Mol fractions		
Separating agent	$1 - n'$	$1 - n''$
Gas	n'	n''
In the gas		
Light component	N'	N''
Heavy component	$1 - N'$	$1 - N''$
Flow through the screen		
Separating agent	ϕ_0	
Light component	ϕ_1	
Heavy component	ϕ_2	
Total flow	ϕ	

The actual diffusion length δ_S of the screen is defined as the diffusion length of an open channel of unitary area, which would offer the same resistance to diffusion as a unit of area of the real screen. It is obvious indeed that the resistance set up by the screen to diffusion is not only a function of thickness but also a function of the size and frequency of the holes in the screen. So, if W_S is the thickness of the screen and λ is the fraction of area open to the flow, we find that

$$\delta_S = \frac{W_S}{\lambda} \tag{7.12}$$

In addition to the presence of the screen, the diffusion is, as we have seen, hindered by the movement of the gas that laps at both sides of the barrier. Hence account must be taken of two actual lengths δ_L and δ_H, referring to the two flows, contributing to which is not the total flow in the two conduits but only a film that sticks to the screen, whose dimensions vary according to flow conditions.

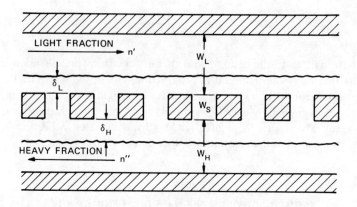

Fig. 7.5 Diagram showing the performance of a porous screen.

When the flow is turbulent, the effective diffusion length of the conduit, given by the thickness of the stagnant gas film adjacent to the screen, is

$$\delta_L = 43\ W_L\,(\mathrm{Re})^{-0.83}\left(\frac{M\rho D}{\eta}\right)^{0.44}$$ (7.13)

where W_L = effective width of the conduit in which the gas flows
      Re = Reynolds number
      M = molecular weight of the gas
      D = diffusion coefficient of the gas in the separating agent
      η = viscosity coefficient

When the flow is laminar, the expression is simpler:

$$\delta_L = \frac{13}{35}\,W_L$$ (7.14)

Similar equations can be found for the conduit through which the heavy fraction flows.

Permeability is defined as the ratio between the total number of masses which flow in a unit of time across a unit section of the screen and the pressure difference between the two faces of the screen:

$$K = \frac{\phi}{\Delta p}$$ (7.15)

If we apply Poiseuille's law for the viscous flow, we find that

$$K = \frac{\rho g d^2}{32 \eta \delta_S} \tag{7.16}$$

in which g is the gravity acceleration, d is the actual mean diameter of the screen pores, and η is the viscosity of the variable composition gas passing through the screen.

These considerations show that, to obtain maximum diffusion through the screen, it is helpful to make the quantity defined in Eq. 7.12 as small as possible, which means making the screen as thin as possible and broadening the free area available for flow of the material. This latter goal cannot be achieved if screens with large holes are being used, because, as can be seen from Eq. 7.16, we would then have a damaging increase in permeability. This means that it is better to have screens with small, very closely spaced holes. The holes must be similar in diameter and form to assure that the separating agent does not tend to pass through the bigger holes and thus cause retrodiffusion of the gas through the smaller holes.

It is also important to make δ_L as defined in Eq. 7.13 as small as possible, which means reducing the stagnant layers of gas on either side of the screen, reducing the aperture of the conduit to a minimum, and using turbulent flows with high Reynolds numbers. However, it is not feasible to reduce the aperture of the conduit or to increase the Reynolds number beyond a certain limit, because the pressure drop along the conduit becomes excessive, and hence control of the installation becomes a problem, given the difficulty of maintaining the optimum pressure differential over a broad enough expanse of the screen. Therefore, for every screen and every specific separation problem, it is wise to establish a suitable compromise between the laminar thickness of the fluid and the pressure drop. In addition, a limitation on the values of Reynolds numbers, particularly in the diffusion column, is imperative by reason of the need to avoid any excessively turbulent movement, which might cause a mixing between portions of the flow at different concentrations.

From the equations written for K and C_D, other interesting data can be gathered on the screen operating conditions. They show us, e.g., that it is desirable to have a high temperature for the fluids since diffusivity is increased by increasing D and permeability is decreased by decreasing ρ/η. Low pressure reduces ρ. With d = 10 μm, we can operate at 1 atm. Efficient functioning at a higher pressure will require a reduction in the pore diameter.

In some diffusion apparatus[11] built in the Soviet Union, the screens were made of cylindrical pipes with the number of pores varying from 20 to 20,000 per square centimeter of surface and with the pores ranging in diameter from 0.5 to 5 μm. Screens with larger pores were also used, and their sizes ran as high as 200 μm. These membranes with relatively widely spaced pores were achieved by using special punches to perforate thin steel cylinders. The screens with tiny holes were made from metal grids run through a rolling mill and then heat-treated. From a nickel grid with 20,000 pores cm^{-2}, it is possible to make a screen having pores with a mean diameter of about 8 μm. In general, porous metallic materials like those used for oil filters are used for screens.

PROCESS OPERATING CONDITIONS

Operating conditions and the efficiency of a stage can be different according to the mode of utilizing the flow of gas and vapor through the screen. The problem of finding the [optimum] operating conditions for a stage can be solved on the basis of the system of equations represented by Eq. 7.6 and referred to the three components present in a mass-diffusion stage. In the solution of the problem, we find three diffusion coefficients: D_{01} for the diffusion of the light component in the separating agent, D_{02} for the heavy component in the separating agent, and D_{12} for the heavy component in the light component. Along with Eq. 7.6, Eq. 7.8 is introduced, written for the three components:

$$\phi = \phi_0 + \phi_1 + \phi_2 \tag{7.17}$$

The system of Eqs. 7.6 and 7.8 has been solved in different cases for different diffusion-coefficient values. The most interesting conditions in the case of mass diffusion are those in which the gain g_0 is much smaller than unity:

$$g_0 = \frac{2(D_{01} - D_{02})}{D_{01} + D_{02}} \ll 1 \tag{7.18}$$

and

$$D_{12} = \frac{D_{01} + D_{02}}{2} \tag{7.19}$$

The different operating conditions of the screen are handled by introducing a nondimensional quantity S, defined by

$$S = \frac{\phi}{C_D} \tag{7.20}$$

Two important special cases are described here:

1. Zero difference in pressure through the screen, hence $S = 0$ and $\phi = 0$, as we find from Eqs. 7.15 and 7.20. This condition occurs in the simple mass-diffusion stage and corresponds to the most efficient way of using the separating agent. The solution to Eqs. 7.6 and 7.8 enables us to find the values of the partial flows through the screen:

$$\phi_0 = C_D (n'' - n') \tag{7.21}$$

$$\phi_1 = C_D [n'N' - n''N'' - g_0 N''(1 - N'')(n'' - n')] \tag{7.22}$$

$$\phi_2 = C_D \left[(1 - N') n' - (1 - N'') n'' + g_0 N'' (1 - N'')(n'' - n') \right] \qquad (7.23)$$

2. Balanced diffusion, where $S = \ln n''/n'$. This condition occurs in the mass-diffusion column when the screen is working in such a way that the flow of the light component through the screen is equal to and in the opposite direction to the flow of the heavy component. In other words $\phi_1 = -\phi_2$ and, from Eq. 7.17, $\phi = \phi_0$. This operating condition is established when $S = \ln n''/n'$. In this case there must be a pressure gradient through the screen. The solution of the usual system of equations leads to

$$\phi_1 = -\phi_2 = \frac{C_D \ln \frac{n''}{n'}}{\frac{1}{n'} - \frac{1}{n''}} \left[(N' - N'') - g_0 N'' (1 - N'') \ln \frac{n''}{n'} \right] \qquad (7.24)$$

The flow of the light component through the screen is found as the sum of two terms with opposite signs. The first term, proportional to $(N' - N'')$, is always positive, and, under the accepted convention of taking as positive the flows running from the light fraction to the heavy fraction, represents a transport of molecules of the light isotope from the light fraction to the heavy fraction; therefore this term tends to remix the isotopes and nullify the separation effect and corresponds to the normal back-diffusion effect set up by the concentration gradient in light isotopes through the screen. However, the second term, proportional to the gain g_0, represents a flow in the opposite direction carrying light molecules to the light fraction. This happens when $n'' > n'$; in other words, there must be a concentration gradient in the separating agent through the screen, i.e., a net flow $\phi = \phi_0$ of the separating agent from the light fraction to the heavy fraction. Thus this second term in Eq. 7.24 gives rise to the separation effect that must be greater than the first, if the separation is to continue to take place. Obviously separation occurs until $(N' - N'')$ has not balanced the second term in parentheses.

The basic operating parameter in a stage is the separation gain g, which refers to the entire stage, and is defined by the following equation into which we have introduced the simplifications allowed by slight enrichments:

$$g = \frac{N_0' - N''}{N''(1 - N'')} \qquad (7.25)$$

The mol fraction N_0' is the mol fraction of the light isotope in the light fraction, which brings the separation process to an end and brings the mixtures on either side of the screen into equilibrium. This condition is satisfied as a rule when

$$\frac{N_0'}{1 - N_0'} = \frac{\phi_1}{\phi_2} \qquad (7.26)$$

or the composition of the flow of gas going through the screen from the light to the heavy fraction is equal to the composition of the gas in the light fraction. In this case, there is obviously no further enrichment of the mixture. In the more common case in which S, n', and n'' have any values whatever,

$$g = \frac{g_0 \left(1 - \frac{n'}{n''}\right) S}{1 - e^{-S}} \tag{7.27}$$

In the case of $S = 0$, Eq. 7.27 becomes simply

$$g = g_0 \left(1 - \frac{n'}{n''}\right) \tag{7.28}$$

as we see from Eq. 7.27, by making S tend toward zero.

The separation gain is proportional to g_0 and increases as the increase of the flow SC_D through the screen and as the decline in the ratio n'/n'' between the heavy and light fractions of the isotopic mixture.

In the case of balanced diffusion, Eq. 7.27 becomes

$$g = g_0 \ln \frac{n''}{n'} \tag{7.29}$$

This result can be obtained directly from Eq. 7.24 if we observe that there is, in equilibrium conditions, cessation of the gas flow through the barrier and that the term in parentheses vanishes. Recalling Eq. 7.25, we obtain Eq. 7.29.

In Eq. 7.24 we can also introduce, in place of the g_0 gain, the g gain:

$$\phi_1 = -\phi_2 = C \left[(N' - N'') - gN'' (1 - N'') \right] \tag{7.30}$$

in which

$$C = C_D \frac{\ln \frac{n''}{n'}}{\frac{1}{n'} - \frac{1}{n''}} \tag{7.31}$$

CASCADES OF SEPARATING ELEMENTS

The equations developed in the two preceding sections can be applied either to simple separating elements like the one shown in Fig. 7.1, or to countercurrent columns in which the elementary separation effect is multiplied (Fig. 7.3).

We will not dwell here on simple separating elements, which have been covered by Benedict and Boas,[7] but will confine ourselves to observing that these elements can be connected in cascade as shown in Fig. 7.6, in which the usual notations have been adopted. The shaded zone on either side of the screen represents, for each separating element, the variation in the mol fraction of the process gas as it runs down the screen. The mol fractions of the desired isotope in the two flows, which, emerging from the heat exchanger X, enter the separating element, are obviously equal.

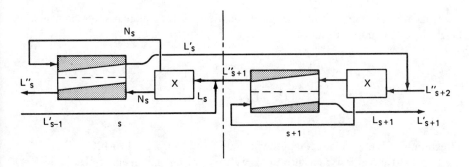

Fig. 7.6 Series connection of separating elements for mass diffusion. X indicates the heat exchangers for condensing and re-evaporating the separating agent. L = feed flow; L' = heads; L'' = tails; s − 1, s, s + 1, s + 2 = subscripts that denote stage numbers; N = desired isotope mol fraction in feed; N' = desired isotope mol fraction in head; N '' = desired isotope mol fraction in tail; x = heat exchangers; broken line = diffusion screen.

As was shown earlier, the cascade of simple stages can offer advantages over the countercurrent column when the solubility of the process gas in the condensate of the separating agent is very high.

COUNTERCURRENT COLUMNS

Let us calculate some of the main parameters for a countercurrent column, adopting some simplifying conditions. The notations are the usual ones.

Suppose that the column operates under conditions of balanced diffusion and that therefore L' and L'', n' and n'' are constant all along the column. We will also call z the height from the feed input point $(0 \leqslant z \leqslant Z)$ and E the circumference of the screen. Next we will combine Eq. 7.30 with the material balance equation

$$L'dN' = -\phi_1 E \, dz \qquad (7.32)$$

In the approximation in which the axial back diffusion is disregarded, we obtain the enrichment equation

$$\frac{dN'}{dz} = \frac{CE}{L'} \left[gN'(1 - N') - (N' - N'') \right] \qquad (7.33)$$

Balance of the desired isotope in the section of the cascade from z to the withdrawal point enables us to write

$$\frac{dN}{dz} = \frac{CE}{L'} \left[gN(1 - N) - \frac{P}{L'}(N_P - N) \right] \qquad (7.34)$$

What we have here is thus the usual equation for the square cascade, in which the height h_0 of the transfer unit is

$$h_0 = \frac{L'}{EC} = \frac{\delta}{\rho D_{12}} \times \frac{\frac{n''}{n'} - 1}{n'' \ln \frac{n''}{n'}} \times \frac{L'}{E} \qquad (7.35)$$

Integration of Eq. 7.34 is accomplished as was shown on pages 116-120.

For $\rho = 0$ and at low concentrations, we have the maximum enrichment

$$A = \exp\left(\frac{g}{h_0} Z\right) \qquad (7.36)$$

In optimum conditions we will have an enrichment

$$a = A^{\frac{1}{2}} = \exp\left(\frac{g}{2h_0} Z\right) \qquad (7.37)$$

(for $a \lesssim 2$) and hence the following separative power per unit of column length:

$$\frac{\delta U_{opt.}}{Z} = \frac{1}{4}(g^2/h_0)L' = \frac{1}{4} g_0^2 \frac{\rho D_{12}}{\delta} \frac{n'' \ln^3 \frac{n''}{n'}}{\frac{n''}{n'} - 1} E \qquad (7.38)$$

Introducing the area, $B = EZ$, of the screen, we have the expression for the area per unit of separating power:

$$\zeta_B = \frac{B}{\delta U_{opt.}} = \frac{4\delta}{\rho D_{12} g_0^2} \times \frac{\frac{n''}{n'} - 1}{n'' \ln^3 \frac{n''}{n'}} \qquad (7.39)$$

Two factors appear in Eq. 7.39; the first factor depends on the properties of the fluids and on resistance to mass transfer through the barrier, whereas the second factor depends solely on the mol fractions n' and n''.

This second term can be minimized in relation to n''. At the same ratio n''/n', it is minimum for $n' = 1$, which, in practice, means for very low mol fractions of the separating agent in the heavy fraction.

This condition also minimizes the specific consumption of the separating agent. In fact, the vapor consumption is $J = \phi_0 B$; therefore, since $\phi_0 = (\rho D_{12}/\delta) \ln n''/n'$,

$$\frac{J}{\delta U_{\text{opt.}}} = \frac{4}{g_0^2} \times \frac{\dfrac{n''}{n'} - 1}{n'' \ln^2 \dfrac{n''}{n'}} \tag{7.40}$$

The availability loss corresponding to the flow of one unit of mass of the separating agent from the center to the periphery of the column, where condensation takes place at temperature T_0, is $w = RT_0 \ln [1/(1 - n'')]$, and hence the specific energy consumption will be

$$\xi = \frac{wJ}{\delta U_{\text{opt.}}} = \frac{4RT_0}{g_0^2} \times \frac{\left(\dfrac{n''}{n'} - 1\right) \ln \dfrac{1}{1 - n''}}{n'' \ln^2 \dfrac{n''}{n'}} \tag{7.41}$$

From this last equation we see that the value $n'' = 1$, although it minimizes the screen area and the quantity of vapor, makes the specific energy consumption infinite. This is true because very low temperatures must be used to condense the separating agent at very low concentrations.

In practice, it is not a very good idea to use temperatures below that of the available cooling water. If water vapor at atmospheric pressure is used as a separating agent, the suitable values of n'' will be close to 0.9. An n' value of 0.1 then represents a reasonable compromise among the work of separation, steam consumption, and screen area.

We shall now see how the column parameters are expressed for a given total separative power ΔU, meaning for a given enrichment and a given extraction of product P, set as input data for the problem.

The optimum height of the column can be found immediately from Eq. 7.37:

$$Z_{\text{opt.}} = \frac{2h_0}{g} \ln a \tag{7.42}$$

Furthermore, under optimum conditions the relative yield must be $\rho \simeq a/(1 + a)$, and hence the normalized product withdrawal $\psi = a\rho = 1/(1 + a)$. Since $\psi = P/gL'$, we have

$L'_{opt.} = P(1 + a)/g$. If we call $f' = L'/E$, the flow per unit of circumference of the screen will be

$$E_{opt.} = \frac{L'_{opt.}}{f'} = \frac{P}{gf'}(1 + a) \tag{7.43}$$

The minimal screen area correspondingly will be

$$B_{opt.} = Z_{opt.}E_{opt.} = \frac{2h_0}{g^2 f}P(1 + a)\ln a \tag{7.44}$$

in which g and h_0 are given, respectively, by Eqs. 7.27 and 7.35.

Determination of optimum f and the width W of the conduits is involved with considerations having to do with the acceptable pressure drop along the light- and heavy-fraction ducts. These flows set up a longitudinal pressure drop as a function of their densities.

This pressure drop is different for the two flows with different densities and their difference may be compensated by friction pressure drops along the ducts, provided flows and conduit dimensions are properly chosen. Determination of this optimum condition makes it possible to hold the pressure difference constant all along the screen.

For a laminar flow the condition is met when

$$f = \frac{g(M_H\rho_H - M_L\rho_L)}{12\left(\dfrac{\mu_H}{n''\rho_H W_H^3} + \dfrac{\mu_L}{n'\rho_L W_L^3}\right)} \tag{7.45}$$

in which the same notations are used as on pages 257-260, and g is the acceleration of gravity. The specific flow f is kept as low as possible to decrease h_0 (Eq. 7.35). Therefore it is better to select minimum dimensions for the conduits as long as the spacing is uniform. Dimensions on the order of magnitude of a centimeter are acceptable. For the pipe that carries the heavy flow, space must be left along the outer wall for the condensed separating agent to run down.

APPLICATIONS

We will next consider separation of ^{13}C by diffusion of CH_4 in water vapor.

With Eq. 3.125 we had already calculated the elementary effect $g_0 = 0.0158$. For example, we want to produce (here we are using a case calculated by M. Benedict) 100 g of ^{13}C per day at 90 mol % from natural methane. Let the waste concentration be 90% of the natural ^{13}C concentration. The external parameters of the cascade are shown in Table 7.2.

The mol fractions of methane in the separating agent are, respectively, $n' = 0.1$ and $n'' = 0.9$, and we will assume that we are working with balanced diffusion. We then find from Eq. 7.29 that $g = 0.0158 \ln 9 = 0.0348$.

We chose to work substantially at atmospheric pressure in columns having the operating and dimensional features shown in Table 7.3.

Table 7.2

OUTER PARAMETERS OF A CASCADE
TO PRODUCE ^{13}C

	P	F	W
CH_4, mol hr^{-1}	0.32	271	270.7
N, mol % ^{13}C	90	1.06	0.955

Table 7.3

COLUMN SPECIFICATIONS FOR $^{13}CH_4$
SEPARATION IN STEAM

	L'	L''
Mol fraction CH_4 (n)	0.1	0.9
Molecular weight (M), g	17.8	16.2
Temperature, °C	99	52
Mol density (ρ), mol m^{-3}	32.7	37.5
Viscosity (η), g msec^{-1}	1.35×10^{-3}	1.2×10^{-3}
ρD_{12}, mol msec^{-1}	1.04×10^{-3}	
Parameter C (Eq. 7.31), mol m^{-2} sec^{-1}	7.6×10^{-3}	
Pipe spacing (W), cm	1.2	
Specific flow rate (f), mol msec^{-1}	9.8	
Screen thickness (W_S), mm	1.2	
Free-area fraction	0.05	
Pore diameter (d), μm	10	

Approximating an ideal cascade with columns of the type described in Table 7.3, the overall screen area is $B = 4000 \text{ m}^2$, and the steam consumption is

$$J = 17.5 \text{ metric tons hr}^{-1}$$

From these numbers we see that even small-output plants require large screen surfaces and a high consumption of separating agent.

The possibility of applying mass diffusion to the separation of ^{235}U has been assessed by Benedict et al.,[5] who assessed the UF_6 system, using N43 as the separating agent. The N43 stands for perfluorotributylamine, or $N(C_4F_9)_3$, whose molecular weight is 671 and whose boiling point is 177°C. The 177°C figure is quite a bit higher than that for UF_6 (sublimation occurs at 56.5°C), which makes it easy to separate the two fluids. The elementary effect as found from Eq. 3.125 is

$$g_0 = 0.00281$$

thus lower than that for gaseous diffusion (0.00429), but higher than that for the best known reversible process, chemical exchange between $NOUF_6$ and UF_6, for which

$$g = 0.0016$$

According to Benedict's reckoning for cascades of simple separating elements, the specific consumption for the process would be no less than 0.97 kW/(kg U year^{-1}) and hence between three and four times that of gaseous diffusion. The use of steam at low temperature would somewhat improve the related costs. The apparatus required is not so demanding as that required for gaseous diffusion and should therefore be less costly.

Mass diffusion can be used effectively for isotope separation on a small scale with elements of medium atomic weight.

Reversible processes (like chemical exchange) may prove more advantageous for such elements as carbon, nitrogen, or sulfur. But for the noble gases the reversible processes are confined to distillation, which involves very low temperatures. Mass diffusion therefore might offer an interesting alternative. Mass-diffusion columns without screens were tested by Cichelli et al.[8] for separating $^{13}CH_4$.

The Soviet Union has operated[11] a cascade of 10 columns in series for separation—on a laboratory scale—of the isotopes of carbon (CH_4), argon, and neon. The separating agent used was xylene ($M_0 = 194$). The height of each column was 1 m, and the screen area of the entire cascade was 1.25 m^2. The absorbed power was 6 to 8 kW. In carbon separation the Russians reported a decline in efficiency caused by the solubility of methane in xylene.

After the satisfactory operation of this laboratory plant, construction was announced[12] for two plants on a larger scale, to be built in Tiflis, Georgia, USSR. The first plant was to consist of 120 simple stages, and the second was to consist of 30 columns. The plants were to be used for isotope separation of carbon, neon, argon, and krypton. Production of 95 to 99% ^{22}Ne was to be about 200 g year^{-1}.

Experiments with a column of the screen type were performed by De Wet and Los[13] to separate the H_2-D_2 system using water vapor and to separate the $^{20}Ne-^{20}Ne$ system using both water vapor and $C_2H_2Cl_2$ as the separating agents.

More recently Nikolaev et al.[14] in the Soviet Union experimented with columns using mercury vapor as a separating agent. This return to the fluid originally used by Hertz was motivated by the need to avoid the harmful effects of solubility of the process gas in the separating agent, as had happened with xylene and other organic substances.

Running three columns in series, Nikolaev et al. obtained [22]Ne at 97% from natural neon (N_0 = 8.8%) with a time to equilibrium of 7 to 8 hr. The pressure was 30 torrs, and the specific flow of the separating agent through the screen ϕ_0 was 2.6×10^{-3} g cm^{-2} sec^{-1}. They also experimented with argon separation. For neon separation, Nikolaev et al. successfully achieved elementary separation gains that were double those obtained in the past by others.

We should also note the separation of [13]CH_4 in water vapor which was done in a column with a screen (0.2 m^2) by Wolf, Konig, and Gross.[15] The pore diameter was 40 μm. With a column height of 79 cm, a total separation factor of 1.13 was obtained.

REFERENCES

General Texts

1. M. Benedict and T. H. Pigford, *Nuclear Chemical Engineering,* p. 473, McGraw-Hill Book Company, Inc., New York, 1957.

2. H. London, *Isotope Separation,* p. 345, Newnes Educational Publishing Co. Ltd., London, 1961.

3. A. M. Rozen, *Teoriya Razdeleniya Izotopov v Kolonnakh,* Chap. 5, p. 149, Goskomitet, Moscow, 1960.

4. J. Schacter and E. von Halle, Diffusion Separation Methods, in *Kirk–Othmer Encyclopaedia of Chemical Technology,* Vol. 7, pp. 119-135, Wiley-Interscience, Inc., New York, 1965.

5. M. Benedict et al., Report on Uranium Isotope Separation, Review, Ad Hoc Committee, USAEC Report ORO-694, June 1972.

Specific Works

6. G. Hertz, A Process for Separating Mixtures of Isotopes by Diffusion in a Stream of Mercury, *Z. Phys.,* **91**: 810 (1934).

7. M. Benedict and A. Boas, Separation of Gas Mixtures by Mass Diffusion, *Chem. Eng. Progr.,* **47**: 51-111 (1951).

8. M. T. Cichelli, W. D. Weatherford, and J. R. Bowman, Sweep Diffusion Gas Separation Process, *Chem. Eng. Progr.,* **47**: 63, 123 (1951).

9. D. Heymann and J. Kistemaker, Separation of Some Isotopes by Convection–Diffusion, in *Proceedings of the International Symposium on Isotope Separation,* p. 545, North-Holland Publishing Company, Amsterdam, 1958.

10. H. Barwich and R. Jueerov, Die neure Entwicklung der Herts-'schen Gegenstromdiffusionsapparate., *ibid.,* p. 551.

11. L. G. Gverdtsiteli, R. Y. Kucherov, and V. K. Takhakaya, Isotope Separation by Diffusion in a Current of Steam, in *Proceedings of the Second United Nations International Conference on the Peaceful Uses of Atomic Energy, Geneva, 1958,* Vol. 4, p. 608, New York, 1958.

12. L. G. Gverdtsiteli et al., Experimental Production of Stable Isotopes, in *Proceedings of the Third International Conference on the Peaceful Uses of Atomic Energy, Geneva, 1964,* Vol. 12, p. 441, New York, 1965.

13. W. J. De Wet and J. Los, The Separation of Eight Gaseous Isotopes by Mass-Diffusion Columns, *Z. Naturforsch.,* **19a**: Part 1, 740; Part 2, 747 (1964).

14. B. I. Nikolaev et al., Rtutnye Mass-Diffusionnye Kolonny dlja Razdeleniya Izotopov, *Isotopenpraxis,* 6: 417 (1970).
15. F. Wolf, P. Konig, and M. Gross, Gas Separation, Using Circulation-Diffusion Methods. Vol. 2, Separation of Stable Isotopes and Commercial Gas Mixtures by Mass or "Sweep" Diffusion, *Isotopenpraxis,* 18: 416 (1972).

THE SEPARATION NOZZLE

OPERATING CONDITIONS

Optimum conditions for operating the separation nozzle (as set forth on pages xxx to xxx in Chap. 3) were determined by calculating the following cost factors per unit of separative power on the basis of the experimental data:

$$\zeta_{\ell} = (1/\delta U)\ell$$

$$\zeta_c = (1/\delta U)\, G^*RT/p'$$

$$\xi_E = (1/\delta U)\, G^*RT \ln (p/p')$$

with

$$\delta U = \frac{G}{2}\, g^2\, \theta(1 - \theta)$$

The terms G^* and G are the mol flow rates, respectively, of the gaseous mixture and of UF_6 alone. Naturally the cut θ refers to UF_6.

The first two terms, ζ_{ℓ} and ζ_c, refer to the relative plant costs, respectively, for the separating element (ℓ is the length of nozzle slit) and to the suction volume (compressors, pipes, valves). The term ξ_E refers to the relative energy consumption for compression of the G^* flow according to the ratio $r = p/p'$. The pressure p'' of the depleted fraction is also very close to p'.

Comparative experiments conducted with sundry dilution gases (N_2, neon, and helium) at varying input pressures led to the choice of helium. Good results can be obtained with hydrogen, but its reactivity with UF_6 makes its use problematical. The most suitable proportions for the helium–UF_6 mixture are 95 mol % helium and 5 mol % UF_6 (a typical mixture).

The feed pressure p naturally increases as the width w of the nozzle throat decreases. The three above-mentioned cost factors—all other conditions being equal—have a minimum as a function of the product pw. For example, with a ratio r = 4, the optimal p pressures of the typical mixture in separating elements of differing dimensions are approximately the following:

$$w(mm) = 0.4 \quad 0.2 \quad 0.03$$
$$p(mm\ Hg) = 48 \quad 80 \quad 600$$

The high incidence of suction volumes on costs pushes the selection of the inlet pressure p toward the higher values.

With an increase of the compression ratio, the cost factor, ζ_ϱ, decreases monotonically. Furthermore, the impact of the separating element on the total costs is far less than that of the suction volume and the energy consumption, both of which level off beyond r = 4. This proves to be the optimum value.

As we have already observed, the cut θ for the typical mixture is exactly determined by p and by r, given a specific geometry of the separation nozzle. Once the width w of the throat has been set, the cut will depend substantially on the distance of the knife blade from the curved wall of the groove. (see Fig. 3.12). The cut increases as that distance is shortened.

The value $\theta = \frac{1}{2}$ cannot, however, be obtained with just any scaling of the nozzle, and, if it is, it will not correspond to the optimum operating conditions. The possible ideal cascades are therefore asymmetrical in design, and the value $\theta = \frac{1}{3}$, which involves the insertion of the heads two stages forward and insertion of the tails one stage behind, is fairly close to optimum conditions for the separating element.

In passing through the nozzle the helium–UF_6 mixture also separates, and so, in the emerging fractions, there is a relative abundance of helium to UF_6 that is different from the input abundance.

THE SEPARATING ELEMENT

In the most recent version of the method, the grooves of the separation nozzle, 10 in number, are arranged equidistantly along the outer wall of a pipe, as can be seen in Fig. 8.1.

The pipe, which is made of aluminum, has an outside diameter of 10 cm and inside is divided into 10 sectors that alternatively constitute the feed and tail ducts for each of the nozzle grooves. The heads are ejected radially from the pipe and are brought together in a vessel that encloses several similar pipes arranged in bundles and fed in parallel. This entire assembly of tubes enclosed in the vessel essentially constitutes the separating element in this process.

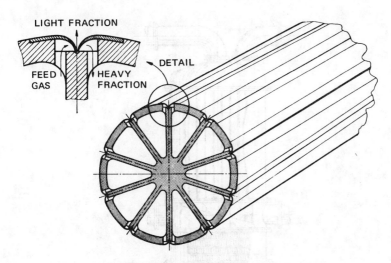

Fig. 8.1 Separation nozzle arrangement.

The detail of Fig. 8.1 shows that the nozzle device is built with two suitably shaped strips along the lip. These strips, which are of aluminum like the pipe, are press fitted by means of spacers into a swallow-tail seat. The typical length is 2 m. Calculation shows that nozzle devices of this type, if mass produced, would affect the specific investment cost of the plan by about $16 per kilogram of uranium (separative work) per year. Several variants of the nozzle device have been developed, whose optimum operating conditions cover the range of input pressures from 400 to 600 mm Hg.

At the German Institut für Kernverfahrenstechnik der Universität und des Kernforschungszentrum Karlsruhe, a prototype separation unit was built containing 81 tubes of the type described above. It has a separative power of about 2000 kg year^{-1}, which is roughly one-third of the separative power of the largest separating element in the U. S. diffusion plants. The feed flow is 100,000 m^3 of gas hr^{-1} at 150 mm Hg. Operating at capacity with the typical mixture, this corresponds to about 80,000 tons U year^{-1}. For plants that produce a few hundred tons per year of 2.4% ^{235}U-enriched uranium, each separating unit coincides with one of the lower stages of the cascade, which would, in practice, be a squared-off cascade.

The separating element was designed as an integrated unit into which are incorporated the compressor and the exchanger that carries off the compression heat. The design of the element is shown in Fig. 8.2. The bundle of separating tubes is placed in the upper part of the vessel, whereas the lower portion contains the heat exchanger with the compressor beneath it. On the bottom is a cylindrical extension of smaller diameter. This extension houses the electric motor that drives the compressor.

The depleted fraction L_s'' is collected at the upper header of the vessel and comes out through the eccentric pipe, while the central pipe is the entry for the tail L_{s+1}'' of

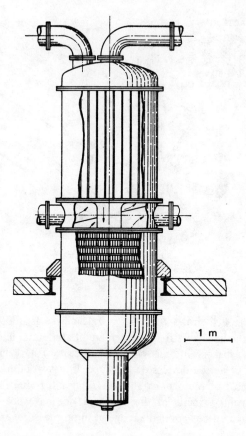

Fig. 8.2 Concentration diagram of a separation nozzle element.

the next stage. The central pipe continues with a conduit that traverses the entire separating element back to the compressor intake on the bottom. This conduit, as it passes through the vicinity of the bundle of separating tubes, has several apertures from which the enriched fraction, L'_S, is drawn off to mix with L''_{s+1}. After compression, the flow $L'_s + L''_{s+1}$ passes through the heat exchanger and is gathered in the median part of the vessel, from which it emerges through piping connected with the s+2 stage. An oblique diaphragm arranged in the median portion of the vessel, as is seen in the figure, divides the outlet collector from the inlet one, in which the feed gas L_s is distributed among the various separating tubes.

The compressor is a radial type with two stages (100,000 m³ hr⁻¹ at 150 mm Hg, with a compression ratio of 4), and the electric motor is designed for 300 cycles and 9000 rpm. The gas passes through the heat exchanger after each compression stage; each time its intake temperature is 40°C.

The separating element has a diameter of 2 m and an overall height of 7 m. The prototype is shown in Fig. 8.3. It was operated in closed circuit for experimental purposes. This is why, as is shown in the figure, the exit conduit of the tail (coming out of the side of the upper cover) is connected by elbows to the recycling conduit (coming into the center of the cover). Similarly the exit and input conduits for the median section of the separating element are connected in short circuit.

Fig. 8.3 Prototype of a separation nozzle element (2 tons δU year^{-1}).

THE CASCADE

The connection of the stages in a cascade does not involve a need to heat pipes or other parts of the plant. In fact, the maximum partial pressure of UF_6 in the process is 30 torrs and hence well below the sublimation pressure at ambient temperature (see Fig. 5.9).

However, flow control and therefore pressure control at all points of the cascade does call for particular attention.

It has already been shown that the passage of the helium–UF_6 mixture through the separation nozzle causes a variation, with respect to the feed, in the helium/UF_6 proportion in the head and in the tail.

Furthermore, in a square cascade, to which a stretch of ideal cascade is approximated in practice, the confluence of heads and recycled tails gives equal feed flows for all stages. This is also true for helium. The change in proportions in the gaseous helium–UF_6 mixture (the heads are far more depleted in UF_6 than are the tails) is felt only at the end of the cascade. The problem is solved by condensing the UF_6 and recycling the helium thus separated at the entry of the cascade.

In a small-scale 10-stage pilot plant at the Karlsruhe Kernforschungszentrum, condensation of the UF_6 is accomplished by alternately connecting with the gas line two traps cooled with liquid nitrogen. At the exit from the final stage, an additional compressor raises the pressure above the level set for feeding the stages.

Proper operation of the cascade requires control of the helium and UF_6 flow rates through each stage. Since these flows are determined substantially by the pressure and UF_6 concentration of the gas coming into the separation nozzle, pressure and concentration must be controlled by suitable adjustment of the cut of each stage.

Mechanical adjustment of the distance of the knife blade from the curved wall does not enable us to optimally adjust to the theoretical cut. A finer tuning of the cut can be obtained by varying the pressure p'' of the gas in the tail fraction. Within certain limits this does not involve any appreciable variations in the elementary separation factor.

The flow level can thus be maintained by means of a set valve for each stage, placed on the compressor intake line.

With their pilot plant, the Germans demonstrated the effectiveness of this control system. This means that there is no need for automatic control, in that the system is intrinsically stable. In fact, the responses of the compressor and the nozzle to variations in pressure and UF_6 concentration give rise to effects that compensate for each other.

It was also possible to show that the plant remains stable even with an inaccurate cut setting. Furthermore, variations of 10% in the reflux rate of UF_6 from the helium-separating unit at the top of the cascade cause no major disturbances. In the 10-stage pilot plant such disturbances (the most spectacular was a 3% pressure variation in the final stage) disappear beyond the fourth from the last stage.

Figure 8.4 is a diagram of a squared-off cascade with separation nozzle stages, with a total separative power of about 600 tons year^{-1}, or about one-tenth of one of the three diffusion cascades in existence in the United States. This value for separative power can be obtained with capacity operation throughout the entire year. The typical parameters of the process are shown in Table 8.1.

The low stages of the cascade are those described on pages 267 to 269, and the high stages (both in the enrichment and in the stripping sections) are of the same type, although scaled for a flow three times smaller.

The plant designed for 600 tons ΔU year^{-1} would consume about 400 MW of electric power. The energy consumption of the process would hence work out to

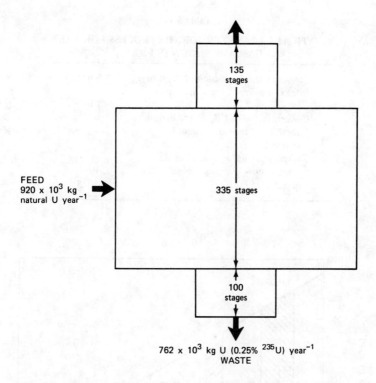

FEED
920 x 10³ kg
natural U year⁻¹

135 stages

335 stages

100 stages

762 x 10³ kg U (0.25% ²³⁵U) year⁻¹
WASTE

Fig. 8.4   Diagram of a squared-off cascade with separation nozzle stages.

about 6000 kWh/kg ΔU, which is at least twice that required for gaseous diffusion.

According to estimates made in 1971, the specific investment for a plant of 600 tons $\dot{\Delta}$U year⁻¹ would be about $160 per kilogram of total uranium separation per year. (About 60% of this sum is chargeable to the separation stages, including the compressors and heat exchangers.) Going on to larger plants (2500 tons ΔU year⁻¹ and over), the estimated values for specific investment drop below those for gaseous diffusion, but this advantage would not be enough today to make up for the higher energy consumption. It is felt that the separation nozzle process would be able to compete with gaseous diffusion on an industrial scale if it proved possible in the future to improve the separation factor, i.e., to raise it from 1.015 to 1.020.

The separation nozzle process, by comparison with the gaseous diffusion process, requires fewer stages and thus, from this viewpoint, as is shown in Fig. 8.5, holds an intermediate position between gaseous diffusion and centrifugation.

One advantage that the separation nozzle process has over the gaseous diffusion process is the shorter time needed to reach equilibrium. That time, as we know, is

Table 8.1

TYPICAL PARAMETERS OF THE PROCESS FOR THE
CASCADE SHOWN IN FIG. 8.4

Pressure forward of the nozzle, mm Hg	600
Intake pressure of the compressor, mm Hg	150
Concentration of UF_6 in the helium forward of the nozzle, mol %	5
Cut (for UF_6)	$\frac{1}{3}$
Temperature before and after the compressor−exchanger block, °C	40
Separation factor	1.015

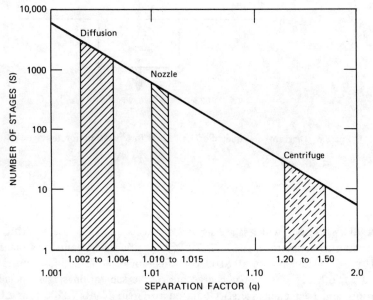

Fig. 8.5 Number of stages S required in three different processes for producing fully enriched uranium, with a separation factor q per stage.

directly proportional to the time the UF_6 spends in the plant and is inversely proportional to ϵ^2. Since the time spent is no higher in the nozzle plant, the equilibrium time is shorter by almost an order of magnitude and could be as much as 100 times shorter.

In the nozzle plant the production capacity and hence the electric power absorbed can be altered by about +20 and −30% with respect to the nominal value (by means of corresponding changes in pressure and temperature), without thereby incurring any major economic penalties. The short time to equilibrium also offers the possibility of temporarily shutting down the plant without any great losses. This plant flexibility is certainly advantageous insofar as the cost of the electric kilowatt-hour is concerned.

REFERENCES

1. E. W. Becker et al., Separation of the Isotopes of Uranium by the Separation-Nozzle Process, *Angew. Chem. Int. Ed. Engl.,* **6**: 507 (1967).
2. E. W. Becker, W. Bier, and R. Schütte, Principles and Economic Aspects of the Separation Nozzle Process, in Problems in the Separation of Uranium Isotopes, Proceedings of the Turin Symposium, 1968, p. 211, Comitato Nazionale per l'Energia Nucleare, Rome, 1968.
3. E. W. Becker, G. Frey, R. Schütte, and D. Seidel, Operation of a 10-Stage Separation-Nozzle Pilot Plant, *ibid.,* p. 225.
4. E. W. Becker et al., The Separation-Nozzle Process for Enrichment of ^{235}U, in *Proceedings of the Fourth International Conference on the Peaceful Uses of Atomic Energy, Geneva, 1971,* Vol. 9, p. 3, New York, 1972.
5. H. Mohrhauer, Status of Uranium Enrichment in Europe, *Atomwirt., Atomtech.,* **17**(6): 300-305 (June 1972).

9 WATER DISTILLATION

ELEMENTARY EFFECT

The elementary separation factor for deuterium separation by means of water distillation is written

$$q_0 = \frac{[N/(1-N)]}{[n(1-n)]} \tag{9.1}$$

in which N is the mol fraction of deuterium in the liquid phase, and n is the mol fraction in the vapor phase.

As was observed earlier, the water molecules, in relation to the two hydrogen isotopes H and D, constitute a ternary system made up of the H_2O, HDO, and D_2O species. If we designate the respective mol fractions in the liquid as N_0, N_1, and N_2, and the mol fractions in the vapor as n_0, n_1, and n_2, we have

$$N = \frac{1}{2}N_1 + N_2 \tag{9.2}$$

$$1 - N = \frac{1}{2}N_1 + N_0 \tag{9.3}$$

The deuterium is distributed between the two molecular species HDO and D_2O on the basis of the following exchange reaction:

$$H_2O + D_2O \rightleftharpoons 2HDO \tag{9.4}$$

If we assume a purely probabilistic distribution, the constant of equilibrium is the "classic" one; that is,

$$K = \frac{[HDO]^2}{[H_2O][D_2O]} = \frac{[N_1]^2}{[N_0][N_2]} = 4 \qquad (9.5)$$

quite independent of the temperature. From Eq. 9.5 we find that

$$N_1 = 2(N_0 N_2)^{1/2} \qquad (9.6)$$

The system of equations made up of Eqs. 9.2, 9.3, and 9.6 enables us to express N_0, N_1, and N_2 as functions of N, as is shown graphically in Fig. 9.1.

So if we write the equations analogous to Eqs. 9.2 and 9.3 for the vapor phase, Eq. 9.1 becomes

$$q_0 = \frac{N_1 + 2N_2}{N_1 + 2N_0} \times \frac{n_1 + 2n_0}{n_1 + 2n_2} \qquad (9.7)$$

Now assume that the vapor phase obeys the law of perfect gases and that the liquid is an ideal solution. Using Dalton's law and Raoult's law will give us

$$p = N_0 \overline{p}_0 + N_1 \overline{p}_1 + N_2 \overline{p}_2 \qquad (9.8)$$

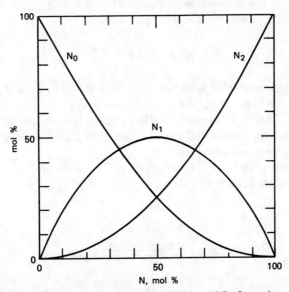

Fig. 9.1 Mol fractions N_0, N_1, and N_2 of the H_2O, HDO, and D_2O species as a function of N [mol fraction $D/(H+D)$].

in which p is the total pressure, whereas $\bar{p}_0$, $\bar{p}_1$, and $\bar{p}_2$ are the vapor pressures for the three components H_2O, HDO, and D_2O.

Hence the corresponding mol fractions in the vapor are

$$n_0 = \frac{N_0 \bar{p}_0}{p}; \quad n_1 = \frac{N_1 \bar{p}_1}{p}; \quad n_2 = \frac{N_2 \bar{p}_2}{p} \tag{9.9}$$

There is no way to make direct measurement of the vapor pressure in the HDO, which cannot be obtained in the pure state. Let us suppose that

$$\bar{p}_1 = (\bar{p}_0 \bar{p}_2)^{\frac{1}{2}} \tag{9.10}$$

With these hypotheses and the substitution of Eqs. 9.9 and 9.10 in Eq. 9.7, the latter becomes

$$q_0 = \frac{2(N_0 N_2)^{\frac{1}{2}} + 2N_2}{2(N_0 N_2)^{\frac{1}{2}} + 2N_0} \times \frac{2(\bar{p}_0 \bar{p}_2 N_0 N_2)^{\frac{1}{2}} + 2\bar{p}_0 N_0}{2(\bar{p}_0 \bar{p}_2 N_0 N_2)^{\frac{1}{2}} + 2\bar{p}_2 N_2}$$

$$= \frac{(N_2)^{\frac{1}{2}}}{(N_0)^{\frac{1}{2}}} \times \frac{(\bar{p}_0 N_0)^{\frac{1}{2}}}{(\bar{p}_2 N_2)^{\frac{1}{2}}} = \left(\frac{\bar{p}_0}{\bar{p}_2}\right)^{\frac{1}{2}} \tag{9.11}$$

And so the separation factor proves to be independent of the concentration level.

Since the vapor pressures of H_2O and D_2O depend in different ways on the temperature, there is a considerable temperature dependency of q_0. This dependency can be expressed by means of the empirical equation

$$q_0 = 0.866 \, e^{63.3/T} \tag{9.12}$$

which will yield q_0 values that agree well with those shown in Table 3.1.

It was shown in Chap. 3 that the square root of $\bar{p}_1/\bar{p}_2$ is 1.052 at 50°C but drops to 1.026 at 100°C. The slight elementary effect and the low concentration of deuterium in natural water ($N_0 = 1.5 \times 10^{-4}$) mean that distillation cascades will have many stages and a very large overall volume.

With optimum enrichment per stage ($\epsilon = g_0/2$), the number of stages required at 50°C to obtain water at $N_P = 99.75\%$ is

$$S = \frac{\ln \dfrac{99.75}{0.0025 \times 0.015}}{0.026} = 600$$

It is readily shown that almost 95% of the separation work is done by bringing the mol fraction of deuterium to about 1%, which will require about 170 stages.

Assuming that a column is being operated at 50°C, with a relative yield $\rho = 0.7$, the steam required per unit of product is

$$\frac{L''}{PN_P} = \frac{1}{\rho g_0 N_0} = 190,000 \, \frac{\text{mol vap.}}{\text{mol } D_2O}$$

which works out to about 170,000 kg of steam per kilogram of D_2O. A representative figure for steam consumption to obtain heavy water in practically pure form is about 200,000 kg of steam per kilogram of D_2O.

PLATE COLUMNS

A classic type of distillation column is the bubble-cap column. The operating principle of such a column is shown in Fig. 9.2, which illustrates two successive plates.

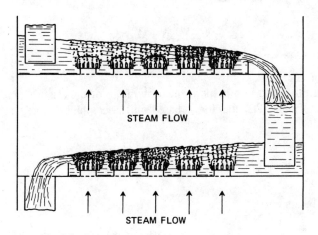

Fig. 9.2 Operating principle of a bubble-cap column.

The steam, after bubbling through the water head of one plate, rises to the one above it. Meanwhile the water runs from one plate to the one below by overflowing on the edge of a dam. Moving from top to bottom, the water is enriched in the less volatile components, to wit HDO and D_2O.

The plates in such a column may be viewed as so many separating elements in a square cascade. The standard plate s in a column is shown schematically in Fig. 9.3, which also shows the mol fractions in the liquid and in the steam both at the inlet and at the outlet.

If the time of contact between liquid and vapor in each individual plate were infinite, we would have

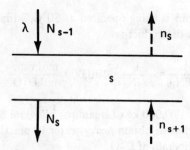

Fig. 9.3 Diagram of a typical plate in a column. λ = water to steam mol ratio; N = deuterium mol fraction in water; n = deuterium mol fraction in steam.

$$N_s^* - n_s^* = (q_0 - 1) N(1 - N) \tag{9.13}$$

and the enrichment obtainable with a column of S plates would be found by integrating the transport equation

$$\frac{dN}{ds} = g_0 N(1 - N) - \frac{P}{L''}(N_P - N) \tag{9.14}$$

as was shown on page 109.

The calculation could also be performed by means of the classical graphic method of McCabe and Thiele. The method is based on the combination of two curves, the "operating line"

$$n_{s+1} = \frac{L'}{L''} N_s - \frac{P}{L''} N_P \tag{9.15}$$

and the "equilibrium curve"

$$n_{s+1} = \frac{N_{s+1}}{1 + g_0(1 - N_{s+1})} \tag{9.16}$$

The operating straight line expresses the mass balance of the desired isotope in the portion of the column from plate s+1 to the bottom.

As shown in Fig. 9.4, the number of stages constructed between the operating straight line and the equilibrium curve gives the number of plates required to move from the top concentration N_0 to the bottom concentration N_P.

However, when $L'/L'' \simeq 1$ and $q_0 \simeq 1$ (a situation that is quite frequent in isotope separation), the graphic method is not very convenient to handle, and so analytical or numerical approaches are preferable.

In the case of low concentrations, the equilibrium curve is also reduced to a straight line:

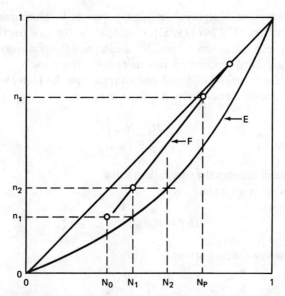

Fig. 9.4 McCabe–Thiele graph for calculating the number of plates in a column: E = equilibrium curve; F = operating line.

$$n_{s+1} = \frac{1}{q_0} N_{s+1} \qquad (9.17)$$

Substituting Eq. 9.17 in Eq. 9.15, we have

$$N_{s+1} - q_0 \lambda N_s = -q_0 \phi \qquad (9.18)$$

where we have set $\lambda = L'/L''$ and $\phi = PN_P/L''$. Integrating Eq. 9.18 with the boundary condition $N(0) = N_0$, we have

$$N_P = \left(N_0 - \frac{q_0 \phi}{q_0 \lambda - 1} \right) [q_0 \lambda]^S + \frac{q_0 \phi}{q_0 \lambda - 1} \qquad (9.19)$$

In fact, the limited time of contact between liquid and steam in the single plate means that the separation attainable with a "real" plate is less than that of the "theoretical" plate discussed on pages 277 to 279. We can allow for this by defining a suitable efficiency factor.

Note first of all that, for a bubble-cap plate like that shown in Fig. 9.2, it is possible to define a point efficiency

$$\beta_0 = \frac{n - n''}{n - n^*} \qquad (9.20)$$

which is also known as Murphree's efficiency [see E. V. Murphree, *Industrial and Engineering Chemistry*, 17: 747 (1925)], in which n is the mol fraction in the steam entering a bubble-cap plate, and n'' and N^* are the mol fractions leaving a bubble-cap plate in the real and ideal (infinite contact time) cases, respectively.

When there is a crossflow of liquid and steam across the plate, we can define for the plate a Murphree efficiency factor $\beta > \beta_0$ as the ratio:

$$\beta = \frac{N_s + N_{s-1}}{N_s^* - N_{s-1}} \tag{9.21}$$

in which the asterisk denotes the equilibrium value.

Isotope mass balance on plate s gives

$$\lambda(N_s^* - N_{s-1}) = n_{s-1} - n_s^* \tag{9.22}$$

and in the case of low concentrations is

$$N_s^* = q_0 n_s^* \tag{9.23}$$

Placing Eqs. 9.22 and 9.23 into Eq. 9.21, we find

$$\beta = \frac{(N_s - N_{s-1})(1 + q_0\lambda)}{q_0 n_{s+1} - N_{s-1}} \tag{9.24}$$

which, when combined with the mass balance equation (Eq. 9.15) made uniform in notation, gives us

$$N_s[1 + q_0\lambda(1 - \beta)] - N_{s-1}[q_0\lambda + (1 - \beta)] = -\beta q_0\lambda \tag{9.25}$$

The solution to this equation with finite differences, written for $s = S_r$, is

$$N_P = \left(N_0 - \frac{q_0\phi}{q_0\lambda - 1}\right)\left[\frac{q_0\lambda + (1 - \beta)}{1 + q_0\lambda(1 - \beta)}\right]^{S_r} + \frac{q_0\phi}{q_0\lambda - 1} \tag{9.26}$$

When this last equation is compared with Eq. 9.19, we see that the number of real plates S_r, corresponding to S number of theoretical plates, is

$$S_r = S \frac{\log q_0\lambda}{\log \dfrac{q_0\lambda + (1 - \beta)}{1 + q_0\lambda(1 - \beta)}} \tag{9.27}$$

When $q_0\lambda = 1$, Eq. 9.27 takes the simpler form

$$S_r = S\left(\frac{2}{\beta} - 1\right) \tag{9.28}$$

In this way it is shown that, for $\beta = 0.50$, the number of real plates necessary to perform a given separation is three times as great as the number of theoretical plates. For $\beta = 0.70$, the number of real plates is 86% higher. Sometimes the mean efficiency of real plates is called simply the S/S_r ratio.

The distance H between two successive real plates is determined by various requirements having to do with the flow of the two phases, liquid and vapor, and above all by the need to make sure that small droplets of water carried along by the steam do not entail a very considerable decline in efficiency.

In practice, in water distillation with bubble-cap plates, the H dimension used is about 30 cm.

Another quantity with which separation efficiency is sometimes expressed is the height of the equivalent theoretical plate (HETP). From what was shown above,

$$HETP = H\frac{S_r}{S} \qquad (9.29)$$

For the earlier case with $\beta = 0.70$, HETP = 60 cm. This is a fairly representative value for water distillation with bubble-cap plates.

With Eq. 9.19 the calculation of the enrichment $a = N_P/N_0$, obtainable with a certain number of plates S, is referred to the hypothesis of an elementary separation factor $q = q_0$, which remains constant over the length of the column. This is not realistic, given the considerable pressure drop along the column. So we have a dependency of q on s:

$$q_s = q_0 \left(\frac{p_0}{p_s}\right)^c \qquad (9.30)$$

with c = constant.

It is shown[7] that the enrichment, in the case of low concentrations, is given by

$$a = 1 + (1 - \rho) g_0 \int_0^S \exp \left[\int_0^s (\lambda q_s - 1)ds\right] ds \qquad (9.31)$$

in which ρ is the relative yield and q_s is given by Eq. 9.30.

As an example, let us take the case of a column with a top pressure $p_0 = 68.4$ torrs ($q_0 = 1.0564$), from which we want to obtain the enrichment $a = 21.5$. In the case $q_0 = $ constant, Eq. 9.19 gives us S = 56, whereas Eqs. 9.30 and 9.31, using $\Delta p = 5.5$ torrs for a theoretical plate, give us S = 67.

Other types of columns, which are of simpler construction, are those incorporating sieve plates. The individual plate consists essentially of a metallic sheet with regular perforations designed to provide the steam with a given transit area. The steam is bubbled through the liquid, forming a sort of froth or foam. Under good operating conditions the level of the foam must keep a distance of at least 2 to 3 cm from the bottom of the plate above.

The movement of the liquid from one plate to the plate beneath it varies for different plate designs. The plate may, for example, be divided into sectors with an opening for the liquid to flow out of each sector. In another variant the liquid moves in a pulsed mode through the same openings used by the steam but alternates with the bursts of steam. Then there are variants in which the liquid is caused to move horizontally over the individual plate.

In sieve-plate columns with independent liquid-effluent apertures, it is possible to achieve an HETP of 30 cm or even less. On the other hand, those plates in which liquid and steam pass through the same holes are as a rule not quite so efficient. A typical value for water distillation with sieve plates is HETP = 45 cm.

PACKED COLUMNS

As was mentioned in Chap. 3, in packed columns the transfer of the less volatile component from the vapor phase to the liquid phase takes place in a continuous mode along the column rather than in a discrete mode as in the plate column.

The quantity of the desired isotope transferred in a unit of time from the steam (in which it is present at mol fraction n) to the liquid across the unit of interface between the two phases is given by

$$\phi = k(N^* - N) \tag{9.32}$$

in which k is the mass-transfer coefficient and N^* is the concentration of the liquid in equilibrium with the vapor, so that for $g_0 \ll 1$

$$N^* - n \cong g_0 N(1 - N) \tag{9.33}$$

In the segment dz of the column, the variation dN in the mol fraction then becomes

$$L'dN = k(N^* - N) \times \sigma \, dz \tag{9.34}$$

in which L' is the mol flow rate of the liquid and σ is the contact surface per unit of column height. Equation 9.34 can also be written

$$h \frac{dN}{dz} = N^* - N \tag{9.35}$$

where we have set

$$h = \frac{L'}{k\sigma}$$

From Eq. 9.35 we see that the column height required to perform a given separation is

$$Z = h \int_{N_0}^{N_P} \frac{dN}{N^* - N} = h \frac{N_P - N_0}{\Delta^* N} \qquad (9.36)$$

in which $\Delta^* N$ is the logarithmic mean of the "driving force" $N^* - N$ along the column.

The quantity Z/h expresses the height of the column in "transfer units," and hence h takes on the name of height of a "transfer unit" (HTU). From Eq. 9.36 we see that h represents that segment of the column in which the axial concentration difference $N_{z+h} - N_z$ equals the mean "driving force."

Since Eq. 9.33 holds good for $g_0 \ll 1$, Eq. 9.35 can be written in the form

$$h \frac{dN}{dz} = g_0 N(1 - N) - \frac{P}{L''} (N_P - N) \qquad (9.37)$$

By comparison with Eq. 9.14, we see that in this case $s = z/h$, which means that HETP and HTU coincide. This is not true, however, in the general case of any q_0 whatever.

For calculating packed columns, it is better to use the HTU rather than the HETP since the former is independent of q_0 and constitutes a measure of the mass-transfer efficiency.

Equation 9.34 does not take into account any axial flow in the direction opposite to that of the concentration gradient. Allowing for this lets the HTU be written as

$$h = h_r + h_a$$

and thus the purely transversal term h_r is compounded with the corrective axial term h_a.

In distillation processes, diffusion in the axial direction—except for special cases of extremely low steam velocities—plays a relatively minor role. A very large contribution may be given to the h_a term, however, by poor transverse distribution of the flow, which causes bypasses with consequent mixing. This is felt the more keenly as the diameter of the column increases, which in turn imposes a set of real practical limits on diameter. In water distillation, for example, using Raschig rings as packing, we dare not go beyond a diameter of about 1 m.

If we are to obtain satisfactory flow distribution, the ratio between the diameter of the column and the diameter of each individual packing body must not be less than 8 : 1.

When water is distilled with Raschig ceramic rings, measuring 15 by 15 by 2 mm, we have an HTU of 20 cm. Spraypak is a "well-ordered" type of packing, as opposed to "random" type packings.[10] The Spraypak is obtained from metallic sheets that have slits cut into them, and the sheets are then stretched, fan pleated, and piled one on top of the other so as to form a cellular structure. Typical values of h for this and other types of columns are shown in Table 9.1.

Here we shall merely mention the existence of high-efficiency packings, which are now used only in a laboratory because of their high cost. Among them are Dixon rings

Table 9.1

DATA ON PLATE AND PACKED COLUMNS

	Bubble-cap plates* (H = 30 cm)	Sieve plates (H = 12.5 cm)	Raschig rings (15 by 15 by 2 mm)	Spraypak No. 5
h, m	0.4	0.4	0.2	0.6
v_{fl}, m sec^{-1}	1.1	2.1	1.1	5.4
h (dp/dz), torrs	5	3 to 4	3	4.5

*We assume a diameter of 4 m.

(metal gauze) and Helipak elements (square-section spirals) that can give an HETP as small as a few millimeters. Similar results can be achieved with film distillation. The column (a typical one is that designed by Kuhn[11]) consists of a bundle of tubes. Inside each tube the liquid flows downward against the flow of the steam, forming a film along the wall.

In all packed columns the efficiency increases if the columns are completely wetted down by flooding at the start of operation. However this procedure must be repeated after each interruption of operation, and this involves some considerations having to do with mixing problems.

COLUMN DIMENSIONS

The column height required to perform a given separation is calculated according to the procedures explained on pages 277 to 284. The diameter of the column is determined by the need to establish an optimum value for the linear velocity or the mass velocity of the steam.

Let us consider first a bubble plate column. The efficiency of the contact between water and vapor on a plate depends to a large degree upon the agitation caused by the steam in its passage through the liquid on the plate. The efficiency of the plate is thus to a considerable degree a function of the steam velocity. When the velocity is too low, the plate efficiency ratings are also low. This phenomenon is due to a decline in the level of liquid in the plates in that, because of the low steam pressure drop, a good part of the liquid passes through the bubble-cap openings and falls onto the underlying plate. At higher velocities the plate efficiency is heightened, thanks to better contact between the two phases. At velocities that are too high, however, efficiency falls off

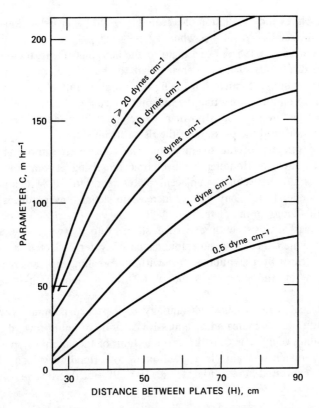

Fig. 9.5 Behavior of the parameter C as a function of the distance H between plates and of the surface tension σ. (After Brown.[5])

because the steam begins a process of picking up and carrying the liquid along with it. Furthermore the steam, instead of splitting up in small bubbles as it comes out of the bubble cap, emerges in bulky slugs and displaces the liquid.

The highest plate efficiency is found in an intermediate velocity range, one for which the following equation, which links the mass velocity ϕ of the steam to the characteristics of the plates and of the flowing material, applies:

$$\phi = C[\rho_v(\rho_\varrho - \rho_v)]^{\frac{1}{2}} \tag{9.38}$$

where ϕ is expressed in kilograms per hour per square meter, C is a parameter depending on the spacing of the plates and the surface tension of the liquid on the plate, and ρ_ϱ and ρ_v are the densities of the liquid and the steam in kilograms per cubic meter.

The values for the C parameter are shown in Fig. 9.5 as a function of the distance between plates and of surface tension. Therefore, with the predetermined spacing between the plates and calculation of ϕ from Eq. 9.38, the cross section of the column results from the relation $A = L''/\phi$, where $L'' = PN_P/g_0 \rho N_0$.

If the steam is to rise from one plate to the next higher one, there must naturally be a pressure difference such as to ensure that the bubbles can pass through the caps and the layer of liquid. Similarly, if the liquid is to drop to the next lower plate, there must be in the conduit connecting the two plates (see Fig. 9.2) a water head sufficient to guarantee the pressure boost, which overcomes the conduit's resistance to the downcoming water and the pressure of the rising steam.

When the velocity of the steam within the column rises too high, there is the phenomenon known as flooding. To overcome the rising pressure of the steam, the connecting conduit between the adjacent plates tends to fill with liquid; when the conduit is completely full, any further increase in steam flow produces an increase in the level of the liquid on the plate.

In the final analysis, with excessive steam velocity we arrive at a situation (flooding) in which there is a superabundance of water collected in the plates. The steam passes through the bubble caps without breaking up, emerging from each of them as a jet and carrying some of the liquid along with it on its upward path.

This same situation applies substantially to a packed column as well, in which flooding conditions are indicated by a massive carry-up of liquid toward the top.

The flooding velocity is thus the extreme limit of the column's operating interval. The nominal operation value is a fraction of the flooding velocity and can even sometimes be expressed in percentages, e.g., 50 to 90% of flooding velocity.

TYPICAL COLUMN PARAMETERS

In consideration of the economics of the process, the most important parameters for any column are (1) efficiency (h; HETP or HTU), (2) steam mass velocity referred to the actual cross-section, (3) liquid content per plate (holdup), and (4) pressure drop per plate.

Obviously it is desirable to have high values for parameters 1 and 2 and low ones for parameters 3 and 4. Since such requirements are, as a rule, conflicting, the best move is to seek a reasonable compromise.

The equilibrium time is determined by the ratio between holdup and flow rate, and so, instead of the absolute holdup, the parameter to remember is rather that ratio (called the "holdup factor") or its inverse, the "efficiency factor."

The pressure drop is usually referred to the theoretical plate, and in this way we allow implicitly for process efficiency. A few of the values for HETP and HTU obtainable with various kinds of columns are shown in Table 9.1.

As for the steam mass velocity, it is advisable first of all to note that it is substantially determined by the free cross section available for its passage. For example, in bubble-cap plates the free section is 10 to 15% of the total, whereas with sieve plates it is 15 to 25%. The Spraypak packing offers a far higher free section, 40 to 45% of the total section. This fact constitutes (more than the HETP, which is not particularly low) the main attraction of this packing, which allows twice the specific throughput and hence a cross section roughly half that of a sieve-plate column. Another advantage of Spraypak is its constant transverse redistribution of the liquid, which makes this kind of packing efficient even at relatively large diameters.

Some comparative data for sieve-plate and packed columns are shown in Table 9.1. These data refer to water distillation at 1 atm pressure, with a steam velocity that is at 90% of the flooding velocity.

Recently a new type of packing called Polpack[12] was devised. It consists of helicoidal metallic strips. Reportedly it has an HETP of 0.25 m and a Δp of 0.7 torr per theoretical plate, with a steam velocity $v = 2.8$ m sec^{-1}.

The flooding velocity varies with pressure according to the equation

$$v_{fl} = \frac{v_{flo}}{p^{1/2}} \qquad (9.39)$$

in which v_{flo} is referred to $p = 1$ atm.

At equal pressures the comparison among various types of columns is made by means of the parameter

$$\frac{\phi}{h} = \frac{p}{RT} \times \frac{v}{h}$$

which expresses the steam load per unit volume of the theoretical plate. Clearly it is advantageous to get high values for v/h.

ENERGY CONSUMPTION

In the simplest plant design, shown in Fig. 9.6(a), all the steam that passes through the distillation column is condensed at the withdrawal point.

With a relative yield ρ from the column, the quantity of steam per unit of product, as was shown on page 277, is $L''/PN_P = 1/\rho g_0 N$, and hence the energy consumption is

$$E_0 = \frac{\lambda}{\rho g N_0} \qquad (9.40)$$

in which λ is the heat of evaporation. At 50°C, E_0 is approximately 110,000 kWh/kg D_2O.

The diagram shown in Fig. 9.6(b), however, makes it possible to reutilize the residual enthalpy of the steam emerging from the column, compressing it by means of a steam compressor and sending it back into the evaporator that supplies the column.

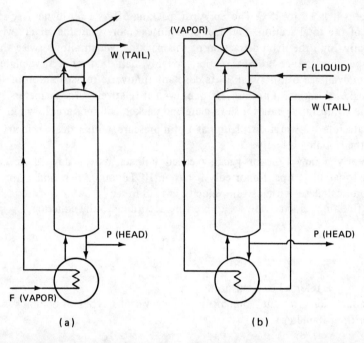

Fig. 9.6 Thermodynamic diagrams for a water distillation column: (a) with condensation at column top; (b) with steam compression.

In this way the process is made reversible to a greater degree, and the compressor must supply only the energy required to compensate primarily for two of the causes of irreversibility: (1) pressure drop in the column, and (2) the temperature drop in the evaporator and in other heat exchangers.

Let us consider point 1. The availability loss derived from the pressure drop across a theoretical plate is given by

$$w_p = T_0 L'' \Delta s \qquad (9.41)$$

in which T_0 is the temperature at the column exit and Δs is the increment of mol entropy of the steam through the plate. So, in the perfect gas approximation, we have

$$\Delta_s = \left(\frac{ds}{dp}\right)_T \Delta p = \frac{R}{p} h \frac{dp}{dz} \qquad (9.42)$$

The loss of availability per unit of separative work therefore turns out to be

$$\xi_p = \frac{w_p}{\delta U} = \frac{4RT_0 h(dp/dz)/p}{g_0^2} \qquad (9.43)$$

With $T_0 = 50°C$ and $h(dp/dz)/p = 0.035$, we have $\xi_p \cong 2$ kWh/kg H_2O. To produce 99.8% heavy water from natural water, we will need separative work $\Delta U/PN_P = 6000$ kg H_2O/kg D_2O, and so the loss of availability per unit of product comes to

$$E_p = \xi_p \Delta U/PN_P \cong 12{,}000 \text{ kWh/kg } D_2O$$

This comparison with E_0 shows that we can have energy consumption lower by an order of magnitude. We must not forget, however, that we are dealing in the first case with thermal energy and in the second case with energy absorbed in the form of mechanical or electrical, and hence more expensive, energy.

Another process aimed at efficient thermodynamic utilization has been suggested by Benedict and Pigford.[14] The process calls for placing the column between the exit of a turbine for electric-power production and the condenser. This would give availability loss corresponding to the pressure jump between the turbine (e.g., 1.5 atm) and the condenser (e.g., 0.1 atm). There would be an advantage over the arrangement in Fig. 9.6(b), in that the theoretical work of compression would be multiplied, rather than divided, for the efficiency factor. In addition, a condenser already required for the electricity-generating plant could be used.

OPERATING PRESSURE

The key parameter in the process is the pressure (or temperature) of condensation. The pressure to a large degree governs costs, either through g (and hence through δU) or through the unit costs proportional to $L''S$, i.e., through the c_1 factor in Eq. 4.148:

$$\frac{1}{\rho}(Sc_1 + c_2)$$

The incidence of the capital cost relative to the column on the total cost is determined by the quantity

$$\zeta_c' = \frac{hL''RT/vp}{\delta U} = \frac{4\,hRT}{p\,g^2 v} \tag{9.44}$$

which expresses the volume of column per unit of separative power.

We can assume that h does not vary appreciably with pressure and that the dependence of v is given by Eq. 9.39. We have $1/g^2\,p^{1/2}$ minimum for

$$g_{opt.} = 4p\frac{\partial g}{\partial p} \tag{9.45}$$

Furthermore, recalling Eqs. 3.9 and 3.10, we find that

$$g = g_1 - \nu \ln p \tag{9.46}$$

in which g_1 is the separation factor at 1 atm and $\nu = (\lambda_2 - \lambda_1)/\lambda_1 = 0.0113$ in the interval 0.02 to 2 atm. This gives

$$g_{opt.} = 4\nu = 0.045 \tag{9.47}$$

and so

$$p^*_{opt.} = e^{(\epsilon_1/\nu)-4} = 0.183 \text{ atm} \tag{9.48}$$

or 140 mm Hg (59°C). So this is the optimum pressure in the extreme case of a very costly packing, whose costs are found to be determining in the economy of the process.

Going on to consider the influence of pressure on energy consumption, we see that it can be expressed by means of the equation

$$E = E_p + E_Q = \frac{c}{g\rho p}\left(\frac{\Delta p_h}{g}\ln\frac{a-\rho}{1-\rho} + \Delta p_Q\right) \tag{9.49}$$

in which Δp_h is the pressure drop per theoretical plate, Δp_Q is the pressure drop corresponding to the temperature drop in the evaporator, and c is a constant.

Equation 9.49 must be minimized if we wish to cut to a minimum the incidence of energy consumption on total cost.

The minimum is found when

$$g^2_{opt.} - (\nu - \pi)g_{opt.} - 2\nu\pi = 0 \tag{9.50}$$

where we have set $\pi = (\Delta p_h/\Delta p_Q)\ln[(a-\rho)/(1-\rho)]$. For relatively small Δp_h levels $\pi \cong 0$, and hence $g_{opt.} = \nu$. From Eq. 9.46 and bearing in mind Eq. 9.48, we then find

$$p_{opt.} = e^{(g/\nu)-1} = e^3(p^*_{opt.}) \tag{9.51}$$

If, on the other hand Δp_Q is negligible, we find $g_{opt.} = 2\nu$, and so

$$p_{opt.} = e^{(g/\nu)-2} = e^2(p^*_{opt.}) \tag{9.52}$$

An economic assessment is needed for accurate determination of $p_{opt.}$, but when we examine the shift from the minima of ζ'_c, E_p, and E_Q as a function of g/ν, we find that, for $g/\nu = 2$ where E_p is minimal, the other two quantities have not grown excessively either.

Thus the optimum pressure will not be too different from Eq. 9.52, that is $p_{opt.} \cong 1.3$ atm. In other words, at pressures between 1 and 2 atm, the steam-compression ratio is about 1.5 as against the ratio of ~10 that we obtain at 1/10 atm, and also the mass velocities are greater. This is more than enough to compensate for the effect of the lower separation factor.

Bebbington and Thayer[16] calculated that, for a plant with 1.2 atm of pressure at the top of the columns and with steam compression, the energy consumption would be about 8800 kWh/kg D_2O.

COLUMNS IN A CASCADE

Since the quantity of steam involved is very large, as is the number of stages, it is clearly a sound idea to approximate the ideal cascade by means of a squared-off cascade.

The general criteria for choosing the dimensions for a cascade are those set forth on pages 145 to 148. The first step in the cascade may be too wide to consist of a single column. The maximum column diameter achieved until now is about 13 m. This means that we may need several columns in parallel. In the first stages it is best to install columns of equal height.

The number of stages per step runs into a limitation in the form of the tolerable pressure drop in the column. In the calculation process, should the column turn out to be too high in relation to the diameter, it can be divided in half (see the first two stages in Fig. 9.7). In this case, the upper half will have the larger diameter since the average pressure will be lower.

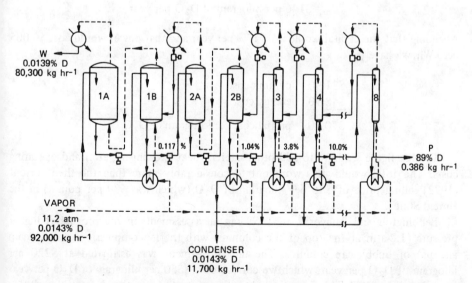

Fig. 9.7 Schematic drawing of the Morgantown, W. Va. (USA), primary distillation plant.

Each stage is equipped with a reboiler in which there is evaporation of a fraction of the liquid flow coming from the previous stage (see Fig. 9.7). Because of the pressure difference between the top and bottom of the column, the steam coming out of the column must be condensed before it can be recycled into the bottom of the preceding stage.

PROCESS ECONOMY

An evaluation of the process with Spraypak packing and utilization of steam at 234 torrs coming from the turbine discharge was made in 1957 by Benedict and Pigford.[14] The column cost was estimated at $70 per cubic meter, and the volume required to produce 1 kg of D_2O annually was 1.3 m^3. This gives an investment per unit of product equal to

$$V_c = \$91 \text{ per kilogram of } D_2O \text{ per year}$$

Energy consumption was assessed at

$$E = 9630 \text{ kWh/kg } D_2O$$

Making a 60% correction for cost escalation [*Chemical Engineering*, **13**: 169(November 1972)], we have

$$V_c = \$146 \text{ per kilogram of } D_2O \text{ per year}$$

Assuming that the capital would cost 15% per year and that power would cost $0.005 per kWh, we have

$$
\begin{array}{ll}
\$21.90 & \text{column cost} \\
\underline{\$48.10} & \text{energy cost} \\
\$70.00 & \text{partial cost per kilogram of } D_2O
\end{array}
$$

To this figure we have to add other capital (heat exchangers, etc.) and operating costs. The total would thus work out to considerably more than the then current (1972) selling price of $86 per kilogram of D_2O (which was $39 per pound) in the United States.

Bebbington and Thayer[16] in 1958 ran an assessment on the process at higher pressure (1.2 atm at the top of the columns) with thermocompression of the steam and use of bubble-cap columns. The unit investment was estimated at $220 per kilogram of D_2O per year, which we corrected to $350 per kilogram of D_2O per year to update it to 1972. This figure included all equipment (even the electrolytic cells for the final enrichment) but not the power plant [1 kW/(kg D_2O year^{-1})]. Energy consumption, as we have already said, was estimated at 8800 kWh/kg D_2O.

With the same economic parameters as in the preceding example, we then find:

$52.50	capital cost
$44.00	energy cost
$96.50	partial cost per kilogram of D_2O

To this figure we must add a quota, albeit a small one, for operating costs. In any case, the cost is higher than the quoted price of $86 per kilogram of D_2O. Use of highly efficient columns might possibly bring the production costs down to more acceptable levels.

As of now, water distillation is applied only in a limited fashion to the final enrichment of preconcentrates. In this way the economic limitations are not so painful, whereas there are technical advantages to be derived from the method, most particularly its simplicity of operation.

A recent study[17] tends to look more kindly on water distillation, even as a basic process. The improvements called for are a high-efficiency packing (Polpack) and a design for multiple-effect steam utilization. In a series of columns in parallel, each one receives the heat of evaporation of the steam emerging from the column next to it. The steam absorbed in the process is said to correspond to a consumption of 37,500 kW(t)h/kg D_2O.

PLANTS

The only primary production plants we know of are the three built in the United States during World War II. Total planned production was about 27 tons D_2O annually. However, only half that much was actually produced because the bubble-cap plates in the columns were defective owing to hasty construction. The plants were shut down after 2 years of operation.

The smallest of the three plants (built at Morgantown, W. Va.) was designed for 4.3 tons D_2O year^{-1} and was the most efficient, producing 3 tons D_2O year^{-1}. Figure 9.7 shows a schematic diagram of the plant, and some construction and operational data are given in Table 9.2.

The columns in the stages from No. 4 on were packed columns with Raschig ceramic rings 16 mm in diameter. After a few modifications the efficiency of the bubble-cap plates was raised to 75% from a lower starting level. Equilibrium time was 90 days. The product [89 mol % D/(H + D)] was further enriched by electrolysis.

The primary exchange-reaction plants, which will be discussed in Chap. 12, enrich the water to an intermediate concentration of 10 to 40%. Further enrichment is done by vacuum distillation. When the work is done under low pressure, there is also

Table 9.2

FEATURES OF THE MORGANTOWN, W. VA., DISTILLATION PLANT

Stage	Columns in parallel	Diameter, cm	Number of plates	Column volume, m³	Steam load, kg hr⁻¹	Pressure, mm Hg		Deuterium concentration bottom, %
						Top	Bottom	
1 A	5	458	80	2,000	80,000	67	238	
1 B	5	366	90	1,440	80,000	238	536	0.117
2 A	1	320	72	175	9,600	129	340	
2 B	1	244	83	118	9,600	340	645	1.04
3	1	101	72	17.3	1,380	124	343	3.8
4	1	46	72*	3.6	330	127	440	10.0
5	1	25	72*		86	127	340	11.5
6	1	25	72*		84	124	328	21.2
7	1	25	72*	4.4	90	124	333	56.4
8	1	25	72*		90	127	308	89
Total	18		757	3,760	91,630			

*Equivalent theoretical plates.

the advantage of cutting down on leaks that are particularly harmful at high concentrations.

In the secondary distillation plants, there is also a stripping section whose tailings (the light fraction) are channeled back into the primary plant. The tailing concentration is kept fairly low (a few percent) to minimize losses in transfer.

At the Savannah River facilities in South Carolina, two distillation plants were built for final concentration, starting with 10% D_2O and returning water at 7% to the primary plant. Each unit consists of six columns in series, the first two of which are actually one column divided in half, with a single reboiler. The feed is introduced at the bottom of the first half. Each of the two units (one is now used to upgrade the depleted water after use in reactors) has a production capacity of about 250 tons D_2O year⁻¹.

The schematic diagram of a Savannah River distillation unit is shown in Fig. 9.8, and Table 9.3 shows some construction and design features.

The efficiency of the bubble-cap plates, spaced at 30 cm, turned out to be about 70%. Columns, condensers, reboilers, and piping are all made of ordinary carbon steel. The plant is fed with steam under 2 atm pressure.

In Canada also, the primary production of heavy water is completed by final enrichment through water distillation.

Water distillation is also the process generally used, either as an alternative to electrolysis or in combination with it, for reconcentrating heavy water that has been used in nuclear reactors and has been depleted for one reason or another.

For this purpose it is better to work at fairly low temperatures, and hence in a vacuum, to cut down on the number of plates needed in the columns. Furthermore,

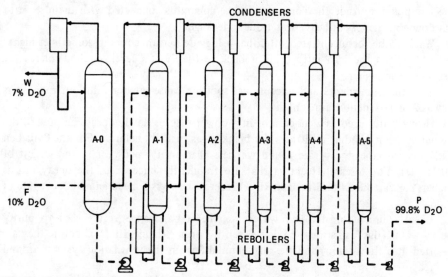

Fig. 9.8 Schematic drawing of a final-concentration distillation unit at Savannah River, S. C. (USA).

Table 9.3

DESIGN FEATURES OF THE SAVANNAH RIVER PLANT
(WATER DISTILLATION)

Stage	1	2	3	4	5	6
Columns*						
Diameter, m	2.30	1.70	1.50	1.20	1.20	1.20
Number of plates	72	84	72	72	72	72
Top pressure, torrs	100	330	100	100	100	100
Bottom pressure, torrs	320	570	320	320	320	320
D_2O concentration at top, %	3	10	20	40	68	90
D_2O concentration at bottom, %	10	20	40	68	90	99.75
Reboilers						
Exchange surface, m²		560	200	140	140	140
Temperature, °C		92	72	72	72	72
Steam load, kg hr⁻¹		5,000	2,300	1,400	1,400	1,400
Condensers						
Exchange surface, m²	280		120	79	79	79

*In all the columns the bubble caps are 10 cm in diameter, and the spacing is 15 cm from center to center.

the low pressure inside the columns and the apparatus connected with them serve to cut down on the loss of heavy water due to leakage.

Water to be reconcentrated often has a high deuterium content, sometimes higher than 99%, and the idea is to bring it back to the 99.75% level required for reactor use—or even higher.

Sometimes accidents and exceptional spoilage cause greater dilution, running as low as 2 to 10% deuterium content.

Heavy water used as a moderator in a power reactor slowly decays because of the humid ambient air that infiltrates the blanket gas (usually helium). For the Canadian NPD reactor, the decay rate found was less than 0.01% per year in the weight of $D/(H + D)$. For research reactors that are frequently uncovered, the decay rate is higher; e.g., at the ZED-II (Chalk River) reactor, there is a mean annual decay rate of 0.06 wt.%.

Usual sources for decayed water are the ion-exchange resins used to purify heavy water (the resins must be deuterized by rinsing them with D_2O before they are inserted into the system) and the air dehumidifiers in the ventilation systems around the reactor.

Before it is upgraded, the decayed water must be purified: decantation (to get rid of oil and other nonmixable organic substances), filtration (to remove solid particles in suspension), treatment with alkaline permanganate (to eliminate organic substances), evaporation, and final purification on exchange resins. Water ready for reconcentration must have a conductivity of 50 μmhos/cm and an organic content of less than 5 mg kg^{-1}.

Table 9.4 shows some data on some reconcentration columns attached to Canadian reactors.

The columns of the NRU reactor are actually two halves of a column, with a single reboiler. The reconcentrated heavy water is drawn off at the bottom of the column with the lesser diameter, whereas the decayed water for concentration is piped in further downstream, at the entry to the reboiler. The columns are made of stainless steel, and each contains 75 sieve plates.

The columns installed at Douglas Point and one of the Pickering columns are built with Sulzer packing. This is a special kind of high-efficiency packing, with an HETP of 7.5 to 8.5 cm and a pressure drop of 0.15 to 0.35 mm Hg per theoretical plate. The columns generally have several feed points, selected on the basis of the concentration level of the water to be reconcentrated.

As was mentioned earlier, there is also another distillation unit at Savannah River, S.C., which consists of six columns and is now being used for reconcentration of decayed water.

Heavy-water reconcentration columns can be considered columns for light-isotope enrichment, which means that the light isotope is present in low concentrations. The calculation is thus simplified accordingly. The productive capacity of the tower is also expressed again here as the quantity of light water removed from the heavy water: for example, the NRU column operating as shown in Table 9.4 removes 0.25 kg H_2O hr^{-1}.

Table 9.4

DISTILLATION COLUMNS FOR RECONCENTRATING
HEAVY WATER: DESIGN DATA

| | NRU | Douglas Point | Pickering | |
			A	B
F, kg hr^{-1}	450	4.5	45	181*
N$_F$, % D/(H + D)	99.77	30	30	38 and 82
N$_W$, % D/(H + D)	96.30	1.0	2.0	1.0
P, kg hr^{-1}	443.5	1.3†	13	115
N$_P$, % D/(H + D)	99.775	99.78	99.0	99.78
No. columns	2	2	1	5
Z, m	24	17	32	52
Diameter, m	0.61 and 0.76	0.25	1	1.8 to 2.3
Type	Sieve plates	Sulzer packing	Sulzer packing	Sieve plates

*Two feed points: (1) for high concentrations (96 kg hr^{-1}) and (2) for low concentrations (85 kg hr^{-1}).

†Obtained in two pass-throughs.

The heavy water coming out of power reactors also contains some tritium. Tritium levels in the moderator reach 10 Ci kg^{-1} after 3 years and 50 Ci kg^{-1} after 30 years of operation. Hence precautions in handling this water must be taken against the hazards of exposure.

REFERENCES

Elementary Effect

1. A. M. Rozen, *Teoriya Razdeleniya Izopopov v Kolonnoakh*, Chap. 2, Goskomitet, Moscow, 1960.

Column-Design Calculation

2. J. H. Perry (Ed.), *Chemical Engineers' Handbook*, Sec. 13, McGraw-Hill Book Company, Inc., 1963.
3. E. Kirschbaum, *Distillation and Rectification*, Chemical Publication, New York, 1948.
4. A. Weissburger, Distillation, in *Techniques of Organic Chemistry*, Vol. 4, Wiley-Interscience, Inc., New York, 1951.
5. G. G. Brown, *Unit Operations*, Part III, John Wiley & Sons, Inc., New York, 1951.
6. E. W. Becker, K. Bier, R. Schutte, and D. Seidel, Separation of the Isotopes of Uranium by the Separation Nozzle Process, *Angew. Chem. Int. Ed. Engl.*, **6**: 507 (1967).
7. E. Cerrai, M. Silvestry, and S. Villani, The Cascading Problem in a Water Distillation Plant for Heavy-Water Production, *Z. Naturforsch.*, **11a**: 694 (1956).
8. See Ref. 1, Chap. 2.
9. H. London, *Separation of Isotopes*, p. 62, Newnes Educational Publishing Co. Ltd., London, 1961.

10. H. R. C. Pratt, Water Distillation as a Process for Heavy-Water Production, in *Heavy-Water Production*, Symposium Proceedings, p. 59, Comitato Nazionale per le Ricerche Nucleari, Rome, 1955.
11. P. Baertschi and W. Kuhn, Final Concentration of Heavy Water by Rectification, in *Progress in Nuclear Energy, Technology, Engineering, and Safety*, Series IV, Vol. 1, p. 57, Pergamon Press, Inc., New York, 1956.
12. A. Selecki, Natural-Water Distillation Plant: A New Technical Approach, in *Techniques and Economy of Production of Heavy Water*, Conference Proceedings, Turin, Italy, 1970, Comitato Nationale per l'Energia Nucleare, Rome, 1971.

Process Assessment

13. M. Benedict, Survey of Heavy-Water Production Processes, in *Proceedings of the International Conference on the Peaceful Uses of Atomic Energy, Geneva, 1955*, Vol. 8, p. 377, United Nations, New York, 1956.
14. M. Benedict and T. H. Pigford, *Nuclear Chemical Engineering*, Sec. 3.1, Distillation of Water, p. 413, McGraw-Hill Book Company, Inc., New York, 1957.
15. H. London, Isotope Separation by Fractional Distillation, in *Isotope Separation*, Symposium Proceedings, p. 319, North-Holland Publishing Company, Amsterdam, 1958.
16. W. P. Beddington and V. R. Thayer, Concentration of Heavy Water by Distillation and Electrolysis, in *Proceedings of the Second United Nations International Conference on the Peaceful Uses of Atomic Energy, Geneva, 1958*, Vol. 4, p. 527, United Nations, New York, 1958.
17. See Ref. 12.

Plants

18. G. M. Murphy, *Production of Heavy Water*, pp. 82-98, McGraw-Hill Book Company, Inc., New York, 1955.
19. See Ref. 16.
20. W. C. Scotten, Separative Work as a Performance Criterion for a Heavy-Water Reconcentration Unit, USAEC Report DP-652, E. I. duPont de Nemours & Co., Inc., Savannah River Laboratory, May 1962.
21. J. A. Morrison, M. H. Thomas, and L. C. Watson, The Management of Heavy Water for Research and Power Reactors, in *Proceedings of the Third International Conference on the Peaceful Uses of Atomic Energy, Geneva, 1964*, Vol. 12, p. 373, United Nations, New York, 1965.
22. H. K. Rae, Heavy Water, Canadian Report AECL-3866, 1971.

10 HYDROGEN DISTILLATION

PROPERTIES OF LIQUID HYDROGEN

A sample of deuterium-enriched hydrogen was first obtained in 1932 by H. C. Urey, F. G. Brickwedde, and G. M. Murphy [*The Physical Review,* **40**: 1 (1932)] by fractional distillation of liquid hydrogen. That experiment proved, by means of spectroscopic monitoring as the concentration rose, that deuterium did indeed exist because of the intensification of deuterium's characteristic lines, visibly separate from the hydrogen lines; i.e., the D line differs by 1.3 A.

Hydrogen has a very low boiling point—about $20°K$. The liquid is colorless and is neither very viscous nor very dense. When placed in a Dewar flask, it boils slowly and creates no foam. See Table 10.1 for some of the typical properties of hydrogen, deuterium, and HD, along with those of nitrogen; the nitrogen data are helpful as terms of reference.

We have used $n-H_2$ and $n-D_2$ to indicate, respectively, normal hydrogen and normal deuterium, which means that they are in equilibrium at ambient temperature. We recall that hydrogen is made up of a mixture of ortho-hydrogen (parallel nuclear spin) and para-hydrogen (antiparallel nuclear spin): these two molecular forms are indicated with the symbols $o-H_2$ and $p-H_2$, respectively. At ambient temperature and above, there is about 25% para- and 75% ortho-hydrogen. At the temperature of liquid oxygen ($\sim 90°K$), the ratio is about half and half. As the temperature moves toward absolute zero, the balance shifts more and more toward para-hydrogen, which

Table 10.1

SOME PROPERTIES OF HYDROGEN AND NITROGEN

	Boiling point, $^\circ$K	Density of liquid at boiling point, g liter^{-1}	Density of vapor at boiling point, g liter^{-1}	Density of STP vapor, g liter^{-1}	Latent heat of evaporation at boiling point, cal mol^{-1}
n-H_2	20.38	70.4	1.309	0.0899	208
HD	22.13	113.4			
n-D_2	23.56	161.4			311.5
N_2	77.35	802	4.59	1.26	1.340

corresponds to a lower energy configuration. At the temperature of liquid hydrogen ($\sim 20^\circ$K) the proportion of para-hydrogen is greater than 99%. The shift to equilibrium, however, is extremely slow (on the order of years) if it is not catalyzed. In distillation plants there is no pure p-H_2 if care is taken to avoid reaching the conversion-reaction equilibrium.

The transformation of ortho- to para-hydrogen is exothermic. The heat of conversion is about 340 cal mol^{-1}, and hence greater than the latent heat of evaporation, as is shown in Table 10.1.

In hydrogen distillation plants the ortho—para conversion increases the demand for coolant and must therefore be held to a minimum. Since—as we have said—the conversion reaction is very slow unless a catalyst is used, it is quite possible to prevent any conversion at all, or at least any considerable degree of it, if care is taken to limit insofar as possible the quantity of highly active catalytic materials present in the plant and specifically in the parts of the plant where the temperature is very low. One especially active material is silica gel, particularly when it is carrying adsorbed oxygen; 1 kg of silica gel will convert 4 mol hr^{-1} of ortho-hydrogen at 17 atm and 40°K, and 1 kg of oxygen adsorbed onto silica gel will convert 1640 kmol hr^{-1} of ortho-hydrogen under the same conditions.

In order to prevent conversion-reaction heat buildup in the lowest temperature parts of the plant, it is also possible, by means of catalysis, to bring about one or more equilibrations in the hydrogen as it gradually cools before being introduced into the distillation columns.

HYDROGEN FRACTIONATION

The marked difference between the boiling points of the molecular species H_2, HD, and D_2 is reflected by a great difference in vapor pressure. The vapor-pressure ratio between H_2 and HD, for example, is about 1.63 at 22°K (about 1.7 atm), as is shown in Fig. 10.1.

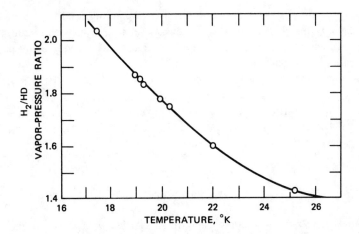

Fig. 10.1 Ratio between the vapor pressures of H_2 and HD.

Under these conditions, however, the relative volatility of H_2 by comparison with HD (meaning the separation factor) is about 1.57 in solutions poor in HD. There are two reasons for this: (1) gaseous hydrogen under the aforementioned conditions of temperature and pressure does not behave like a perfect gas,* and (2) the HD–H_2 solutions are not ideal but show positive deviations from Raoult's law.†

Distillation can be done with bubble plate columns for relatively large column diameters or with packed columns for small diameters.

Experiments conducted at Cambridge University by D. R. Augood (Thesis, Cambridge University, January 1955) using an experimental column 1 in. in diameter, with bubble-cap plates, showed overall efficiencies of about 0.5 with linear vapor velocities u several times higher than the values acceptable according to the familiar semiempirical equation, analogous to Eq. 9.38.

$$u = K \left[\frac{(\rho_L - \rho_V)}{\rho_V} \right]^{\frac{1}{2}}$$

in which K is a constant characteristic of the column and ρ_L and ρ_V are the densities of the liquid and the vapor, respectively [see J. H. Perry (Ed.), *Chemical Engineers' Handbook*, Sec. 13, McGraw-Hill Book Company, Inc., New York, 1963].

For industrial plate columns, Malkov[8] cites overall efficiency values of 30 to 35%, whereas Gami and Rapial[13] give 35 to 40%. Gami and Rapial have calculated that

---

*H. Wooley, R. B. Scott, and F. G. Brickwedde, *Journal of Research of the National Bureau of Standards*, **41**: 379 (1948).

†H. J. Hoge and R. D. Arnold, *Journal of Research of the National Bureau of Standards*, **47**: 63 (1951); R. B. Newman, Thesis, Bristol University, October 1954.

their columns could go as high as 50% if just a few operating conditions were changed.

The relatively high values for the elementary separation factor in liquid-hydrogen distillation make it possible to achieve high enrichment without very many plates; such is not the case in water distillation.

For example, the total reflux enrichment A from 0.003% in HD (in view of the considerable value of liquid hydrogen as a raw material, the upper portion of the column operates as a stripping section and the lower portion operates as an enrichment section, with the feed introduced between the two) to 3% in HD, with $q_0 = 1.57$, is achieved with a number of theoretical plates

$$S = \frac{\log A}{\log q_0} = \frac{3}{0.195} = 15$$

which would correspond—assuming an overall efficiency of 0.4—to about 40 real plates. Of course, this number increases if we wish to achieve the same enrichment and withdraw rich material. That would raise the number of plates to 80 or so for absolute yields near the optimum yield.

With two columns attached in series (drawing off, from the first column, hydrogen at 5 to 10% HD), practically pure deuterium (about 99.8%) can be obtained by starting with hydrogen at natural concentration. In this case the second column is in practice a double column, the first half of it yielding practically pure HD.

If we consider that, for a production of 1 ton D_2O month^{-1}, the diameter of the first column will be roughly 1.2 m, the plant volumes are shown to be lower by two orders of magnitude than those found in water distillation.

For liquid-hydrogen distillation, therefore, the problem of optimum scale for the cascade is not a very serious problem. Once an efficient thermodynamic cycle for the process has been established, the difficulties tend to center around problems like purification of the feed gas and insulation of the plant.

ENERGY CONSUMPTION

From the discussions about water distillation in general (Chapter 3) and water distillation in particular (Chapter 9), it is shown that energy consumption in any distillation process is linked primarily with the irreversible transformations that occur in such a process.

In any case, hydrogen distillation is more advantageous than water distillation for two reasons:

1. The higher q_0 involves lower flows L'' to be evaporated per unit of product PN_P.

2. The heat of evaporation of the n-H_2 at 20°K is only 200 cal mol^{-1} (that of n-D_2 is about 310 cal mol^{-1}) and hence 50 times smaller than that for H_2O (9700 cal mol^{-1} at 373°K).

These facts mean that losses of availability involved with the various causes of irreversibility (most of all the temperature drops in the heat exchangers and the inefficiency in the compressors) lead to a specific energy consumption—referred to the unit of D_2O produced—which is markedly lower than that required for water distillation.

A diagram of the principle of hydrogen distillation is shown in Fig. 10.2. A portion $(L'' - W)$ of the deuterium-depleted gas coming out of the top of the column is recompressed by the compressor C_R and recondensed in the coils of the reboiler R at the bottom of the column, after which it is introduced into the head to form the liquid reflux. The usual reflux ratio $(L'' - W)/W$ adopted is in the range of about 2.5 to 1.

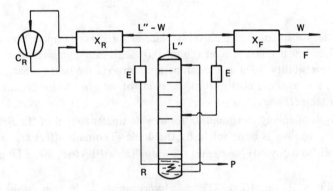

Fig. 10.2 Schematic flow sheet for hydrogen distillation. C_R = reflux compressor. X = heat exchanger. E = cooling devices. F = feed. L'' = gas flow in the column. P = product. R = reboiler. W = waste.

The reflux gas $L'' - W$ and the feed gas F pass through the heat exchangers X_R and X_F, respectively, but cooling devices (E) must be added to heat exchangers to compensate for heat losses in the exchangers and other causes of irreversibility.

These cooling devices are made up of one or more combined systems among the following: (1) auxiliary cooling cycles (liquid NH_3 or N_2), (2) fast expansion (Joule–Thomson effect), and (3) expansion turbines.

These systems are used in various ways in the plants that will be described later. Expansion turbines are particularly well suited for relatively high flow rates and pressure ratios that are not too high.

In the conventional processes of liquefying gases and separating them by distillation, the practical efficiencies (ratios between availability absorbed in the ideal cycle and actual work) are 3 to 30%. Such an efficiency is an index of the irreversibilities inherent in the process.

By way of example, the various terms in which energy consumption can be analyzed for air distillation at 120°K are shown in Table 10.2.

Table 10.2

ENERGY CONSUMPTION IN AIR DISTILLATION

	cal mol^{-1}	%
Reversible work	83	3.8
Compression losses	820	37.7
Column losses	1000	45.5
Heat exchanger losses	283	13.0
Total	2186	100.0

In hydrogen distillation, which takes place at far lower temperatures (20°K), the practical efficiency is much smaller (about 0.01%). It is easily understood that certain causes of irreversibility, such as the temperature drop in the heat exchangers of even a few degrees, are far more costly from the point of view of thermodynamic efficiency at these low temperatures.

An analysis of energy consumption for a cycle similar to that of the Soviet plant in Fig. 10.6 (the cooling is done solely by the Joule–Thomson effect and auxiliary N_2 cycles, but without any NH_3 cycles) is shown in Table 10.3 for 1000 STP m^3 H_2 to be processed.

If a column is fed 1000 STP m^3 hydrogen hr^{-1}, it is possible to produce about 850 kg D_2O year^{-1}. The D_2O will contain from 5 to 10% D/(H + D), or 0.097 kg D_2O hr^{-1}. Hence the specific consumption of energy (see Table 10.3) is

$$E = 616/0.097 = 6400 \text{ kWh/kg } D_2O$$

With larger plants and an improvement in the thermodynamic cycle, however, it is possible to achieve lower specific consumption.

For the feed gas F (see Fig. 10.2) there are substantially two alternatives: (1) electrolytic hydrogen and (2) gas for ammonia synthesis (usually from processed methane).

In the first case the hydrogen is at practically atmospheric pressure and must be compressed at the entry to the distillation plant (up to 4 to 5 atm, for example) and further compressed at the exit before being used for ammonia synthesis.

In the second case the gas in the ammonia-synthesis process is compressed at very high pressures (100 to 1000 atm), but the distillation plant can be inserted at any of several points of the primary process at intermediate pressures (e.g., from less than 20 atm to more than 200 atm). The gas available for distillation can then be compressed or expanded, depending on which is required by the particular coolant cycle.

Table 10.3

ENERGY CONSUMPTION FOR A HYDROGEN-DISTILLATION SYSTEM

	kcal	%
Reversible work	40	0.0076
Loss due to temperature drop along the column	900	0.17
Minimum work to compensate for the heat losses	8300	1.57
Loss due to temperature drop in heat exchanges	116,800	22.10
Loss due to pressure drop in heat exchanges	46,500	8.80
Loss due to irreversibility in the reboilers	53,500	10.10
Loss for irreversible expansion of reflux gas	10,300	1.95
Loss in the compressor (isothermal efficiency = 0.6)	158,000	29.80
Consumption of energy for the N_2 cycle	135,000	25.50
Total	529,340 (616 kWh)	99.9976

As we shall see in the next section, the incoming gas, particularly if it is ammonia synthesis gas, must be carefully purified. This purification occurs along the line of X_F heat exchangers (see Fig. 10.2) while the temperature of the feed gas gradually drops to approach the process temperature.

HYDROGEN PURIFICATION

A liquid-hydrogen distillation plant cannot be fed with hydrogen produced solely for the extraction of deuterium. The feed cost alone would make the production of heavy water prohibitive from the economic point of view. In fact, if we assume a plant yield of 90%, the plant must be fed with about $(6700/0.9) \times (1000/20)$ mols H_2/kg D_2O produced, the equivalent of about 8300 STP m^3 H_2/kg D_2O. For example, since hydrogen produced from methane re-forming costs about $0.03 per STP cubic meter, the cost of feed alone would have a product impact of at least $250 per kilogram of D_2O.

Unless hydrogen is used in a closed cycle, with reintegration of the deuterium content by means of exchange reactions, according to the system to be discussed later, liquid-hydrogen plants can be used only to produce heavy water as a by-product of industrial hydrogen production, which—as we know—is used primarily for making ammonia.

The gas for synthesis consists of approximately 75 vol.% hydrogen and 25 vol.% nitrogen. The hydrogen, usually produced as a gas from water or by methane re-forming, also contains a number of impurities (CO, Ar, CH_4, CO_2, etc.) in small but still not negligible quantities. Electrolytic hydrogen is far purer (normally it contains only 0.01 to 0.06% N_2), but its production on a large scale is less common, for readily understandable economic reasons.

Since in liquid-hydrogen distillation the feed gas must be cooled to temperatures of about $20°K$, at which any other gas (except helium) would solidify (nitrogen solidifies at $63°K$), clearly there must be extremely thorough purification of the feed gas.

Without such a scrupulous cleansing process, there would be a buildup of solid substances in various plant components (distillation columns, heat exchangers, connecting pipes, etc.), which would cause a blockage. In practice, the nitrogen content (nitrogen is the commonest and most abundant impurity) should be held below a few parts per million.

In a plant that processes 4000 STP m^3 hydrogen hr^{-1}, if the N_2 impurities in the feed gas come to 5×10^{-5} mol mol^{-1}, there is a buildup of about 0.25 kg hr^{-1}, which amounts to 360 kg in 2 months of operation.

Purification is done gradually all along the feed line, in which the gas is gradually cooled by heat exchangers, by the deuterium-depleted gas emerging from the distillation plant.

The principal methods of purification consist (1) in deposition of the solidified impurities into suitable containers (regenerators) or into heat exchangers, with subsequent sublimation of the impurities, and (2) in adsorption of the impurities on beds of activated charcoal or silica gel (up to about $80°K$).

Without going into the details of any specific purification line (this will be done later in a general description of planned and existing plants), let us now discuss the deposition of solidified impurities.

One method is based on the use of heat exchangers with conduits that are used alternately at specified intervals of changeover. The impurities in the feed gas are deposited on the channel walls for a certain period, and at the end of that time the pure gas coming from the plant is directed into the channels through which the feed gas had previously traveled and vice versa. In this way the impurities deposited over a given period are swept up and carried away in the next period by the deuterium-depleted gas.

Heat exchangers of particularly simple design which can be used in the way described above are Marston exchangers. Marston exchangers are built by alternating thin corrugated sheets of aluminum alloy or other metals and flat sheets. In the channels thus formed, the two currents of gas are made to flow countercurrently. Until now, exchangers of this type had been developed only for pressures below 15 atm.

Determining dimensions and operating conditions for reversible conduit exchangers for eliminating impurities from hydrogen presupposes a familiarity with the state diagrams for the vapor—solid equilibrium of the major systems involved in the process, and especially those for the H_2-N_2 system.

Z. Dokoupil of the Kamerlingh Onnes Laboratory in Leiden (Netherlands) demonstrated in his thesis at Leiden University (Nijhoff's Book Shop and Publishing Company, The Hague, 1955) that the vapor pressure of solid nitrogen is greatly increased by the presence of hydrogen.

For example, using as a reference term the vapor pressure of pure N_2 at 33°K, we obtain—corresponding with various values of the total pressure—the factors of increase shown in Table 10.4.

Table 10.4

INCREASE IN THE VAPOR PRESSURE OF N_2
IN THE PRESENCE OF H_2 AT 33°K

Total pressure, atm	Partial pressure, N_2, torrs	Factor of increase
0.0012	0.0012	1
1.3	0.0016	1.3
5	0.005	4
10	0.025	20
15	0.15	125
25	1.9	1,600
50	14	12,000

If reversible-conduit exchangers are to operate, the concentration gradient of N_2 in the gas which evaporates the impurities must be greater than or equal to the gradient in the gas which deposits the impurities. The equality of the concentration gradient determines the maximum temperature difference between the two flows of gas in the exchanger.

Figure 10.3 shows, as a function of temperature, the nitrogen-concentration gradients at three different total-pressure values.

If we assume, for example, that the feed gas is at 5 atm and the exhaust gas is at 1.3 atm, we can see from Fig. 10.3 that the gradients reach equality at 29°K. Below this temperature the gradient in the gas at 5 atm is greater than that in the gas at 1.3 atm. Hence, with these conditions, a changeable-channel exchanger could not operate below 29°K, since the exhaust gas would not be able to sublimate the entire mass of impurities deposited by the feed gas.

Also used to remove impurities from hydrogen are the so-called regenerators, frequently encountered in low-temperature technology and used particularly for removing CO_2 from the air. These are vessels containing a suitable filler with high

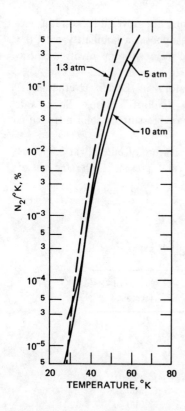

Fig. 10.3 The N_2 concentration gradient in hydrogen as a function of temperature at various total pressures.

thermal capacity, over which the exhaust gas and the feed gas are passed alternately. As the feed gas passes over the regenerator, it deposits its impurities, which are then reevaporated by the pure exhaust gas. The best filler material is lead since many other metals have a specific heat that declines sharply as the temperature drops.

As will be shown later in dealing with the plants built in the Soviet Union, a good way of removing the residual impurities in N_2 is adsorption on beds of activated charcoal or silica gel at 80°K.

THERMAL INSULATION

Clearly, the distillation plant operating at about 20°K must be adequately insulated. Insulation must cut heat losses down as much as possible, even though such losses constitute a relatively minor term in the energy balance by comparison with the loss caused by the temperature difference between the feed hydrogen and the exhaust.

Insulation can be achieved by means of a dead space in which a vacuum is set up and maintained or by means of insulating materials in contact with the cold walls of the plant.

However, the use of insulating materials in direct contact with apparatus at temperatures close to 20°K runs into a limitation in the form of the liquefaction of the air contained in the pores or in the structure of the insulating material. This can be avoided by dividing the material into two layers by means of an airtight container. The layer inside the container and next to the plant walls at very low temperature is kept in a hydrogen (or helium) atmosphere at low pressure, while the outer layer—at temperatures above the dew point of air—is left in contact with the air at normal pressure (or nitrogen may be used).

For insulating plants of medium dimensions, like some pilot plants, for example, the insulating materials would have to be extremely thick, so thick that space would be taken up out of all proportion to the volume of the plant proper. In this case it is better to decrease the thickness of the insulating material by inserting a metal screen (e.g., copper) into it, and chilling the screen with a stream of liquid nitrogen. Calculation will show that the optimum position for such a screen is that which divides the insulating material considered as a whole into two slices, one 70% and the other 30% of total thickness, with the larger one being the one between the screen and the plant wall.

Santocel is an insulation particularly suitable for such uses. It is a powder of silica gel, whose grains, thanks to a cellular structure, are far more porous than ordinary silica gel. Furthermore, Santocel has a very low specific heat, which means it can reach stationary temperature very quickly.

Studies run on Santocel and other powdered insulation materials[6] have shown that their thermal conductivity declines with the grain size. In addition, conductivity, which is a rapidly declining function of the pressure of the gas present in the powder, stabilizes below a certain pressure level that is specific to each grain. These typical pressures are roughly inversely proportional to the grain dimensions, whereas the values on which the conductivity levels are stabilized are proportional to them.

Figure 10.4 shows, as a function of gas pressure, the thermal conductivity K of Santocel and silica gel in grains no larger than 74 μm. For comparison the conductivity of slag wool is also shown. It is obvious from the figure that, with the above-mentioned powders and with pressures lower than about $\frac{1}{10}$ mm Hg, the conductivities obtained are just about equal to those obtainable with a high vacuum (10^{-5} mm Hg), which is equal to about $\frac{1}{100}$ of the value obtained with slag wool and air at atmospheric pressure.

PLANTS

Following earlier experiments run in Germany, Clusius and Starke[3] in 1949 suggested a plant design for production of practically pure deuterium from hydrogen at natural concentration by means of liquid-hydrogen distillation. That design is shown in Fig. 10.5. Enrichment is accomplished by means of two columns linked in series. The first, fed with natural hydrogen through expansion valve 1, produces hydrogen

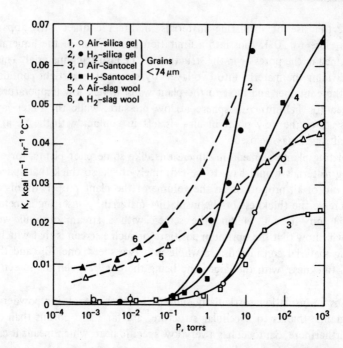

Fig. 10.4 Heat conductivity of various insulating materials as a function of the pressure of the gas present.

with a 5 to 10% HD content. This hydrogen, which is withdrawn from the reboiler of the first column, is fed through valve 3 into the top of the second column, which is a Linde double column.

Highly concentrated HD is drawn off from the upper portion, and, through exchanger 4 and valve 5, it is equilibrated according to the exchange reaction $H_2 + D_2 \rightleftharpoons 2HD$, in a catalysis chamber at ambient temperature. For this reaction the most commonly used catalysts are those containing platinum, palladium, or nickel, the same ones that are discussed in Chap. 12 for reactions between hydrogen and water vapor. The equilibrium constant for the reaction is 3.26 at 298°K.

The depleted gas emerging from the top of the second column is returned to the bottom of the first. The evaporation heat for the reboilers for both columns comes from a (preponderant) portion of the deuterium-depleted hydrogen emerging from the top of the first column. This hydrogen is recompressed and circulated (as already shown in Fig. 10.2) through the reboiler coils, after which it is sent through expansion valve 2 into the top of the first column to provide the liquid reflux for that column.

On the basis of their experience accumulated in operating two pilot plants for processing 70 STP m³ gas hr⁻¹ (one for electrolytic hydrogen and the other for ammonia synthesis gas), the Russians built an industrial plant for deuterium concentration by means of electrolytic hydrogen distillation. This plant consists of a

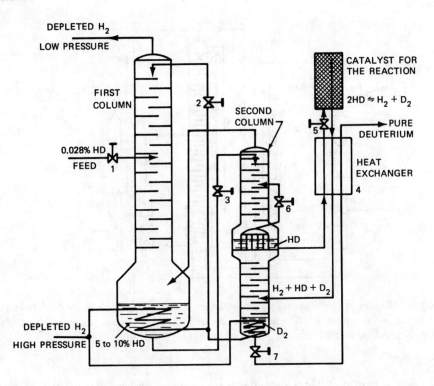

Fig. 10.5 Diagram of the distillation plant suggested by Clusius and Starke.[3]

number of identical units, each supplied with 4000 STP m^3 feed gas hr^{-1}. The design of one such unit is shown in Fig. 10.6.

The feed hydrogen, compressed to 2 to 4 atm by the C-1 compressor, flows through exchangers X-1 and X-2, the latter being cooled with ammonia. In these exchangers the water and oil contained in the feed gas are frozen. Then the gas itself is still further cooled by passage through exchangers X-3 and X-4. The nitrogen is eliminated by adsorption on a bed of activated charcoal or silica gel contained in vessel A. When, after passing through exchanger X-5, the hydrogen has reached a temperature of 24 to 26°K, it is introduced into the distillation column through expansion valve V-1.

While part of the deuterium-depleted hydrogen coming out of the top of the column flows into exchangers X-5, X-3, and X-1 in countercurrent to the feed gas, most of this hydrogen is compressed in compressor C-2 to provide the liquid reflux for the column. The column operates with a 2.5 reflux ratio.

The hydrogen compressed by compressor C-2 is divided into two flows. The more abundant flow emerges at 5 to 6 atm and, after passing successively through exchangers X-6 to X-9, flows through a boiler coil and is reintroduced into the top of the column through valve V-2. The smaller flow of hydrogen, on the other hand, is

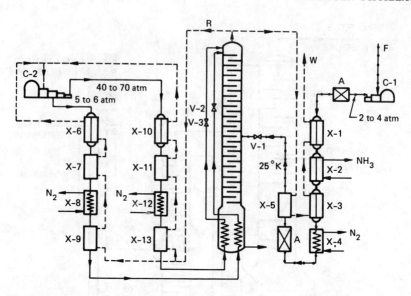

Fig. 10.6 Diagram of the liquid-hydrogen distillation plant now operating in the Soviet Union. R = reflux. A = adsorbers. W = flow recycled to the chemical plant. C = compressors. F = feed. V = valves. X = heat exchangers.

compressed to 40 to 70 atm and, after passing through exchangers X-10 to X-13, also goes through a boiler coil and is fed into the top of the column through valve V-3. Exchangers X-4, X-8, and X-12 are cooled with liquid nitrogen produced in a separate circuit (not shown in Fig. 10.6). In this circuit the cooling (about 60,000 kcal at 80°K for this particular plant) can be achieved either by using the Joule–Thomson effect or by means of expansion turbines.

Refrigeration losses occurring in the feed line are partly compensated for by the N_2 cycle and partly by the expansion of the gas at 60 atm (in V-3).

The column has 77 plates, each 1050 mm in diameter. The overall plate efficiency has been estimated at about 30 to 35%. Fed with hydrogen containing 0.03% HD, it yields a product of about 7 to 9% HD. The final concentration is done by water electrolysis and exchange reactions.

The plant consists of two units that are individually insulated. The first unit consists of a column (about 10 m high) and of exchangers that operate below 80°K. Insulation for this unit is provided by a hydrogen atmosphere with a liquid-nitrogen-cooled intermediate screen.

The second unit contains the exchangers and filters that operate above 80°K. In these exchangers the temperature differences at the hot end are 5 to 8°C. The vertical section of the Soviet plant is shown in Fig. 10.7.

The cooling required by the plant, broken down into its several items, is shown in Table 10.5. Note that there is no heading for ortho-/para- conversion in it. Thanks to

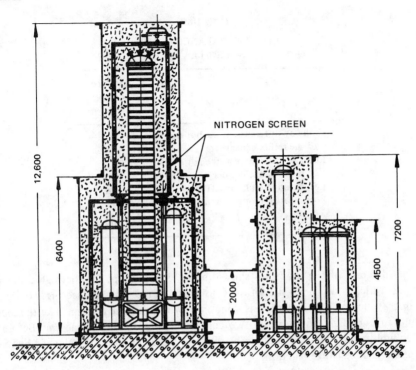

Fig. 10.7 Vertical section of the Soviet distillation plant (heights are given in millimeters).

the absence of catalysts and the closed-cycle circulation of most of the hydrogen, this item does not amount to much. It involves a cooling increment of 3 to 5% in the nitrogen cycle at 80°K.

The plant takes 80 to 90 hr to reach operational status and is operated for 2 months at a time. The specific energy consumption is about 5000 to 5500 kWh/kg D_2O.

Between 1954 and 1958 the French designed and built an industrial pilot plant to process 4000 STP m^3 ammonia synthesis gas hr^{-1}. The plant, which is connected with the ammonia-synthesis installations of the National Nitrogen Industry Office, was built by Société de l'Air Liquide.

The data derived from operating this pilot plant helped to complete the planning and design of a large distillation plant which, fed with 66,000 STP m^3 ammonia synthesis gas hr^{-1}, was to produce about 40 tons D_2O $year^{-1}$. The specific investment estimate for the D_2O was \$425 per kilogram of D_2O per year (1958), and an energy consumption of about 4000 to 6000 kWh/kg D_2O.

The composition of the ammonia synthesis feed gas for the plant is H_2, 75%; N_2, 24.5%; Ar, 0.25%; CH_4, 0.2%; with the remainder being impurities in the form of CO, CO_2, O_2, and traces of H_2O.

Table 10.5

**COOLING BALANCE IN THE
SOVIET PLANT**

	Required cooling, %
Enthalpy difference at the hot end of the reflux exchangers	54
Enthalpy difference at the hot end of the feed exchangers	20
Loss through faulty insulation	24
Loss through product extraction	2
Total	100

The diagram of the process is shown in Fig. 10.8, except for the high-concentration part which is similar to that of the Clusius and Starke[3] design (see Fig. 10.5).

In the pilot plant, distillation is done in a two-stage plate column (like the second column in Fig. 10.5), followed by two columns with a Dixon ring packing. Before the last column, which yields a product at 99.95%, the deuterium is rebalanced by means of a catalyzed exchange reaction.

The plant is subdivided into two units. The "cold" unit contains all the components that operate below 64°K, fitted into a cylindrical vessel (3 m in diameter

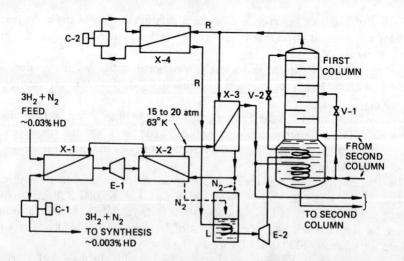

Fig. 10.8 Partial diagram of the French distillation process. C = compressors. E = expansion turbines. L = nitrogen evaporator. R = reflux. V = valves. X = heat exchangers.

and 12 m high) containing Santocel under a moderate vacuum (10^{-2} mm Hg), with a screen of liquid-nitrogen-cooled copper. The "hot" unit contains all components operating at temperatures above 64°K. It has conventional magnesium carbonate insulation. For safety reasons, both units are housed in a cubic cell of reinforced concrete. The productive capacity of the pilot plant is about 1.5 tons D_2O year^{-1}.

The refrigeration cycle of the French process is peculiar in that it lacks N_2 auxiliary cycles and N_2 and NH_3 cycles for preliminary cooling (except for an N_2 cycle for the insulation screens).

The feed gas is under considerable pressure (230 atm). It is therefore possible to obtain all the cooling required for the feed line by means of a single expansion turbine (E-1) and a single valve (V-1). Along the reflux line the coolant is provided by the evaporator L, the turbine E-2, and the valve V-2.

Let us now discuss the purification process of the French plant. First the ammonia synthesis gas is cooled in exchanger X-1; then the gas is expanded into E-1 and piped from there into exchanger X-2 where the N_2 is condensed and separated. The condensate, also containing a little hydrogen and impurities, is collected in the evaporator L. The hydrogen emerging from X-2 is under 15 to 20 atm pressure, and its temperature is a little higher than nitrogen's triple point, which is about 63°K. It still contains about 2% N_2; purification down to a few parts per million is done by means of solidification in switchable-conduit exchangers. In Fig. 10.8 these conduits are indicated in outline with X-3. Actually they constitute a more complex system. The pressure interval from 15 to 20 atm is the one corresponding to the smallest residue of gaseous nitrogen.

The reflux hydrogen R, recompressed by compressor C_R between the first and second passages through exchanger X-4, evaporates the nitrogen in L, is expanded in E-2, passes again into a coil of the column reboiler, and finally is piped in as feed through valve V-2 to the top of the same column.

A pilot plant for distilling 400 STP m^3 electrolytic hydrogen hr^{-1} has been built at Ems (Switzerland) by the Sulzer Company. The feed hydrogen is enriched electrolytically to 0.15 mol % HD/H_2, and the distillation plant turns out 1 STP m^3 hydrogen hr^{-1} at 60 mol % HD. Final enrichment is done by water distillation (about 2 tons D_2O year^{-1}).

Figure 10.9 is a diagram of the Sulzer plant. The process, analogous to the French one, is characterized by its lack of ancillary cycles for preliminary cooling. The cooling is done primarily by the three expansion turbines E on the reflux line and by the expansion valves on the feed line.

The purification procedure is the following. After the oxygen is eliminated in deoxo units, the feed gas is further purified in regenerative heat exchangers. Final purification before entry into the column is done by condensation and reevaporation in the liquefaction device L.

The column consists of 90 packed tubes, fed in parallel by means of capillaries. Both the column and the other "cold" components are housed in high-vacuum containers protected with aluminum foil to minimize cooling losses.

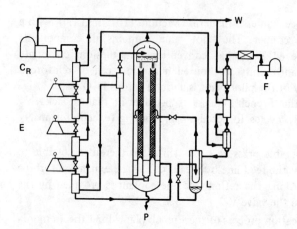

Fig. 10.9 Diagram of the Sulzer plant for hydrogen distillation. F = feed. P = product. W = gas shunted back to the synthesis plant. L = liquefaction apparatus. C_R = reflux compressors. E = expansion turbines.

In Frankfurt, Germany, Linde AG has built a pilot plant for Farbwerke Hoechst AG which can produce about 4 tons D_2O year^{-1}, processing ammonia synthesis gas (about 70% H_2 and 30% N_2) at 20 atm pressure. The diagram for the process is shown in Fig. 10.10.

Cooling is provided by an auxiliary N_2 cycle and by expansion valves both on the reflux line and on the feed line. In the feed line the incoming gas, precooled to 100°K

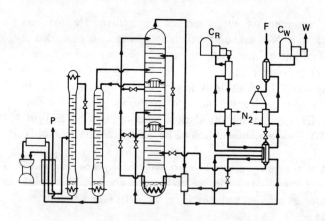

Fig. 10.10 Diagram of the Linde plant for hydrogen distillation. F = feed. P = product. W = gas shunted back to the synthesis plant. C_R = reflux compressor. C_W = compressors for recycling to the ammonia plant.

with the depleted hydrogen (by means of which the H_2O and CO_2 are eliminated) is further cooled by means of an expansion turbine (8 atm exhaust pressure).

The rest of the purification occurs after passage into the exchangers downstream from the turbine, where the N_2, CO, Ar, O_2, and CH_4 are condensed (for subsequent reevaporation by the depleted hydrogen). After decompression at 5 atm, the feed gas goes into a series of regenerators cooled by the processing gas. In these regenerators there is a deposit (at $27.5°K$) and subsequent sublimation of the remaining impurities (particularly nitrogen).

The reflux compressor C_R recompresses the hydrogen at ambient temperature up to about 100 atm.

Distillation takes place in three columns. The first column, containing 166 plates, consists of three stages at approximately 3.2, 2.0, and 1.2 atm, respectively. This multistage system makes it possible to reduce the reflux ratio ($\sim$1).

The second column (40 plates), which is fed by the 4% HD liquid drawn off from the bottom of the third stage, enriches to 90% HD. Next comes a catalytic reequilibration of the deuterium, after which the final enrichment (99.8 mol % D_2) is effected in the third column, which contains 90 plates.

The cold components of the plant are arranged in two concentric units insulated with slag wool, the inner one kept under a hydrogen atmosphere and the outer one under a nitrogen atmosphere.

At Nangal (India), Linde AG has built another plant similar to the one described above. It was designed to process 5000 STP m^3 electrolytic hydrogen enriched in deuterium to about three times the normal concentration. The capacity of the Nangal plant is 14 tons D_2O year^{-1}. The plant began operations at the end of 1962 and has provided a remarkable accumulation of experience and data. Some of the interesting points are these:

1. The plant operates for an average of more than 8000 hr year^{-1} and has gone as long as 15 months in operation without interruption.

2. A shutdown of about 3 weeks year^{-1} is required for ordinary maintenance. Defrosting is required for safety reasons as well. It is necessary to get rid of the oxygen (1.1 kg month^{-1}) which along with nitrogen (6.5 kg month^{-1}) is deposited in the plant. The accumulated oxygen for just 1 month would be the equivalent, in the presence of H_2, of 1.15 kg TNT.

3. On one occasion a fire was caused by a leak of hydrogen under high pressure.

4. Deposits of solid nitrogen in the plant can cause trouble in the various mechanical components (valves and the like). Fortunately the solid nitrogen does not stick to metal and can be easily removed mechanically.

5. The feed rate and hence the plant's productivity can be raised considerably beyond the design level.

On the basis of the experience acquired with the Frankfurt and Nangal plants, Linde AG has prepared an improved plan for processing 177,000 STP m^3 ammonia synthesis gas hr^{-1} (74% H_2, p = 25 atm, T = 300°K), which can produce 1500 tons NH_3 day^{-1}.

The distillation plant would produce about 100 tons D_2O year^{-1} with a content of 250 ppm HD in the feed hydrogen.

The suggested improvements are the following:

1. Elimination of the auxiliary N_2 circuits. The required cooling is provided entirely by hydrogen-expansion turbines, two on the feed line and one on the reflux line.

2. Greater pressure in the three sections of the first column. The minimum pressure would be 2.2 to 3 atm. The compression ratio in the reflux gas is reduced, as is the power required to drive the reflux compressor.

3. Simplification of the insulation system. Instead of two concentric units as in earlier plants, there would be a single unit with a hydrogen atmosphere.

The assessed energy consumption for such a plant is only 2400 kWh/kg D_2O, and hence the absorbed power would be 31.5 MW.

Table 10.6 shows some of the data for comparison among the Soviet, Air Liquide, and Linde processes. The last column refers to the 100-ton D_2O year^{-1} Linde plant discussed above. The plant's larger size, the application of turbines to expand higher flow rates of hydrogen, and the increased pressure on the gas emerging from the primary column are some of the principal reasons for the great cut in energy consumption.

Table 10.6

COMPARATIVE DATA ON SEVERAL HYDROGEN DISTILLATION PROCESSES

	Plant			
	Soviet	Air Liquide	Linde–Nangal	Linde design
Feed	Electrolytic H_2	Ammonia synthesis gas	Electrolytic H_2	Ammonia synthesis gas
F, STP m^3 hr^{-1}	4000	4000	5000	180,000
p_F, atm	2 to 4	230	25	25
Reflux ratio	2 to 2.5		1	1
p_R (reflux), atm	5 to 6 / 40 to 70	15 to 40	50	10
		Cooling		
Feed	NH$_3$ cycle / N$_2$ cycle / H$_2$ expansion	H$_2$ turbine / H$_2$ expansion	H$_2$ turbine / N$_2$ cycle / H$_2$ expansion	H$_2$ turbine
Reflux	N$_2$ cycle / H$_2$ expansion	H$_2$ turbine / H$_2$ expansion	N$_2$ cycle / H$_2$ expansion	H$_2$ turbine
		Final purification		
	Adsorption	Reversing exchangers	Regenerators	Regenerators

A hydrogen-distillation plant* can be made independent of the production of hydrogen as a raw material for industrial purposes by reintegrating the deuterium in the exhaust hydrogen and returning it to feed the plant all over again.

*Proceedings of the Second United Nations International Conference on the Peaceful Uses of Atomic Energy, Geneva, 1958, Vol. 4, p. 628, United Nations, New York, 1958.

This can be done by causing a chemical exchange between the hydrogen treated in closed cycle (see Fig. 10.11) in the distillation plant and a flow of water vapor containing deuterium at natural concentration. As was shown in Chap. 3, deuterium at low concentrations is distributed between hydrogen and water according to the equilibrium constant of the $HD + H_2O \rightleftharpoons H_2 + HDO$ exchange reaction. The reaction should occur at the highest possible temperature to get an equilibrium constant as close to unity as possible so as to encourage the deuterium to move from the water to the hydrogen. In practice it is not wise to go above 600°C, since at temperatures higher than that the reaction rates become very fast and there is also a swift inverse

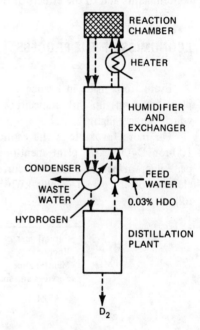

Fig. 10.11 Diagram of the process with hydrogen circulation in a closed cycle.

reaction during cooling of the gas mixture. At 600°C the equilibrium constant is K = 1.3. From the material balance equation and using N_0 to indicate the deuterium concentration in natural water, y to indicate the mol ratio between hydrogen and steam, and η to indicate the yield of the distillation plant, we find that the deuterium concentration n_F in the feed hydrogen can be expressed as follows:

$$n_F = \frac{N_0}{K + y\eta}$$

For example, with K = 1.3, y = 0.2, and η = 0.9, we have $n_F \simeq 0.02\%$ HD, a value slightly below that for the hydrogen in the ammonia synthesis gas (usually 0.025%). Of course, the process just now described involves plant costs that are higher than those of plants using ammonia synthesis gas.

Finally, we should point out that, with high-temperature exchange, more weight must be given to the resistance of the catalyst to heat than to its activity. We must make absolutely sure that the powdered and dispersed catalyst does not stop and stick in the coldest parts of the plant, where it could encourage inversion of the reaction.

Although we still lack direct industrial experience, the likeliest catalysts would seem to be those supported on various oxides with great specific surface, particularly iron oxides. Also under study are catalysts supported on metal.

As for activity, the platinum and palladium catalysts are more efficient than those using nickel on chrome oxide, but the latter catalysts are more resistant to contaminants and to the effects of temperature.

ECONOMICS OF THE PROCESS

Evaluations made in France in 1958 on the basis of Société de l'Air Liquide's pilot plant had come up with a specific investment of $425 per kilogram of D_2O per year, which is fairly high.*

Far more favorable is the economic analysis of the Linde design (1970) for the 100-ton D_2O year^{-1} plant mentioned earlier. The specific investment is about $190 per kilogram per year in 1973 currency. With a capital cost of 15% per year and an electric-power cost of 6 mills kWh^{-1}, the unit cost of production can be analyzed as follows:

Capital cost	$28.50
Energy	14.40
Maintenance	3.90
Services and manpower	3.20
Total	$50.00
	per kilogram
	of D_2O

This is obviously a most attractive figure, but, unfortunately, direct experience with the process is thus far confined to plants on a scale 20% smaller than that of the project cited.

From what we have just seen, any ammonia-synthesis plant is a potential source of deuterium. The yield of deuterium extracted from hydrogen is about 90%.

Roughly speaking, the production of 1 ton D_2O year^{-1} can be associated with 15 tons NH_3 day^{-1}, or 1200 STP m^3 treated hydrogen hr^{-1} containing about 120 ppm $D/(H + D)$.

---

*For the distillation plant in Nangal, India, the investment as reported in 1960 was $2.9 million.

The additional cost of the closed-cycle hydrogen process has been evaluated at about \$10 per kilogram of D_2O if the exchange is run at 250°C (with which we obtain no more than about 80 ppm deuterium in the hydrogen). By raising the temperature to about 600°C, we have about 100 ppm deuterium in the feed, but the costs deriving from energy consumption for heat are extremely high.

REFERENCES

General

1. M. Benedict, Survey of Heavy-Water Production Processes, in *Progress in Nuclear Energy Series IV, Technology and Engineering*, Vol. 1, pp. 3-56, R. Hurst and S. McLain (Eds.), McGraw-Hill Book Company, Inc., New York, 1956.
2. E. W. Becker, *Heavy-Water Production*, Review Series, No. 21, International Atomic Energy Agency, Vienna, 1962, p. 20 (STI/PUB/15/21).

Process Studies

3. K. Clusius and K. Starke, Rectification of Mixtures of H_2–HD–D_2 for the Production of Deuterium and Heavy Water, *Z. Naturforschu.*, **4a**: 7 (1949).
4. L. Weil and A. Lacaze, Heat Transfer from Boiling Hydrogen at Various Pressures, in Ninth International Congress on Coldness, Paris, 1955, Comptes Rendus des Travaux des Comissions I et II, p. 13, Paris, 1955.
5. T. E. Hall, in *Heavy-Water Production*, Symposium Proceedings on Heavy Water Production, p. 71, Comitato Nazionale per le Ricerche Nucleari, Rome, 1955.
6. E. Kanda et al., Experimental Research on the Rectification of Liquid Hydrogen to Obtain Deuterium, in *Proceedings of the Second United Nations International Conference on the Peaceful Uses of Atomic Energy, Geneva, 1958*, Vol. 4, p. 550, New York, 1958.
7. B. M. Bailey, Some Aspects of Heavy-Water Production by Distillation of Hydrogen, *ibid.*, p. 556.

Plants

8. M. P. Malkov et al., Industrial Separation of Deuterium by Low-Temperature Distillation, *ibid.*, p. 491.
9. E. Roth et al., Production of Heavy Water in France, *ibid.*, p. 499.
10. P. Akar and G. Simonet, Industrial Production of Heavy Water by Distillation of Liquid Hydrogen, *ibid.*, p. 522.
11. J. Hänny, *Kaeltetechnik*, **12**(6): 158 (1960).
12. W. Lehmer, A. Sellmaier, and W. Baldus, *Linde Ber. Tech. Wiss.*, **5**: 3 (1959).
13. D. C. Gami and A. S. Rapial, Analysis of Operating Experience of a Hydrogen Distillation Plant, in *Proceedings of the Third International Conference on the Peaceful Uses of Atomic Energy, Geneva, 1964*, Vol. 12, p. 421, United Nations, New York, 1965.
14. K. S. Bimbhat, Operational and Economic Aspects of Heavy-Water Production at Nangal, Based on Liquid-Hydrogen Distillation, in *Techniques and Economy of Production of Heavy Water*, Conference Proceedings, Turin, 1970, Comitato Nazionale per Energia Nucleare, Rome, 1971.
15. H. Gutowski, Technical Developments of the Low-Temperature Process for Heavy-Water Recovery and Its Economic Results, *ibid.*, p. 91.

11 *ELECTROLYTIC PLANTS*

ELECTROLYTIC PLANTS FOR PRELIMINARY ENRICHMENT

The process of separating heavy water by means of water electrolysis can be helpful for final enrichment of preconcentrates, for which the quantities to be processed are relatively small. The high separation factor, the practicality of the operation, and the possibility of holding losses to very low levels make this method particularly suitable for final concentration.

Preconcentration of natural water by electrolysis, on the other hand, encounters a considerable limitation in the high unit cost of the plant and in the heavy consumption of electric power. The process is economically suitable for producing heavy water only as a by-product of electrolytic hydrogen, and the unit cost of the heavy water thus obtained then becomes an increasing function of the plant yield.

To obtain preconcentrated water from an electrolytic plant with the least modification and supplementary structures, we need only to divide the cells into groups hydraulically connected in series. Each group of cells, whose number declines as the concentration rises, constitutes a stage in the cascade. The electrolyzed flow of each stage, instead of being recycled to the previous stage, is collected and sent to the user, as shown in Fig. 11.1.

The flow withdrawn from each stage, which goes to feed the next stage, is obtained by condensing the steam which accompanies the hydrogen and oxygen produced in that stage. For a given electrolyzed flow, the flow drawn off is determined by the temperature of the cells, the nature and concentration of the electrolyte, and the temperature of the condensers. Consequently, since all these factors cannot be arbitrarily changed, the cut is subject to certain limitations.

322

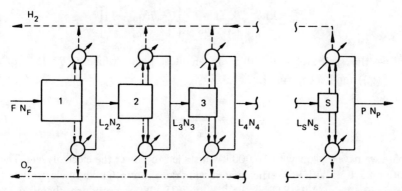

Fig. 11.1 Electrolysis plant for preconcentration without recycling. (From M. Benedict and T. H. Pigford, *Nuclear Chemical Engineering,* Fig. 11.9, p. 432, McGraw-Hill Book Company, Inc., 1957.)

The yield of the installation $(\eta = PN_P/FN_F)$ is necessarily small since the deuterium contained in the hydrogen is going to be lost anyway, even when it is in higher than natural concentration. In the low concentration approximation, the enrichment α of a stage is found to be, as was shown on pages 102 to 105.

$$\alpha = \frac{q_0}{1 + \theta\,(q_0 - 1)} \tag{11.1}$$

in which q_0 is the elementary separation factor of the cells and θ is the cut. Establishing a value of θ which is constant for all the stages, we find that the enrichment is constant too, and we obtain, for the yield of a plant with S stages, the expression (see pages 123 and 124).

$$\eta = (\alpha\theta)^S = \left(\frac{q_0\theta}{1 + \theta\,(q_0 - 1)}\right)^S \tag{11.2}$$

or, with θ from Eq. 11.1,

$$\eta = \left(\frac{q_0 - \alpha}{q_0 - 1}\right)^S \tag{11.3}$$

The electrolyzed flow is

$$L'' = (1 - \theta)F \sum_{i=1}^{S} \theta^{\,(i-1)} = (1 - \theta^S)F \tag{11.4}$$

and so, calling k the unit consumption of electric power, we find the specific consumption to be

$$E = \frac{kL''}{\eta_F N_F} = \frac{k}{N_F} \frac{1 - \theta^S}{\theta^S} \left[\frac{1 + \theta(q_0 - 1)}{q_0} \right]^S \tag{11.5}$$

Adopting the same value for θ as in an ideal plant, which is $\theta = 1/(1 + q_0^{1/2})$, we find $\alpha = (q_0^{1/2})$ and hence, from Eq. 11.3,

$$\eta = \left(\frac{q_0^{1/2}}{q_0^{1/2} + 1} \right)^S \tag{11.6}$$

Suppose we have a plant with 10,000 kW installed to power the electrolyzers. The cells operate on 2.1 V. With 95% efficiency, it will take about 6.6 kWh to electrolyze 1 liter of water, producing 1.25 STP m^3 hr^{-1}. With 5.25 kW, one produces therefore 1 STP m^3 hr^{-1} of hydrogen, and the whole plant of 10,000 kW yields 1870 STP m^3 hr^{-1}.

If, starting with natural water, we want to produce water at concentrations no lower than 1.5% with a separation factor of $q_0 = 5$ ($\alpha = q_0^{1/2} = 2.235$), we shall need

$$S = 2 \frac{\log 100}{\log 5} = \frac{4}{0.69} \simeq 6 \text{ stages}$$

and the plant yield will be $\eta = (2.235/3.235)^6 = 0.11$. Since $\theta^S \ll 1$, we see from Eq. 11.4 that the feed flow F practically coincides with the electrolyzed flow L'', which is $1,870,000/22.4 = 83,500$ mols hr^{-1}. The plant thus produces $PN_P = \eta FN_F = 0.11 \times 8.35 \times 10^4 \times 1.5 \times 10^{-4} = 1.38$ mols D_2O hr^{-1} contained at about 1.5%. With 8000 hr of operation per year, the plant's production is 11,040 mols, equal to about 221 kg of heavy water. The specific power consumption proves to be $8 \times 10^7/2.21 \times 10^5 = 362$ kWh g^{-1}. This consumption is enormous, but it is charged off to the cost of the hydrogen, which is the installation's principal product.

The power rating of the initial stage is given by the expression $(1 - \theta)Fk$, in which Fk coincides for all practical purposes with the power of the entire plant. The power required for the other stages is found by multiplying the flow of the first stage successively by θ. For the plant in question, the power distribution is more or less the following:

Stage No.	1	2	3	4	5	6
Power, kW	6900	2140	665	210	65	20

The only plant costs to be charged against heavy-water production are those having to do with the piping for the water supply to the stages in the cascade and possibly those costs having to do with the need for more thorough condensation of the steam that saturates the electrolytic gases.

In several countries, existing electrolytic plants have been adapted to produce heavy-water preconcentrates as by-products. Norsk Hydro in Norway, which was the first company to produce heavy water in large quantities, produced heavy water as a by-product of electrolytic hydrogen for use in ammonia synthesis. A plant in operation in 1942 at Rjukan, Norway, was using a mean electric power of 91,000 kW to produce about 17,000 STP m^3 hydrogen hr^{-1} and about 1.5 metric tons D_2O $year^{-1}$ at 15%.

The plant consisted of nine stages in cascade without recycling, with a cut $\theta = 0.27$ by condensation of the vapor that saturates the electrolytic gases. This cut was obtained by maintaining the electrolyte (a solution of KOH) at 60°C. The separation factor q_0 was 5.3.

The final concentration was done in a second electrolytic plant consisting of nine stages with recycling, according to the pattern to be explained below. The Norsk Hydro electrolysis plants were subsequently modified to increase deuterium recovery by means of the method described on pages 328 to 330.

An electrolytic preenrichment plant was built in India, in northern Punjab. With the damming of the Sutlej River at Bhakra and Nangal, 450,000 kW of electric power have become available at a low unit cost. About 130,000 kW are used to produce 25,000 STP m^3 hydrogen hr^{-1} for ammonia synthesis (about 250 tons day^{-1}) and 14 metric tons D_2O $year^{-1}$. The electrolyzers are Italian-built De Noras, with a separation factor of 6.26 at the maximum operating temperature, which is 85°C.

The electrolytic cells are subdivided into three stages without recycling, and the third stage yields 5000 STP m^3 hydrogen hr^{-1} at concentrations of about three times the natural level. The deuterium is extracted from this hydrogen (with a yield of about 90%) in the distillation plant referred to on page 317. The overall yield of the process is better than 50%.

ELECTROLYTIC PLANTS FOR THOROUGH ENRICHMENT

To increase the yield of an electrolytic plant, we can modify the stages that process water at higher concentrations in such a way as to recycle the electrolyzed flow from each stage. This is done by burning the hydrogen produced in those stages and recycling the resulting water. The conceptual diagram of this process is shown in Fig. 11.2, which shows S electrolytic stages connected in a cascade. From stage m on, the hydrogen is burned in burners B and recycled so as to form a symmetrical cascade.

Of course, if the highest yield is to be obtained from the burning stages (which means the lowest specific consumption too), these stages must operate like an ideal cascade. The cuts must be set so that there is no remixing at the points of confluence of the flows, and hence the enrichment per stage must be $\alpha = q_0^{\frac{1}{2}}$. If there are no complications involved, the same enrichment in the stages can be kept also in the stages without recycling.

The m-1 stage too is, in effect, part of the ideal cascade since it is fed in part with water from the stage m burner, at n_m concentration. The hydrogen produced in the m-1 stage, which is withdrawn and sent to utilization, constitutes the waste W of the

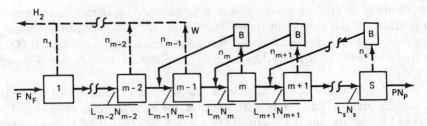

Fig. 11.2 Conceptual diagram of an electrolysis plant with hydrogen burning and recycling in the higher concentration stages. (From M. Benedict and T. H. Pigford, *Nuclear Chemical Engineering*, Fig. 11.11, p. 435, McGraw-Hill Book Company, Inc., 1957.)

ideal cascade. The mol fraction N_{i+1} of deuterium in the water produced by the stage i is given by

$$N_{i+1} = \frac{q_0^{i/2} N_F}{q_0^{i/2} N_F + 1 - N_F} \qquad (11.7)$$

whereas the mol fraction n_i in the hydrogen generated by the same stage is

$$n_i = \frac{q_0^{i/2-1} N_F}{q_0^{i/2-1} N_F + 1 - N_F} \qquad (11.8)$$

The flow H of hydrogen produced, burned, and recycled in the stages from m on is given by the equation that expresses the total recycled flow rate in an ideal symmetrical cascade:

$$H = \frac{P}{q_0^{1/2} - 1} \left\{ \frac{[N_P(1 + q_0^{1/2}) - q_0^{1/2}] \, 2 \ln (R_P/R_m)}{\ln q_0} \right.$$
$$\left. + \frac{N_P - N_m}{N_m(1 - N_m)} \frac{q_0 - (q_0 + 1) N_m}{q_0^{1/2} - 1} \right\} \qquad (11.9)$$

Furthermore, recalling the handling of ideal cascades, the flow of hydrogen W produced by the m-1 stage can be obtained from the equation

$$W = \frac{P \, q_0^{1/2} (N_P - N_{m-1})}{(q_0^{1/2} - 1) N_{m-1} (1 - n_{m-1})} \qquad (11.10)$$

Of course, the cost of the burned hydrogen in the recycling stages will be added onto the price of the heavy water by-product. One of the most important points in the design of an electrolytic plant with recycling in its higher stages is the determination of

Table 11.1

ASSESSMENT OF THE COSTS OF HEAVY WATER RECOVERED IN AN
ELECTROLYSIS PLANT THROUGH RECYCLING OF BURNED H_2

Stage	N_i, %	n_i, %	H, mols hr^{-1}	PN_P, mols hr^{-1}	$\Delta H/\Delta(PN_P)$	Unit costs (PN_P), dollars kg^{-1}
1	0.0149	0.00563				
2	0.0394	0.0149				
3	0.1042	0.0394	29,300	12.4	6530	326
4	0.275	0.1042	8,700	9.23	2460	123
5	0.725	0.275	2,420	6.69	940	48
6	1.89	0.725	675	4.84	361	18
7	4.84	1.89	195	3.51	59	3
15	99.17	97.85	. . .	. . .		
Production	99.69	Plant without burners 0.23				

the stage m at which it is best to begin recycling. Taking $\Delta(PN_P)$ as the increase in production to be obtained by moving the start of burning from stage i to stage i-1 and taking ΔH as the additional loss of hydrogen that such an increase would involve, we clearly see that the $\Delta H/\Delta (PN_P)$ ratio becomes greater as we move closer to the low concentrations.

The m stage is thus determined by the maximum value of $\Delta H/\Delta(PN_P)$, which does not push the price of heavy water above the going market level. This determination is made in steps by developing the calculation for various plants, each with a different starting point for burning.

In Table 11.1 are the findings of one such study, done for an electrolytic plant producing 4250 STP m^3 hydrogen hr^{-1}. (The example is a reelaboration of the one given by Benedict and Pigford in Ref. 8, Sec. 4.3.)

It is assumed that the cells, operating on a current of 2.1 V, have a separation factor q_0 of 7 and an electrolytic yield of 95%. The plant, fed with natural water, produces water at 99.69%. Even the stages without recycling are run with an enrichment $\alpha = q_0^{\frac{1}{2}}$, like those of the ideal symmetrical cascade. Under these conditions, 15 stages are needed to achieve the desired enrichment.

In the various cases considered in Table 11.1, the net production of hydrogen is constant: 4250 STP m^3 hr^{-1} (about 190,000 mols hr^{-1}). So there is a case-to-case variation in the number of electrolytic cells installed and in the total electric-power rating of the plant.

The last column in Table 11.1 shows the marginal costs for the additional production obtainable by gradually advancing the burning of hydrogen. These costs are calculated on the basis of a price of $0.03 per cubic meter STP for both hydrogen and oxygen. Since $\frac{1}{2}$ mol oxygen is burned for every mol hydrogen, the consumption of the latter will cost $0.045 per cubic meter STP, or $1 per kilomol, which shows that the increase in recovery obtained by burning stage 3 hydrogen is not altogether profitable. If, on the other hand, we burn the hydrogen produced in stage 4, the increase in production that we obtain in comparison with a plant that starts burning at stage 5 is at a unit cost that is not grossly in excess of the market price. In this case, the total cost of the burned gases is

$$\frac{8700 \times \$1}{9.23 \times 20} = \$47 \text{ per kilogram of } D_2O$$

This value, which is fairly low, leaves a comfortable margin for amortization of the supplementary equipment (burners, more efficient condensers, piping, etc.) required for the separation process.

If burning begins at stage 4, we obtain a yield of

$$\eta = \frac{9.23 \times 100}{190 \times 10^3 \times 1.49 \times 10^{-4}} = 32.6\%$$

and the specific consumption (since it takes 0.118 kWh to produce 1 mol hydrogen and since the overall production is about 200,000 mols) is

$$E = \frac{0.118 \times 200,000}{9.23 \times 20} \simeq 127,000 \text{ kWh/kg } D_2O$$

One system for increasing the yield of an electrolytic plant, while avoiding the burning of hydrogen, consists in enriching the feedwater for the individual stage by means of chemical exchange with the hydrogen produced in the same stage.

The process can be set up as shown in Fig. 11.3 for three successive typical stages. The steam that saturates the hydrogen generated in the electrolytic cells E of stage s is richer in deuterium than the hydrogen itself, because of the electrolytic separation factor. Therefore it is first depleted in the scrubber column (L) in countercurrent to the water coming from the s-3 stage. Thus, when it reaches the reaction chamber R, the hydrogen can be balanced chemically with the depleted vapor that accompanies it and releases part of its deuterium to it. If the reaction is run at 70°C, the equilibrium constant is $K \simeq 2.80$. The depleted hydrogen then flows into the scrubber column of the preceding stage (s-1). In this way the hydrogen is repeatedly depleted of its deuterium along its route in favor of the water that feeds the later stages of the electrolytic cells.

The design shown in Fig. 11.3 was used for the three Norsk Hydro electrolytic plants at Glam-Fjord in Norway. Each plant consists of 29 stages. In the first nine stages (all except the first stage is equipped with a reaction chamber), a deuterium concentration of about 2% is reached, whereas the final concentration takes place in the later 20 stages, in which recycling is achieved by burning the hydrogen. Total production of the three Norwegian plants is about 20 metric tons D_2O year^{-1}. An

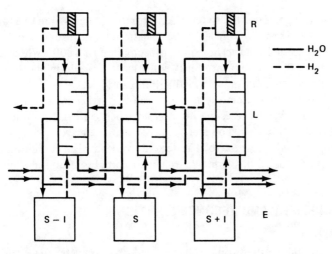

Fig. 11.3 Stages in an electrolysis plant with cells (E) combined with scrubber columns (L) and reaction chambers (R).

Table 11.2

DISTRIBUTION OF ELECTRIC POWER IN THE SABIÑÁNIGO PLANT IN SPAIN

Stage	Maximum power, kW	No. of cells
1	9,600	532
2	4,300	240
3	1,900	104
4	940	52
5	410	23
6	160	9
Total	17,310	960

electrolytic plant with reaction chambers has also been built in Sabiñánigo, Spain. The Oerlikon electrolytic cells, most of them of the filter-press type, were subdivided as shown in Table 11.2.

The actual plant design, however, is simpler than that shown in Fig. 11.3. The hydrogen in each stage (although of course no deuterium is recovered from the first) passes through a condenser, and the condensate feeds the next stage. The same hydrogen is resaturated with natural water vapor (75 to 80°C), goes to the reactor, after which the water vapor is recondensed and goes to feed the previous stage, whereas the hydrogen mixes with that of the preceding stage and is then put through another exchange reaction.

At the Sabiñánigo plant, the water is concentrated in deuterium to about 2%, with a production of 0.5 ton D_2O year^{-1}. The specific steam consumption is 8000 kg/kg D_2O, to which is added an electric-power consumption of 1800 kWh/kg D_2O for the compressors and other equipment. Final enrichment is made in another electrolytic plant with hydrogen burners and in a distillation plant.[11]

Deuterium recovery in electrolytic plants can be further increased by putting the hydrogen through several successive reaction chambers, rather than just one, in each individual stage. In this case, however, the role of the electrolytic separation factor becomes secondary with respect to that derived from chemical equilibrium. Therefore this case will be discussed in Chap. 12, which is devoted to chemical-exchange plants.

FINAL ENRICHMENT AND RECONCENTRATION

The electrolytic method can well be used to complete final enrichment of preconcentrates, even those produced by other methods. For this purpose the method can be applied in three different types of plants, i.e., plants having continuous, semicontinuous, and discontinuous operation.

The continuous plants are like those already described, meaning the plants that consist of a number of stages connected in series, with burning and recycling. Semicontinuous- and discontinuous-operation plants also perform enrichment in successive stages. These stages, however, unlike those for continuous-operation plants, do not all work at the same time. They are not materially connected, nor is the enriched mixture drawn off during operation. The stages follow one another in time, and use is made of a smaller number of cells in the same plant for each subsequent stage.

A stage in a semicontinuous-operation plant consists of one or more cells, each equipped with a feed vessel and a recovery vessel. Before electrolysis is started, each cell and its feed vessel are filled with the mixture to be concentrated. Electrolysis is then initiated. The gases produced are burned, and the resultant water is gathered in the recovery vessel. From the feed vessel a load of water continuously flows into the cell, so that the level of liquid in the cell remains constant. During electrolysis the mixture contained in the cell is gradually enriched.

Electrolysis is continued until the load in the feed vessel is gone. After this the electrolysis is halted, and the enriched mixture is removed from the cells and is used to fill the feed vessels and cells of the next stage, which produces further enrichment.

During the operation of a semicontinuous plant, the several electric parameters (voltage, current density, etc.) remain constant, as do the electrolytic concentrations and the cell temperatures. Varying over time, however, are the concentration of the contained mixture within the cells and hence the concentration of the mixture collected in the recovery vessels.

Discontinuous-operation plants are similar in all respects to semicontinuous-operation plants except that they have no feed vessels. The relatively large cells are filled with the water to be concentrated and are not fed any more water during electrolysis, so that they are gradually emptied. Hence in the discontinuous-operation plants, in addition to variations in the D_2O, there are also variations in the concentration of the electrolyte, in the various electric parameters, and in cell temperature.

For the theory of semicontinuous plant operation, the reader is referred to a specialized work (see Ref. 3), where as for discontinuous plant operation the reader should see in Chap. 4 the discussion of "batch" processes like Rayleigh distillation.

As was mentioned earlier, at the Norsk Hydro plant in Rjukan, Norway, a continuous-operation plant was used for the final concentration of heavy water.

A continuous-electrolysis plant having hydrogen burning was built at the Junta de Energia Nuclear (JEN) in Madrid to process 2% preconcentrated water from the Sabiñánigo plant (see page 230) up to 20 to 30% concentration. The final enrichment is then performed by distillation. The JEN electrolysis plant consists of five stages: three stages form the enrichment section, and the other two are the recovery section.

The cells are single-pole cylinders. The vessel itself acts as the cathode, and the anode is a nickel-plated metal cylinder suspended from above. The voltage drop is 2 V, and the current is supplied at 700 A. The electrolyte temperature is 50°C. Separation factors of 7 to 8 have been achieved.

The U. S. Atomic Energy Commission (USAEC), on the contrary, adopted the discontinuous process for the final concentration of the heavy water produced in the Morgantown, W. Va., distillation plant. The discontinuous process was also used in the Trail, B. C., plant. The Trail plant will be described below. Some time ago the electrolytic plant at Savannah River was shut down, and final concentration is now done solely by distillation.

The Trail electrolysis plant was in operation until 1956, producing about 0.5 ton D_2O month^{-1} at 99.8% from 2.14% water. The plant had three "batch" type stages, with 126, 20, and 4 cells per stage, respectively. The cells had steel cathodes and yielded a separation factor q_0 of 8 at a temperature of 23°C. The electrolytic solution was made with KOH at 2.5 wt.% initially. In the first two stages 85% of the load was electrolyzed, and in the third stage 67% was electrolyzed. When electrolysis was completed, the KOH was converted into K_2CO_3 by bubbling with CO_2 after which the water was evaporated out of the K_2CO_3.

A semicontinuous electrolytic plant is now operating in Canada at Chalk River. When fed with water with 90% deuterium, the plant can produce 330 kg D_2O hr^{-1} at 99.8% concentration.

The plant consists of seven units. Five of the units have Chalk River Nuclear Laboratories' cells (10,000 A cell^{-1}) and two have 12 each of the Trail-type cells (7000 A cell^{-1}). The total maximum absorbed current is 1,068,000 A. The cells are cylindrical, single pole in design, 0.3 m in diameter, and 1.5 m high. The mild-steel vessel is the cathode, and the anode is nickel-plated sheet steel. Some features of the cells are shown in Table 11.3.

The electrolyte is a solution of KOH at 15 to 25 wt.%. The separation factor q_0 is normally about 9 to 10. One of the seven units in the plant is shown schematically in

Table 11.3

CHARACTERISTICS OF THE ELECTROLYTIC CELLS OF THE CHALK RIVER PLANT

Cell type	Trail	Chalk River
Distance between electrodes, mm	6	3
Holdup, V	3.5	4
Current, A	6700	10,000
Total power, kW	23	37
Temperature	25	30
Current density, A cm^{-2}	0.6	0.32
Voltage, liters	50	4

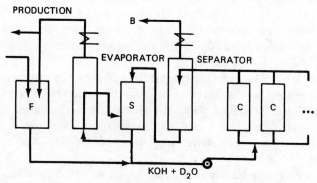

Fig. 11.4 Diagram of a unit of the Chalk River electrolysis plant: F, feed vessel; S, electrolyte recycling vessel; C, electrolytic cells (18 or 12); B, to the burner.

Fig. 11.4. The figure shows that the enriched product is extracted continuously through the evaporator, whereas the electrolyte stays in the cycle, and there is no need to replace it for every enrichment operation.

When the electrolyte is replaced, it is transformed into a carbonate that is freed of its heavy water by heating in an oven. An oven can be seen in the foreground of Fig. 11.5, which shows a general view of the installation. The three prism-shaped objects on wheels with cylinders on top of them are tritium contamination detectors. The heavy water used as a reactor coolant contains 2 to 2.5 Ci liter^{-1}, while that used as a moderator in power reactors generally contains from 10 Ci liter^{-1} up.

Tritium tends to stay in the cells since there is an electrolytic separation factor of about 20 for tritium. Tritium can be removed from the plant when necessary by rinsing it down with plain water.

The small volumes involved and the possibility of using whatever number of cells is suitable for the load to be processed means that an electrolytic plant is more flexible than a distillation plant for reconcentrating depleted water.

Fig. 11.5 View of the Chalk River electrolysis plant (Atomic Energy of Canada Limited) for reconcentrating depleted water.

REFERENCES

1. M. Benedict, Survey of Heavy-Water Production Processes, in *Proceedings of the International Conference on the Peaceful Uses of Atomic Energy, Geneva, 1955,* Vol. 8, p. 377 (Sec. 5), United Nations, New York, 1956.
2. D. C. Gami, D. Gupta, N. B. Prasad, and K. C. Sharma, Production of Heavy Water in India, in *Proceedings of the Second United Nations International Conference on the Peaceful Uses of Atomic Energy, Geneva, 1958,* Vol. 4, p. 534, New York, 1958.
3. L. Orsoni and M. Silvestri, Electrolytic Concentration of Heavy Water: Theory, Italian Centro Informazioni Studi Esperienze (CISE) Report 16, Milan, 1950.
4. L. Orsoni and M. Silvestri, Electrolytic Concentration of Heavy Water: Applications in Continuous-Operation Plants, Italian CISE Report 17, Milan, 1950.
5. P. G. Deshpande and D. C. Gami, Design of an Electrolytic Plant for the Concentration of Heavy Water, in *Proceedings of the Second United Nations International Conference on the Peaceful Uses of Atomic Energy, Geneva, 1958,* Vol. 5, p. 568, New York, 1958.
6. E. Cerrai, L. Orsoni, and M. Silvestri, Description of a Small Electrolytic Plant for Thorough Concentration of D_2O, Italian CISE Report 32, Milan, 1952.
7. E. Cerrai and M. Silvestri, Plant for Neutralizing and Distilling Solutions of H_2O-D_2O, Italian CISE Report 33, Milan, 1952.

8. M. Benedict and T. H. Pigford, *Nuclear Chemical Engineering*, Sec. 11.4m, McGraw-Hill Book Company, Inc., New York, 1957.

9. E. W. Becker, *Heavy-Water Production*, Review Series, No. 21, p. 51, International Atomic Energy Agency, Vienna, 1962 (STI/PUB/15/21).

10. J. A. Morrison, M. H. Thomas, and L. C. Watson, The Management of Heavy Water for Research and Power Reactors, in *Proceedings of the Third International Conference on the Peaceful Uses of Atomic Energy, Geneva, 1964*, Vol. 12, p. 373, United Nations, New York, 1965.

11. J. Alvarez et al., Studies Performed by the JEN on Obtaining Heavy Water Through Electrolysis and Isotopic Exchange Reaction, *ibid.*, p. 406.

12. H. K. Rae, Heavy Water, Canadian Report AECL-3866, Chalk River, 1971.

12 *EXCHANGE-REACTION PLANTS*

MONOTHERMAL PROCESSES: GENERAL REMARKS

As was seen in Chap. 3, there are several isotope-exchange reactions between hydrogenated compounds which offer very high separation factors for deuterium. Thus, for example, in the reaction

$$H_2O + HD \rightleftharpoons HDO + H_2$$

at $80°C$, the equilibrium constant is $K = 2.8$. If the system is a two-phase one, e.g., liquid (water) and gas (hydrogen), the elementary separation effect can be multiplied by running the two phases in countercurrent flow in a "transfer column" similar, at least in design, to distillation columns. This is shown in Fig. 12.1. As in distillation the countercurrent flow of vapor is obtained by evaporating water in the boiler at the bottom of the column, so in a water–hydrogen chemical-exchange process the countercurrent flow of gas may be achieved by converting water to hydrogen at the bottom of the transfer column.

For such conversion we can use (and some plants have already used them) electrolytic cells or even water–metal reaction beds at high temperature (although no application has been reported).

Further on it will be shown that countercurrent flow can also be achieved by circulating one of the two phases in closed cycle and using the change in the equilibrium constant of the exchange reaction at two diverse temperatures. This is why

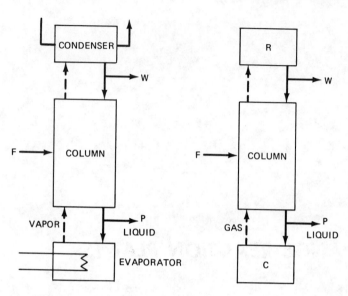

Fig. 12.1 Analogy between the distillation process and the gas–liquid exchange reaction. R = reflux converter; C = chemical reactor or electrolytic cell; F = feed; P = product; W = waste.

such processes are called "dual-temperature" processes. "Monothermal" is the term used for processes in which the chemical exchange takes place at a single temperature level, and the countercurrent flow is obtained by chemical conversion.

In addition to water–hydrogen exchange, the monothermal process has been applied to the ammonia–hydrogen system. For this system, phase conversion is obtained by heating the ammonia to break it down at the bottom of the column. In the water–hydrogen exchange process, with electrolytic conversion, the electrolytic separation factor is added to that of chemical exchange, so that actually there is a combined process from the point of view of separation effect as well. It must be stressed, however, that the presence of an electrolytic separation effect is not essential.

MONOTHERMAL H_2O/H_2 PROCESSES

In Chap. 11 it was shown that the yield of an electrolytic plant can be increased by adding reaction chambers. Rather than considering a single reaction chamber for each electrolytic stage, we now see that several reaction chambers can be arranged according to the square-cascade design, as shown in Fig. 12.2.

The hydrogen produced by the battery of cells A, which constitutes a particular stage of the electrolytic plant, is mixed at point O with water vapor generated in the evaporator E_1. The hydrogen–steam mixture crosses a catalytic bed housed in the reaction chamber R_1 and, after reacting, enters the condenser C_1. The two phases are

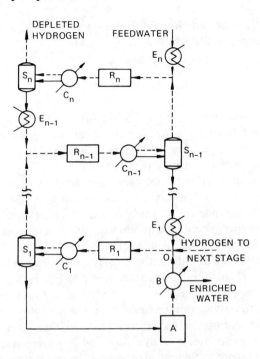

Fig. 12.2 Procedure for recovering deuterium from electrolytic hydrogen by means of the exchange reaction with water vapor. A = electrolytic cells; C = condenser; E = evaporator.

separated in the separator S_1. The water from it is fed into the electrolytic cells A, and the hydrogen goes to react again with steam in a successive reaction chamber. If the water–vapor exchange is repeated S times, according to the diagram in Fig. 12.2, the result is a countercurrent-flow process in which the feedwater is gradually enriched by the hydrogen coming from the cells.

The enriched water extracted from the cells, condensing at B the steam that is formed there, goes to feed the next enrichment stage in the plant. The depleted hydrogen coming from that stage is combined at point O with the hydrogen coming from A, to undergo further depletion.

It is easy to see that every series of S reaction chambers, each equipped with an evaporator, a condenser, and a separator, behaves, insofar as the transfer of deuterium from the gaseous phase (hydrogen) to the liquid phase (water), like a distillation column with S theoretical plates, having an elementary separation factor equal to the equilibrium constant K of the water–hydrogen exchange reaction.

In fact, each complex of evaporator, reaction chamber, condenser, and separator can be thought of as a plate in that ideal column. The ratio between the relative abundances of deuterium in the water and in the hydrogen leaving the complex is K. With a column consisting of a very large number of plates and operating with equal mol flows for the two phases at a temperature of 80°C, for which K = 2.80, the maximum yield is practically achieved (see Chap. 4).

$$\eta_\infty = 1 - \frac{1}{K} = 0.643$$

The plant yield coincides with the yield of the first-stage column and even though, in actuality, with not too large a number of plates we obtain only 90% of the maximum value ($\eta \simeq 58\%$), recovery is substantially increased by comparison with the electrolytic plant with partial burning of the hydrogen.

In the process shown in Fig. 12.2, the water must be evaporated and condensed as many times as there are beds of catalyst for the exchange reaction, which naturally calls for considerable expenditure of thermal energy. This expenditure can be cut down by adopting another procedure that requires, for a whole series of catalyst beds, only a single evaporation and a single condensation operation. This second process uses suitable exchange columns, in which the catalyst beds are alternated with usual bubble-cap plates, according to the arrangement shown in Fig. 12.3.

The hydrogen coming from the battery of electrolytic cells A is saturated with the steam coming from the evaporator E, which vaporizes the water coming from the transfer column. The hydrogen gives up deuterium to the steam with which it is saturated each time it passes over a catalyst bed. The hydrogen—steam mixture must bubble through one or more bubble-cap plates where the steam gives up the deuterium to the water, the hydrogen remaining inert.

In this way, with several repetitions of alternate exchange reactions and scrubbings, a countercurrent flow process is obtained in which the water flowing down the column is progressively enriched in deuterium, while the hydrogen flowing up is depleted. At the top of the column, the condenser C condenses the steam that saturates the outcoming hydrogen. The condensate constitutes the reflux liquid, together with the water coming from the preceding enrichment stage.

In the transfer column the hydrogen—steam mixture is heated by a superheater R [see Fig. 12.3(b)] before reaching each catalyst bed. This is done to prevent condensation in the bed itself, with a consequent decline in activity.

The transfer column for hydrogen—vapor exchange (called a Trail column after Trail, B.C., Canada, the place at which it was operated until the 1950s) can thus be considered as made up of a number S of plates, each consisting of a catalyst bed and one or more bubble-cap plates. For the entire series of S plates, the water is evaporated and condensed only once, at E and at C, respectively [Fig. 12.3(a)]. With the column shown there, however, with S and the water and hydrogen flow rates being equal, a smaller fractionation is obtained than with the multiple-evaporation and -condensation process.

While for the multiple-evaporation process the enrichments are easy to calculate, we can see that, using the formulas for distillation columns, a specific calculation is required for exchange columns of the Trail type. Only the low concentrations will be discussed here. Fig. 12.4 is a diagram of the standard plate s in a Trail column,

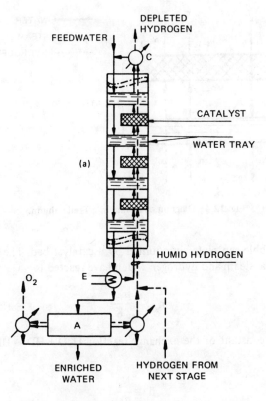

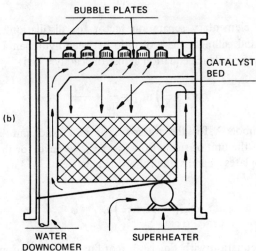

Fig. 12.3 Process for recovering deuterium from electrolytic hydrogen by exchange reactions. (a) Transfer column. (b) Plate design.

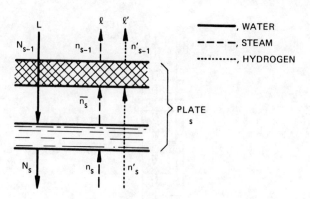

Fig. 12.4   Diagram of a plate in a Trail column.

consisting of a bubble-cap plate surmounted by a catalyst bed. The ratio between the mol fractions of the steam and hydrogen which have reacted is

$$n'_{s-1} = \frac{n_{s-1}}{K} \tag{12.1}$$

in which K is the constant of the exchange reaction $H_2O + HD \rightleftharpoons HDO + H_2$. We also have the equation

$$\bar{n}_s = \frac{N_s}{q_0} \tag{12.2}$$

in which q_0 is the elementary separation factor for distillation. Keeping in mind Eqs. 12.1 and 12.2 and calling y the mol ratio between hydrogen and steam, we can write the desired isotope balance equation across the catalyst bed:

$$\left(1 + \frac{y}{K}\right) n_{s-1} = \frac{N_s}{q_0} + \frac{yn_s}{K} \tag{12.3}$$

Introducing the symbols λ for the water–vapor mol ratio and φ for the isotope transport referred to the unit of steam flow ($\varphi = \phi/l$), we have, for the isotope crossing the section between plates s-l and s, the following balance:

$$\lambda N_{s-1} - \left(1 + \frac{y}{K}\right) n_{s-1} = \varphi \tag{12.4}$$

Combining this last equation with Eq. 12.3, reordinating, and dropping the index by one unit, we have

$$N_{s+1} - AN_s = -B \tag{12.5}$$

with

$$A = \frac{q\lambda(1 + y/K)}{1 + y/K + q\lambda\, y/K} \quad \text{and} \quad B = \frac{q\varphi}{1 + y/K + q\lambda\, y/K} \tag{12.6}$$

The relative yield of the column $\rho = \eta/\eta_\infty$ [in which $\eta_\infty = 1 - (1 + y/K)/q\lambda$] is given by $\rho = B/N_0(A - 1)$, and hence the solution to Eq. 12.5, integrated with the boundary condition $N(0) = N_0$, is written

$$N_S = N_0\, [1 - \rho]\, A^S + N_0\rho \tag{12.7}$$

The enrichment a, which is obtained with a column having S = 10, K = 2.80 (80°C), y = 3, qλ = 4, and ρ = 0.90, may be calculated as follows:

$$a = 0.1 \times A^{10} + 0.9 \quad \text{with A} = 1.30$$

and so

$$a = 0.1 \times 14.1 + 0.9 = 2.3$$

Developing S from Eq. 12.7, we have the known relationship

$$S = \frac{\ln\,[(a - \rho)/(1 - \rho)]}{\ln A} \tag{12.8}$$

Hence the quantity A corresponds, for ρ = 0, to the enrichment factor per plate.

For the multiple-evaporation process, we correspondingly have A = Kλ (in this case λ is the mol ratio of water to hydrogen). In the multiple-evaporation process with λ = 1, we find A = K, e.g., A = 2.80 at 60°C. In the Trail column fed with equal mol flows of water and hydrogen (equal at the outside, or before the evaporator and after the condenser), there is inside the column a mol ratio of water to steam of λ = 1 + y. With y = 3 and q$_0$ $\simeq$ 1, we have, as shown above, A = 1.30. Hence we obtain markedly lower fractionation, the number of plates being equal, than we could with the multiple-evaporation process.

In the above-mentioned calculation, we have assumed that, in the exchange processes, equilibrium has been reached. In other words, we have been talking about theoretical plates rather than real ones. Of course, in calculating for a plant, we have to take into account the percentages of equilibrium achieved. For low concentrations the calculation can be approached analytically, with suitable generalization of the exchange-column equation.

Calculation of the number of plates needed to achieve a certain enrichment with Trail columns can be done graphically.[5] Such calculation shows that, if all the catalyst beds in a Trail column are to be equally used, meaning that each will convert the same proportion of the HD coming in to HDO, the isotope transport across the column must be zero. If the transport is not zero, in the upper plates of the column the single catalyst bed will transform a smaller proportion of HD than is transformed in the lower plates.

During World War II, the Manhattan District encouraged application of the method for recovering deuterium from the electrolytic hydrogen produced in the Trail, B.C., plant by Consolidated Mining and Smelting Company. Hydrogen production was about 14,000 STP m^3 hr^{-1}. The enrichment plant started operation in June 1943 and reached its stationary level of concentrations after 8 months. Production of heavy water was about 0.5 metric ton $month^{-1}$. Operation continued until 1956, the year in which the plant was shut down because in the meantime more economical plants had been built, plants incorporating the principle of dual-temperature exchange reactions.

The electrolytic plant with exchange reaction consisted of four stages, each made up of one group of electrolytic cells C, with one or more exchange columns T. The plant produced 2.14% preconcentrated water. Final enrichment was performed by means of a three-stage discontinuous electrolytic plant, which was described on page 331.

The design of the exchange reaction plant is shown in Fig. 12.5. In the figure, an exchange column and its evaporators and condensers are shown as a unit. The product drawn off in the form of enriched water from each stage consists of the condensate that is obtained by cooling the electrolytic gases. Concentrations and flow rates shown in the figure are those actually observed over a specific period during 1945 and do not lead to any exact balance of materials.

The cells were the diaphragm type with steel cathodes and were run at 60 to 70°C with a voltage of 2.1 V; they gave a separation factor q_0 of 3.8. The electrolyte used was KOH (28 wt.%) and NaOH (20 wt.%).

The cut of the electrolytic cells was very small in the first stage (about 7.5%). The cut increased to 25% in the second stage and to about 30% in the other two stages. In Fig. 12.5 we can see that the condensate obtained at the top of the first column is removed from the plant and is not used as reflux because it is too depleted. The oxygen produced by the plant carries with it a little rich water, which is scrubbed with natural water. The natural water is thereby enriched by 1% in deuterium and is introduced into the cascade, bypassing the first stage. Finally, some of the feedwater is introduced directly into the C-0 cell group without going through the first exchange column because, since these cells are not watertight, it is preferable to have any leaks as low as possible in concentration. It is an interesting fact that the feedwater, even though it is natural water, has a deuterium concentration considerably lower than normal (138 ppm as against 149 ppm). This fact was commented on in Chap. 1.

In Table 12.1 are the data relating to the various plant components. The first stage in the cascade contains two exchange columns (plus one reserve column), whereas the other three stages have only one column each. The number of bubble-cap plates shown on the table includes six plates beneath the catalyst bed at the bottom of the column and five more at the very top. Note also that, of the 2693 electrolytic cells in the first stage, 288 are those of the 0 group (see Fig. 12.5).

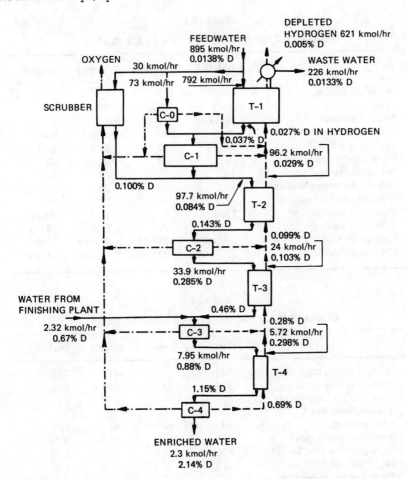

Fig. 12.5 Diagram of the Trail plant. C = electrolytic cells; T = exchange columns.

The operating conditions of the exchange columns in the Trail plant are shown in Table 12.2. The data shown for flow rates do not precisely coincide with those shown on Fig. 12.5.

The temperature of the various columns ranges from 60 to 73°C since it was found experimentally that, working with temperatures between 60 and 75°C, the maximum recovery was made. The temperature is a little higher in the first-stage columns because they operate at a little higher pressure. If the temperature is lowered, there is the disadvantage of cutting down the steam flow, which means that there is also a drop in deuterium transfer from the hydrogen to the steam over the catalyst beds. However, if the temperature is raised too high, there is an excess of steam and hence too slight a variation in its concentration after each reaction. Furthermore, as the temperature rises, there is a drop in the equilibrium constant K of the exchange reaction. At the

Table 12.1

MAIN SPECIFICATIONS FOR THE TRAIL PLANT

	Stage 1	Stage 2	Stage 3	Stage 4
No. of electrolysis cells	2693	378	96	30
No. of columns	2(+1)	1	1	1
Column diameter, m	2.6	1.5	0.76	0.46
Column height, m	34.2	32.9	29.6	29.4
No. of bubble-cap plates	35	32	32	32
No. of catalyst beds	13	13	13	13
Distance between plates, cm	20	20	20	20
Depth of catalyst beds, cm	11.5	15	15	11
Volume of catalyst, cm^3	13	3	0.73	0.146
Type of catalyst	Pt	Pt	Pt	Ni−Cr
Evaporator, kcal hr^{-1}	570,000	146,000	47,000	4700
Condenser, kcal hr^{-1}	1,070,000	293,000	54,000	14,700

Table 12.2

OPERATING CONDITIONS FOR TRAIL COLUMNS

	Stage 1	Stage 2	Stage 3	Stage 4
Pressure at top, torrs	833	716	712	713
Pressure at bottom, torrs	927	798	798	764
Mean catalyst temperature, °C	73	67	64	62
Mean bubble-plate temperature, °C	69	64	61	60
Water flow rate, kmol hr^{-1}	756	125	31.1	9.22
Hydrogen flow rate, kmol hr^{-1}	620	96.3	24	5.72
Steam flow rate, kmol hr^{-1}	212	30	6.26	1.44
Steam volume through plates, m sec^{-1}	0.53	0.53	0.44	0.34
Volume of hydrogen flow through catalyst, STP m^3 m^{-3} hr^{-1}	13,300	8800	8200	10,800
Efficiency ratings, %				
Bubble-cap plates (Murphree)	53	37	48	48
Catalyst beds (fresh)	95	95	95	95

two extremes of the variability range of the mol ratio y between hydrogen and steam, we have, on the one hand, $y \to \infty$, the extreme case of a column that does not enrich because it has no steam and, on the other, $y = 0$, the extreme case of a column that, being without hydrogen, enriches like a simple distillation column.

It is shown in the table that the percentage of equilibrium reached with a fresh catalyst was very high (95%). Even after 2 years in operation the percentage was still between 80 and 95%. However, for good catalyst performance, we need pure hydrogen since any substances tending to accumulate on the catalyst (substances known as "poisons") decrease the portion of the surface available for reaction and hence cut down the efficiency of the catalyst itself.

Poisons can be attached to the catalyst by chemical reaction with an impurity present in the reagents (such as sulfate compounds or H$_2$S, the latter leading to the formation of metal sulfide that has a very low or even zero catalytic action) or by heavy adsorption of the impurity itself.

Although in the case of heavy adsorption the poisoning action is temporary and disappears on simple physical treatment of the poisoned catalyst, in the first case the poisoning is more stubborn. Both platinum catalyst and nickel—chromium catalyst are poisoned by KOH, CO, and such sulfur compounds as H$_2$S. This is why, with the catalysts available now, water—steam exchange for deuterium recovery is confined to use with electrolytic hydrogen, the water—gas hydrogen or the hydrogen derived from methane processing being too rich in impurities.

From the material balances (139 mols hr^{-1} D$_2$ incoming as against 111 mols hr^{-1} outgoing), we find that the plant has many losses (this is seen notably in the cells), which means that the yield is only 39.3% as compared with the 63.7% there would be without the losses. This latter value is quite close to the theoretical maximum (67%) yield for the 73°C temperature. Calculated in 1945 for a production of 0.5 ton month^{-1}, the specific investments and operating costs were, respectively, $500 per kilogram of D$_2$O per hour and $60 per kilogram of D$_2$O. In 1954 the operating cost was $132 per kilogram of D$_2$O. The process thus has typically very low capital costs and very high operating costs.

In the Trail version the process is certainly not an economical one, but Benedict and Pigford[1] have suggested an improved version based on the following assumptions: (1) cutting losses from the cells to a minimum; (2) a higher electrolytic separation factor ($q_0 = 7$); and (3) zero transport in the transfer columns. This last requirement can be met by having about 70% of the feedwater for each stage bypass the exchange column and go directly to the cells. This will ensure that isotope transport takes place along the cell cascade rather than along the columns.

Flows must be so proportioned that there is no mixing at the points of confluence and, furthermore, that the enrichment is the same for every group of cells and for each exchange column. The higher separation factor makes a purely electrolytic first stage attractive. The result is that the hydrogen flow in the columns is only 45% of that in the Trail plant, with total hydrogen production being equal. Despite the fact that the waste hydrogen will have a slightly higher concentration, the production and yield (61%) are 56% higher than the corresponding quantities of the Trail plant.

MONOTHERMAL NH$_3$/H$_2$ PROCESSES

With the NH$_3$/H$_2$ system, the exchange reaction

$$NH_3 + HD \rightleftharpoons NH_2D + H_2 \qquad (12.9)$$

can be run at very low temperatures. Theoretically the lower limit is the temperature at which ammonia solidifies, which is $-78°C$. At this temperature the elementary separation factor q_0 is 9. However, even at temperatures not so low, the separation factor remains high. For example, we find

for T = $-40°C$ $+25°C$ $0°C$
    $q_0 =$ 7   5   4.2

For the dependence of q_0 on the absolute temperature, Bigeleisen and Perlman[7] have suggested the equation

$$\log q_0 = \frac{237}{T} - 0.2428 \qquad (12.10)$$

as valid for the interval from -73 to $+227°C$.

By operating a transfer column at low enough temperature, we can obtain a very high separation rating with a modest number of theoretical plates. However, as we shall see, the efficiency of the ammonia–hydrogen contact at low temperature is not very good. This increases the number of real plates and in practice means that it is better to use nonconventional plates.

The exchange reaction (Eq. 12.9) must be catalyzed. The catalyst most commonly used is potassium amide (KNH_2) in ammonia solution. This compound is obtained by dissolving 99.8% pure metallic potassium in ammonia and hence has a fairly high cost. Potassium amide is broken down by oxygen and such oxygen compounds as H_2O, CO, and CO_2. With water it is transformed into potassium hydrate, whereas with oxygen it leads to the formation of explosive compounds. Therefore the processing gas must be subjected to careful purification, so that the residual content of water and oxygen is less than 1 ppm.

The monothermal NH_3/H_2 exchange process was developed in France, primarily for recovering deuterium from the hydrogen which is part of the gas used for synthesizing ammonia. The diagram of the process is shown in Fig. 12.6. The process was adopted in France at Mazingarbe, in combination with a plant producing 650 tons ammonia year^{-1}. Deuterium recovery from the feed hydrogen (132 ppm deuterium) has a yield of 63%, and so production is about 20 tons D_2O year^{-1}.

The gas for synthesis, at 450 atm pressure, is first subjected to the purification process. This is done in two steps. In the first, the oil, the oxygen (by means of catalysts), and the humidity (by means of alumina) are eliminated. In the second step, the remaining impurities are removed by scrubbing with an ammonia solution of potassium amide. After purification the gas enters a transfer column at $-25°C$; this column operates as a stripping section, at the head of which the synthesis plant sends back part of the ammonia produced (115 tons year^{-1} out of 650) to the same column as liquid reflux. There are two reasons why lower temperatures were not part of the design: (1) very expensive steels would not have to be used in construction, and (2) a simple type of cooling plant could be used.

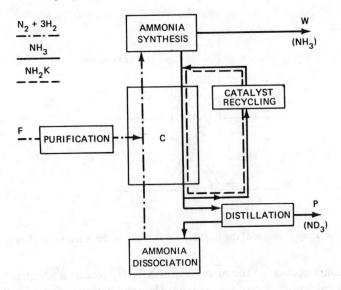

Fig. 12.6 Diagram of the monothermal NH$_3$/H$_2$ exchange process. C represents the transfer column or two columns in series; F = feed; P = product; W = waste.

The contact units (10 or so theoretical plates) are a special type, as shown in Fig. 12.7. The plate consists of a ring of nozzles in which the gas (3H$_2$ + N$_2$) breaks up and scatters the liquid (NH$_3$ + KNH$_2$) in tiny droplets. The large contact surface makes up to a degree for the slowness of the diffusion processes in the liquid phase. The ammonia is pumped into the nozzles by pumps submerged below the surface of the liquid. The −25°C column is attached in series with a second column that operates as an enrichment section. In this second column a concentration of about 1.5% D/H is reached, and this second column operates at −10°C. A lower separation factor was accepted in exchange for more efficient contact.

At the output of the enrichment column, the ammonia is separated from the potassium amide by evaporation (at 20 atm), is recondensed, and is subjected to final enrichment by distillation at atmospheric pressure and −30°C. The potassium amide is depleted in deuterium and flows into a transfer column at +35°C in countercurrent with a flow of process gas, which is then reinserted at the bottom of the enrichment column. The catalyst in turn is recycled at the top of the stripping column. For replacement of the lost catalyst, the potassium consumption amounts to 0.6 kg for every 100 metric tons of gas treated.

Reconversion of the ammonia to hydrogen and nitrogen is done by heating (with a suitable catalyst) to 550 to 580°C at 55 to 60 atm. The gas must then be recompressed to the process pressure (450 atm) by means of a special dry-piston high-capacity compressor.

The Mazingarbe plant has operated for several years quite satisfactorily, with an availability factor of 92%.

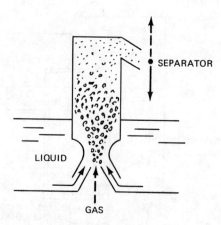

Fig. 12.7 Operating principle of the H_2/NH_3 contact unit in the Mazingarbe plant in France.

Energy consumption for the monothermal NH_3/H_2 process is associated primarily with the thermal dissociation of the ammonia (E_T) and with recompressing the process gas (E_C). We find $E_T = 2.5 \times 10^6$ kcal/kg D_2O, and $E_C = 1110$ kWh/kg D_2O. Estimating the cost of thermal energy at \$2.50 per million kcal and that of electrical energy at \$0.006 per kilowatt-hour, we arrive at a partial cost of \$12.85 per kilogram of D_2O for the major energy-consumption costs.

A plant technically derived from Mazingarbe was built at Baroda, India. It is associated with an ammonia synthesis plant producing 1000 metric tons day^{-1}. The production will be about 67 metric tons D_2O year^{-1}, with a yield of 89%. Several modifications were made in the Mazingarbe design for Baroda. For example:

1. The temperature in the transfer columns is $-27°C$ (stripping) and $0°C$ (enrichment).

2. The ammonia is broken down at 140 atm (rather than 60), which cuts down the energy consumption for recompressing the gas.

3. The enrichment column also operates at 140 atm, which means that the compressor can be located at its outlet and that the gas can be recycled to the purification section. This makes possible the use of an ordinary oil-lubricated compressor.

4. Final enrichment is made in a second dual-temperature stage rather than by distillation of the ammonia.

DUAL-TEMPERATURE PROCESSES: GENERAL REMARKS

As was mentioned earlier, the countercurrent in a transfer column may be by a method other than phase conversion. This method is shown in Fig. 12.8. The gas coming from the transfer column at temperature T_1 is depleted in deuterium by the liquid (according to the equilibrium constant K_1) and is recycled at the bottom of the

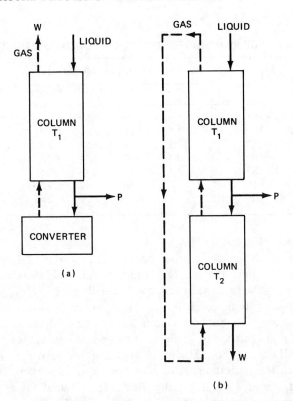

Fig. 12.8 Diagram of a dual-temperature process (b) compared with a monothermal process with phase conversion (a). P = product; W = waste.

second column at a temperature $T_2 > T_1$. This second column is fed with the liquid coming from the first column. Furthermore, the equilibrium constant K_2 at the higher temperature is less favorable to the liquid, and so it restores to the gas some of the deuterium it gathered in the first column. Thus the gas enters the bottom of the first column enriched. Between the two columns, part of the enriched-liquid flow is drawn off as product. A variant on this design consists in circulating the liquid in a closed cycle and extracting the rich fraction of the gas. The processes that make use of exchange at two different temperatures are called dual-temperature processes.

Of course it is better to have the two temperatures as far apart as possible, compatible with technical and economic requirements. Having them very different will give the maximum K_1/K_2 ratio, which is important if a good separation factor is to be obtained. The dual-temperature process can be run with several pairs of substances, as can be seen in Table 12.3. In the table are shown, for the various exchange reactions (all at low deuterium concentrations), the elementary separation factors q_0 at several temperatures (the figures are taken from Refs. 2 to 5 and Ref. 10), as well as the q_{25}/q_{100} ratios of the separation factors at 25°C and 100°C, respectively.

Table 12.3

EXCHANGE REACTIONS BETWEEN HYDROGEN COMPOUNDS

Reacting substances (phases: liquid–gas)	q_0/K	Separation factor (q_0)					q_{25}/q_{100}
		0°C	25°C	100°C	125°C	227°C	
$H_2O + NH_2D \rightleftharpoons HDO + NH_3$	$\frac{3}{2}$	1.02	1.00	0.99	...	0.98	1.01
$H_2O + HDS \rightleftharpoons HDO + H_2S$	1	2.52	2.26	1.86	1.77	...	1.21
$H_2O + DCl \rightleftharpoons HDO + HCl$	$\frac{1}{2}$	2.87	2.51	1.98	1.87	1.59	1.27
$H_2O + DBr \rightleftharpoons HDO + HBr$	$\frac{1}{2}$	3.57	3.07	2.34	2.17	1.79	1.31
$H_2O + DI \rightleftharpoons HDO + HI$	$\frac{1}{2}$	4.55	3.80	2.78	2.56	2.05	1.37
$NH_3 + HD \rightleftharpoons NH_2D + H_2$	$\frac{2}{3}$	4.22	3.56	2.47	2.33	1.70	1.44
$H_2O + HD \rightleftharpoons HDO + H_2$	1	4.69	3.87	2.69	2.47	1.94	1.44

The reaction speeds for the first five systems listed in Table 12.3 are fairly high, so that they do not require the use of a catalyst. All these systems, however, are corrosive, except for the first, water–ammonia, but then its q_{25}/q_{100} ratio is rather low. The last two systems listed in the table, ammonia–hydrogen and water–hydrogen, are not corrosive, but both require the use of a catalyst.

Of the various systems, the only ones thus far applied on an industrial scale are the H_2O/H_2S and NH_3/H_2 systems. Studies are now under way on the amine–hydrogen systems, in which the separation factor is at least equal to within ±10% that of the NH_3/H_2 system. Figure 12.9 graphically illustrates the variations in the separation factor with temperature for the H_2O/H_2S, H_2O/H_2, and NH_3/H_2 systems.

To calculate the separation factor of dual-temperature separating elements, we must know the enrichment produced in each of the two phases, liquid and gas, when they are in countercurrent flow through an exchange or distillation column.

Distillation columns, whether plate or packed, and exchange columns, whether the Trail design (for water–hydrogen exchange in the gaseous phase) or the bubble-cap design (for uncatalyzed reactions), behave alike insofar as the dependence of enrichment on the number of plates and on the ratio between the mol flow rates of the two phases is concerned. We shall therefore refer to both types of columns with the more general term of "transfer column."

We can clarify the preceding analogy by first considering a bubble-cap column in which q_0 is the elementary separation factor (it makes no difference whether it is derived from distillation or from chemical exchange). Our considerations will be confined to the case of low concentrations, and we shall also assume that contact between the two phases has an efficiency rating of $\beta = 100\%$. In this case Eq. 9.19 is applicable and can be written in this form:

$$N_S = fq_0n_S + (1 - f)N_0 \tag{12.11}$$

in which

$$f = \frac{(1/q_0 \, \lambda)^S - 1}{(1/q_0 \, \lambda)^S - q_0 \, \lambda} \tag{12.12}$$

From Eq. 12.12 we see that, for any value of λ, $0 \leqslant f \leqslant 1$ and that for $\lambda = 1/q_0$ we have $f = S/(1 + S)$. When $S \to \infty$ with $\lambda \leqslant 1/q_0$ (a condition of "little liquid" or of "balanced flows"), we have $f = 1$, and, from Eq. 12.11, we find that the two phases reach equilibrium at the base of the column. But if, on the contrary, $\lambda > 1/q_0$ (condition of "much liquid") at the limit for $S \to \infty$, i.e., $f = 1/q_0\lambda$ is obtained, and therefore the equilibrium between the two phases is reached at the top of the column, as in the case of the fractional distillation of water, where the mol flow of the liquid is always greater than that of the steam.

From these considerations and from Eq. 12.11, we see that, for any value of $\lambda \leqslant 1/q_0$, the parameter f will coincide with the ratio between the quantity of isotope transferred from one phase to the other in a column of S plates and the quantity transferred in a column made up of an infinite number of plates. But, if it is

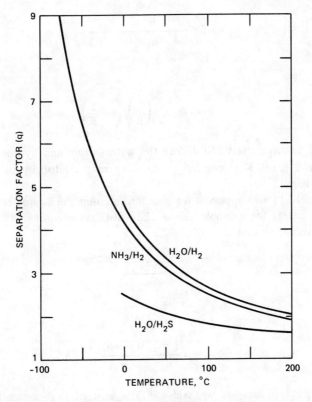

Fig. 12.9 Dependence of the separation factor on temperature in the H_2O/H_2, NH_3/H_2, and H_2O/H_2S systems.

$\lambda > 1/q_0$, the parameter f will not coincide with that ratio but will be proportional to it according to the $1/q_0\,\lambda$ factor. We shall call f the "transfer parameter." It is easy to show that any transfer column can be described by Eq. 12.11 with a suitable expression for the f parameter, which will, of course, retain its significance no matter how it is expressed.

For example, for a packed column we find

$$f = \frac{\exp\,[(1 - q_0\lambda)S] - 1}{\exp\,[(1 - q_0\lambda)S] - q_0\lambda} \tag{12.13}$$

in which S indicates the number of transfer units. This latter quantity is defined by the relation $S = Z/h$ in which Z is the height of the packing, L is the flow rate of the liquid, and h is the height of the transfer unit.

Similarly a Trail column (consisting of alternating bubble-cap plates and catalyst beds), fed by steam and hydrogen in equilibrium, is described by the same equation (Eq. 12.11) in which f is given by

$$f = \frac{B^S - 1}{B^S - q_e\lambda(1 + y/K)} \tag{12.14}$$

where

$$B = 1/q_e\lambda + \left(\frac{y}{K}\right)\Big/\left(1 + \frac{y}{K}\right) \tag{12.15}$$

using λ and y, respectively, to denote the water–steam and hydrogen–steam mol flow ratios and q_e and K, respectively, for the separation factors by distillation and by chemical exchange.

Equation 12.11 also applies if we take into account the limited efficiency of the interphase contact; for example, for a plate distillation column with a Murphree efficiency rating β, we find

$$f = \frac{\gamma^S - 1}{\gamma^S - q_0\lambda} \tag{12.16}$$

in which

$$\gamma = \frac{1 + q_0\lambda(1 - \beta)}{1 + q_0\lambda - \beta} \tag{12.17}$$

Equation 12.11 applies—as we said—in the area of low concentrations and is particularly helpful in calculating the separation factor in dual-temperature processes since it sets up a simple linear ratio between the concentrations at either extremity of any transfer column. Of course the calculation of the distillation-column systems can all be done via the familiar McCabe–Thiele graphic method.

THE DUAL-TEMPERATURE H_2O/H_2S PROCESS

The water–hydrogen sulfide system affords the considerable advantage of not requiring the use of catalysts in a dual-temperature process, which means that the contact between the two phases can be achieved in such columns of conventional design as bubble-cap plate or sieve plate columns.

Another important feature of the dual-temperature process in the water–hydrogen sulfide system is that it frees the production of heavy water from other industrial processes since most of the raw material used in the process is natural water. An enrichment plant can be designed by connecting in cascade a number of separation elements, each one consisting of two columns, as shown in Fig. 12.10. Three stages are shown by way of example.

At the outlet of the cold column of each stage, a certain flow of enriched water is removed to feed the next stage. The depleted water from the second stage is piped in above the hot column. We can readily see that, with the possible exception of the final stage, in all the other stages the extracted rich flow and the depleted input flow between the two columns are practically equal, and hence the flow rates of water flowing in both columns of any given stage are also practically equal.

In each stage, of course excepting the last one, we thus have a withdrawal of isotope but not of mol flow. This means that there is a second-species withdrawal.

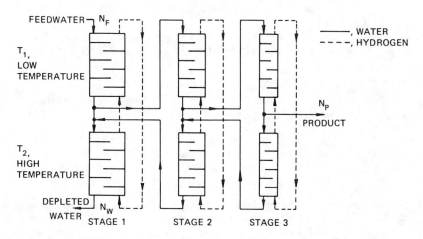

Fig. 12.10 Flow diagram for a three-stage plant for dual-temperature water–hydrogen sulfide exchange.

The diagram shown in Fig. 12.10 is not the only possible one for connecting the stages in cascade, but it is the best. As we shall see later on, the design has been used for all plants built in the United States, with only one variant. The gas circuits in the stages after the first one, rather than being autonomous as they are in the diagram in Fig. 12.10, are each derived from the preceding stage, as are the water circuits. In this way, in exchange for a more complex flow-control system, we have a decrease in the quantity of steam needed to humidify the gas in the hot columns; humidifying is now required only for the first stage.

The first design that anyone would think about when connecting stages in a cascade is the ideal symmetrical design, in which the depleted water coming from the hot column of a given stage would be recycled back into the top of the cold column of the previous stage, rather than into the top of the hot column, as indicated in Fig. 12.10. However, in the ideal-cascade design it would be necessary, to avoid mixing at the points of confluence, for the enrichment of the stage to be equal to the square root of the stage separation factor $[a = (q)^{1/2}]$. This, as we shall see, involves a marked limitation of enrichment, which might otherwise reach far higher levels, thus decreasing the number of stages in the cascade, with a consequent decrease in the unit cost of the plant.

The fact is that, with columns consisting of an infinite number of plates and with $1/K_1 < \lambda < 1/K_2$ (K_1 and K_2 are the constants of equilibrium for the low and high temperatures, respectively), the mol fraction of the gas coming from the cold column (for low deuterium contents) will be $n = N/K_1$, in which N is the mol fraction of the water feeding the column. Furthermore, at the bottom of the hot column, we find $N'' = K_2 n$, and hence $N''/N = a/q = K_2/K_1$. The enrichment factor for the separating element is accordingly

$$a = 1 + \frac{K_1 - K_2}{K_1} \frac{1 - \theta}{\theta} \tag{12.18}$$

in which θ is the cut. With small values for the cut, it is possible to obtain rather good enrichments. Further, if, e.g., the concentration in the feedwater for the second stage is aN_F, the depleted water coming out of that stage has a concentration of $N_F \times a$ K_2/K_1. The no-mixing requirement means that "a" must be equal to K_1/K_2, whereas, in general, it could be much higher.

If we adopt values for "a" higher than K_1/K_2, we might consider bringing in the depleted water from one stage at a suitable spot in the cold or hot column upstream so as to avoid causing any mixing. However, the design shown in Fig. 12.2 is the best anyway because, even if it is theoretically less efficient, it is simpler to build.

It is easy to see that for an element with second-species withdrawal—and hence for a cascade as well—the maximum yield is

$$\eta_\infty = 1 - \frac{K_2}{K_1} \tag{12.19}$$

For example, for $T_1 = 30°C$ and $T_2 = 130°C$, we have $\eta_\infty = 21\%$.

The energy consumption for a dual-temperature plant is made up not only of the power for pumping for circulation of both phases but also of the unrecovered heat losses in the heat exchangers positioned between the cold and hot zones of the plant. Heat exchange can be accomplished in several ways. In general, most of the required heat is obtained from the gas emerging from the hot column, whereas preheating of the water that feeds the hot columns is done by the depleted water emerging from the same columns.

The choice of operating conditions for a dual-temperature plant, which means choosing the pressure and the low and high temperatures, is governed by the phase diagram of the water–hydrogen sulfide system shown in Fig. 12.11 and by the dependence of the equilibrium constant K on the temperature. The latter is shown in some detail in Table 12.4 where, according to various temperature levels, we show the equilibrium constants K for the heterogeneous liquid–gas phase.

Obviously it would be desirable to operate the exchange columns at the highest possible pressure so as to cut down the column cross section as much as possible. On the other hand, there is a ceiling on pressure at temperatures below 28 to 30°C in the formation of the hydrate of H_2S which, as a solid, would swiftly clog the columns (see Fig. 12.11). At higher temperatures there is a similar limitation in the liquefaction point of H_2S.

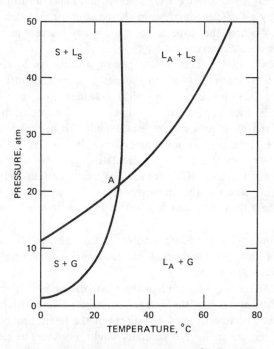

Fig. 12.11 Phase diagram for the H_2O/H_2S system.

Table 12.4

EQUILIBRIUM CONSTANT FOR THE
$H_2O + HDS \rightleftharpoons HDO + H_2S$ REACTION

Temp., °C	K	Temp., °C	K
0	2.524	80	1.939
10	2.390	90	1.897
20	2.299	100	1.858
30	2.222	110	1.823
40	2.153	120	1.790
50	2.091	130	1.761
60	2.035	140	1.732
70	1.985	150	1.706

The equilibrium curves for the various phases meet at the "triple point" A (29.4°C, 22.2 atm) and cut the plane into four regions. In Fig. 12.11, G is the gas, L_A is the aqueous solution, L_S is the liquid H_2S, and S is the solid H_2S hydrate. Since, in addition to high pressure, it is desirable to have a temperature T as low as possible, it is easy to see that the optimum conditions for both temperature and pressure will be found near point A. And, in fact, to the left of point A the slope of the curve of equilibrium (between S + G and L_A + G) is steep, and hence a drop in pressure is not compensated for by a sufficient increase in the equilibrium constant $K(T_1)$. Whereas to the right of A—where the slope is less steep—any increase in pressure entails a marked drop in the equilibrium constant.

Because of these considerations, we set the low temperature T_1 at about 30°C and the plant pressure at about 20 atm. In the design stage the final pressure level is established on the basis of certain practical considerations as well, such as the availability of standard valves with given maximum pressure specifications.

Once T_1 and the plant pressure are established, it is natural to seek the highest possible level for T_2 (the hot-column temperature). In this way the yield is increased and—the product remaining equal—the circulating gas flow and the column cross section are cut down. However, if T_2 is raised beyond a certain limit, the yield tends to remain constant, whereas the quantity of steam needed to saturate the gas continues to rise, and thus the result is a further increase in cross sections and in heat consumption.

Determining the T_2 temperature involves evaluating several economic factors, which will be different in each situation. However, as a general rule it will be somewhere between 120 and 150°C.

The existence of the L_A + L_S zone in the phase diagram leads us to consider the additional possibility of working the dual-temperature process with both components in the liquid phase. The advantage of getting rid of the latent heat of evaporation for the saturation of the gas in the hot columns would, however, be eliminated by two drawbacks: a higher operating pressure and a T_2 temperature limited by the critical point ($T_C = 100.4°C$; $P_C = 89$ atm). The results are lower yields and hence higher circulating flows. In addition, the efficiency of the liquid—liquid contact is probably lower than that of the liquid—gas contact, which means that longer columns would be needed and there would be greater holdups of hydrogen sulfide.

The equilibrium constant K of the exchange reaction between the water (liquid) and the hydrogen sulfide (gas), the values for which are shown in Table 12.4 for various temperatures, does not exactly constitute the elementary separation factor in an exchange column. In fact we must allow for the solubility σ of the H₂S in the water and for the steam that saturates the H₂S (i.e., the humidity H of the gas).

M. L. Eidinoff and C. H. Hiskey, defining the elementary separation factor q_0 as the ratio between the abundances of deuterium in the liquid and the gaseous phases, worked out the approximate expression

$$q_0 = \frac{q_e(\sigma + K')(1 + H)}{(1 + HK')(1 + \sigma)} \tag{12.20}$$

in which q_e is the separation factor for the distillation effect of the water and K is the equilibrium constant for the exchange reaction in the gaseous phase ($K' = K/q_e$). Equation 12.20 is valid, with good approximation, for any deuterium concentration. The error is less than 2/1000, up to concentrations of 15%. At temperatures of 30 and 130°C, Eq. 12.20 gives the q_0 values of 2.16 and 1.59, respectively. The 1.59 value particularly differs appreciably from the corresponding value of K. Precise calculation of the enrichment obtainable with a dual-temperature separating element is rather involved because of the complications introduced at the various mixing points. Figure 12.12 is a flow diagram in a separating element with second-species withdrawal and with an autonomous gas circuit.

The water from the cold column T_1 is heated in the heat exchanger E_L, and the water develops a quantity of gaseous H₂S because of the diminished solubility. This deuterium-rich gas is joined with the gas flow coming from the hot column T_2 and enters the heat exchanger E_G (for the sake of simplicity, we have omitted in Fig. 12.12 the auxiliary heating and cooling circuits needed because of the limited recovery of the exchangers). The condensate of the gaseous mixture cooled in E_G is joined with the liquid coming into E_L. In addition, a portion of the depleted liquid is used to saturate the gas coming from the cold column and heading toward the hot column. The H₂S dissolved in the water coming out of the cold column is evaporated in a small scrubber S by means of a steam flow. In the gas circuit, as in the water circuit, the greatest differences in concentration due to mixing are, respectively, $n_2 - n_P$ and $N' - N$.

The enrichment calculation on which the scale of the plant and the various flow rates are based can be done on a simplified pattern, like the one shown in Fig. 12.13, in which there is no mixing except that due to second-species withdrawal.

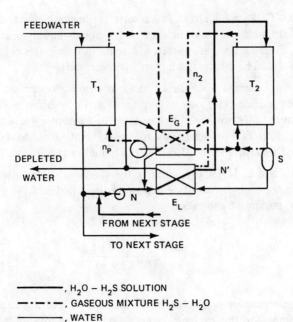

Fig. 12.12 Flow diagram of a dual-temperature separating element for the H_2O/H_2S system.

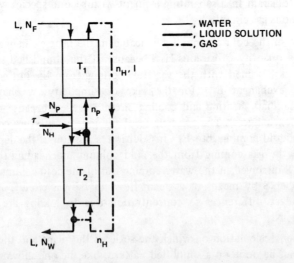

Fig. 12.13 Simplified diagram of a dual-temperature separating element for the H_2O/H_2S system.

The enrichment factor $a = N_P/N_F$, in the case of low-deuterium concentrations, is found by solving the linear system

$$N_P = f_1 q_1 n_P + (1 - f_1) N_F$$
$$N_P - N_H = \frac{\tau}{L'}$$
$$N_W = f_2 q_2 n_H + (1 - f_2) N_H \qquad (12.21)$$
$$N_F - N_P = \gamma_1 (n_H - n_P)$$
$$N_F - N_W = \frac{\tau}{L}$$

in which q_1 and q_2 are the elementary separation factors given by Eq. 12.20 for the two columns (T_1 for the low-temperature column and T_2 for the high-temperature column), $\gamma_i (i = 1$ or $2)$ are the gas–liquid mol ratios in the two columns ($\gamma_i = 1/\lambda_i$), τ is the cascade transport, L is the water flow that feeds the element, and the terms f_i are the transfer parameters of the columns, as defined by Eq. 12.12. When the yield $\eta = \tau/LN_F$ is introduced, the solution to the Eq. 12.21 system gives the following expression for enrichment:

$$a = 1 + \frac{1 - q_2/q_1 - \eta}{q_2/f_1 q_1 - q_2/\gamma_2 + 1/f_2 - 1} \qquad (12.22)$$

Equation 12.22 enables us to find the optimum value for the mol ratio (H$_2$S/water), meaning the value that, for a given yield and a given number of plates, makes the enrichment highest. Overlooking the effect of the solubility of H$_2$S and of the humidity of the gas, and assuming that we have an equal number of plates in each of the two columns, the optimum value for γ is

$$\gamma_{opt.} = (K_1 K_2)^{\frac{1}{2}} \qquad (12.23)$$

In particular, with $T_1 = 30°C$, $T_2 = 130°C$, and $p = 20$ atm, we find that $\gamma_{opt.} = 1.98$.

The yield (and hence the enrichment) best for operating a separating element is determined on the basis of economic considerations, such as getting the minimum column volume per unit of product. For example, with 50 theoretical plates per column and under the above-cited pressure and temperature conditions, we find the optimum value for the yield is $\eta \simeq 0.20$, scaling the element according to the criterion of minimum volume for columns. Accordingly we find from Eq. 12.22 that $a = 10$. In this way, with three stages, starting with natural water, we obtain a product at 15% concentration. In fact, the number of stages required to achieve enrichment on this order of magnitude (i.e., 1000) is not critical with respect to overall production cost, and so a plant can be built with almost any number of stages between 2 and 5. There is a tendency, however, to keep the number of stages as small as possible for practical reasons. Taking the above-found values for γ and η, we see that in a stage the flow of H_2S circulating per unit of product $(1 = \gamma/\eta \, N_F)$ is about 60,000 mols $H_2S/mol \, D_2O$ or about 100,000 kg $H_2S/kg \, D_2O$.

Energy consumption in a dual-temperature H_2O/H_2S plant is determined mainly by the limited recovery in the heat exchangers and, to a lesser degree, by the compression of the circulating gas. Figure 12.14 shows two designs for heat recovery. In the first, the saturation heat of the gas at temperature T_2 is recovered from the gas emerging from the column by means of the liquid–gas exchanger G. In the second design, on the contrary, recovery is handled by direct liquid–gas contact by means of liquid–liquid and liquid–gas condensing exchangers, which are far more efficient. Direct liquid–gas contact occurs in the plates at the bottom of each column.

The thermal balance of the plant is integrated by the introduction of steam into the H_2S recovery column S (stripping); in plan (b) there is an introduction of steam into a heat exchanger for heating the water at the bottom of the hot column as well.

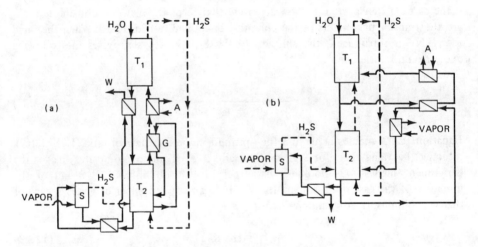

Fig. 12.14 Diagrams for heat recovery in dual-temperature H_2O/H_2S plants. (a) With liquid–gas heat exchangers G. (b) With liquid–liquid heat exchangers. (S = H_2S recovery column; A = cooling water.)

H_2O/H_2S PROCESS PLANTS

In the United States, during the years 1951 and 1952, two dual-temperature plants using the water–hydrogen sulfide system to produce 450 metric tons $D_2O \, year^{-1}$ were built, incorporating the Girdler–Spevack (GS) process. The first plant, which was built at Dana, Ind., was shut down in 1957 because of a lack of demand for heavy water. The second plant, however, built at Savannah River, S. C., is still in operation, although with only 8 of its original 24 units, and producing about 150 metric tons

D_2O year^{-1}. It is performing satisfactorily, and its reliability factor is laudable: better than 98%. Recently the bubble-cap plates were replaced with sieve plates.

In both plants the cold columns are run at temperatures between 30 and 40°C and the hot columns between 120 and 140°C. Operating pressure is 20 atm; the gas is circulated from the tops of the cold columns to the bottoms of the hot ones by means of centrifugal compressors.

The main difference between the Dana plant and the one at Savannah River is that the Dana plant consists of 6 independent units, each one consisting of 5 stages (4 pairs of columns in parallel in the first stage), whereas the Savannah River plant consists of 24 independent units, each one made up of only 2 stages (a single pair of columns in the first stage). In both plants the first stages are the same: diameter 11 ft (3.35 m), number of plates, 70 in the cold columns and 60 in the hot columns (with another 10 used for gas saturation).

In the second stage of the Savannah River plant there are 85 plates in the cold columns and 70 in the hot columns (diameter about 2 m); the difference is aimed at compensating the lower efficiency of the plates in the cold columns. Figure 12.15 gives an overall view of the Savannah River plant. It develops that the Savannah River plant has considerable advantages over the Dana plant: greater control facility, lower production loss due to maintenance, and greater flexibility.

For this reason we shall describe the unit of the Savannah River plant in greater detail (Fig. 12.16). The feedwater, after passing through the cold column (CT-1) of the first stage, is heated in the heat exchanger LH-1 and goes through the hot column HT-1, from which it emerges before the last 10 plates. This water is discarded after it has been stripped of the H₂S dissolved in it, passing into the small recovery tower S-1, which uses steam injection.

The gas is circulated by means of the centrifugal compressor GB-1 from the top of the cold column to the bottom of the hot column where it is heated and saturated as it goes through the first 10 plates. The required heat is supplied by a water flow that circulates through the PC-1 and PC-2 heat exchangers. The gas, after going through the hot column, goes through the exchanger—condensers PC-1 and SC-1 and then completes the circuit by going through the cold column. The second stage amounts to a bypass for about a third of the flow rates, inside the LH-1, PC-1, and SC-1 heat exchangers of the first stage.

All the heat lost from the system because of incomplete recovery in the exchangers is resupplied to the system by the steam injected at S-1, where the steam also serves to remove the H₂S from the waste water. Elimination of the H₂S is facilitated by preheating the water coming into S-1 in the SX-1 exchanger. In this way there is also lower consumption of steam. The (depleted) waste water is the heating fluid, both in the LH-1 exchanger in the first stage and in the LH-2 exchanger in the second stage. The SC-1 and SC-2 exchangers for cooling the gas have fresh water flowing through them (CW).

The heat carried off by this water and the waste water coming from the LH-1 and LH-2 heat exchangers constitutes the biggest heat loss in the system. The enriched water is drawn off as a condensate from the PC-2 and SC-2 exchangers since the

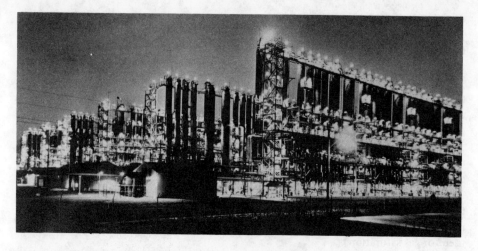

Fig. 12.15 Overall view of the Savannah River plant in the United States.

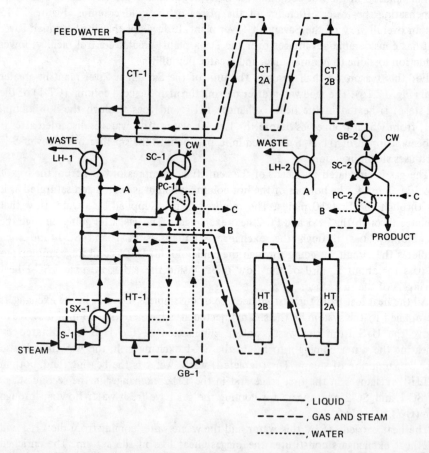

Fig. 12.16 Diagram of a unit in the Savannah River plant (GS process).

condensate is cleaner than the liquid flowing between the cold column and the hot column.

The main flow-rate values and operating conditions for one unit of the Savannah River plant are shown in Table 12.5. The H$_2$S required for the process is produced by reaction of NaHS with H$_2$SO$_4$ in a small auxiliary plant.

Designing the Dana and Savannah River plants required solution of three important practical problems: (1) corrosion, (2) inspection, and (3) safety. We will discuss these three problems in succession.

Table 12.5

FLOW RATES AND OPERATING CONDITIONS FOR
A UNIT OF THE SAVANNAH RIVER PLANT

Flow rates	
Cold gas (first stage), kg hr^{-1}	280,000
Cold gas (second stage), kg hr^{-1}	77,000
Feedwater, kg hr^{-1}	71,000
Steam flow rate (at 60 atm), kg hr^{-1}	13,000
Pressure at top of cold column (first stage), atm	20
Temperatures, °C	
Cold column (first stage)	33
Hot column (second stage)	133
Output concentrations, mol % D$_2$	
From first stage	0.085
From second stage	15

1. Steel is corroded by H$_2$S in solution, but the ferrous sulfide resulting from corrosion forms a protective layer that prevents further corrosion. Thus the corrosion, which is very rapid at first, becomes negligible after about 1000 hr of exposure. Of course care must be taken that erosion does not destroy the sulfide layer. Therefore ordinary steel was used for all components (column and exchanger shells, most of the piping, etc.) in which there is no great flow turbulence or splashing of drops against the walls, whereas elsewhere (bubble-cap plates, exchanger pipes, etc.) austenitic steel was used (chromium–nickel). Type 304 AISI stainless steel is advisable, even though type 316 is tougher. Type 410 (12 to 14% chromium) can be used only for operating periods of about 5 years.

Some of the nascent hydrogen that is formed in the reaction of H$_2$S with steel is diffused into the crystalline structure of the steel and thus greatly diminishes the breaking strength. This hydrogen then returns to the molecular state and builds up in the points of discontinuity of the metal. This is why careful ultrasonic examinations must be made of all the steel laminates so as to make sure there are no flaws in which the hydrogen might lodge, with consequent rupture of the metal. It is also necessary to limit the hardness of the steel used—e.g., in the bolts—and stresses must be limited as well.

Other precautions for controlling corrosion are regular inspections of the plant and the use of minimum-thickness holes in areas where corrosion is likely. No corrosion inhibitors were used in the Dana or Savannah River plants.

2. The gas–liquid mol ratio γ, whose optimum value is expressed by Eq. 12.23, is extremely critical to the plant yield. The yield will dip to practically zero for γ deviations of 15% over or under $\gamma_{opt.}$. For good plant operation, the variations in γ are best held below ±1%. Furthermore, the accuracy of the usual flowmeters, which are generally used to measure such flows, is practically never more than about ±10%. Hence it is not a good idea to base the flow control on absolute measurements from these. The problem was solved in the AEC plants by controlling the flows on the basis of the deuterium content at the intermediate points in the cold and hot columns, respectively. These concentrations will be equal if γ is equal to $\gamma_{opt.}$, but they will draw apart if γ gets away from its optimum value. The samples are taken from the intermediate points in the columns, usually at intervals of 8 hr. The samples are analyzed with a special high-sensitivity mass spectrograph. With this system the flows can be regulated and kept constant within the desired limits, even without accurate knowledge of the absolute values of the flow rates.

3. Leaks of H_2S from the plant as a result of breakdowns or ruptures in pipes are very dangerous because of the high toxicity of the gas. (Each of the two AEC plants contains a large amount, 800 tons or so.) Each unit in the plant is equipped with a remote-controlled fast isolation system, as well as with vent valves, to prevent massive leaks of H_2S following accidents. In this way the maximum loss of H_2S is held to about 8 tons. In case of accident, the moment the section in which the leak is occurring is located, the vent valves are opened to discharge the gas into a special holding tank. At the top of this tank, the gas is flamed off.

Other safety standards consist in constant monitoring of H_2S in the air in the vicinity of the plants and in checking on wind velocity and direction, which is helpful in deciding the evacuation plan. Personnel, carefully trained in emergency procedures, operate in pairs at all times for mutual protection. They wear masks with respirators in the immediate vicinity of the plants or masks with absorbent filters in the more distant areas.

Proctor and Thayer[19] improved the process by suggesting several modifications, chief among them being:

1. Arrangement of the columns in three stages.

2. Use of more efficient sieve plates, larger in diameter.

3. Elimination of the liquid–gas heat exchangers and adoption of a design similar to that shown in Fig. 12.14(b).

4. More compact arrangement of the apparatus so as to cut down on connecting piping, valves, and supporting structures.

In this way there is a substantial reduction in plant volume and hence of costs.

The Proctor and Thayer[19] design concepts were incorporated in the CGE/Lummus process, adopted for two large plants in Canada, the Port Hawkesbury plant in Nova Scotia and the Bruce plant near Douglas Point in Ontario. The Port Hawkesbury plant, which went into operation in 1970, was planned for a production of 380 metric tons D$_2$O year^{-1}, whereas the Bruce plant, consisting of two units almost the size of the one at Port Hawkesbury, will produce 800 metric tons D$_2$O year^{-1}. The Bruce plant went into production in 1973.

The basic operating parameters of these plants (pressure, temperature, etc.) are substantially the same as those of Savannah River. What is different, however, is the layout of the process, as shown in Fig. 12.17. Note particularly that the interstage connection is made only through gas circulation, whereas in each stage (except the first) the liquid flows in a closed circuit.

The first stage consists of three columns in parallel, each column made up of a cold section (the upper part) and a hot section (at the base). These columns are 9.2 m in diameter and 92 m in height. The walls are 89 mm thick. The sieve plates are spaced at intervals of about 0.46 m. Figure 12.18 shows one of these plates during assembly in the shop. There are about 130 plates in each column, plus 15 or 20 more for gas humidification and as many again for dehumidification. The second stage consists of a single column, also in two sections, not quite so tall as that of the first stage and about three-quarters of its diameter. In the third stage, however, high- and low-temperature exchange is done in two different columns having about one-fourth of the diameter of the second-stage column.

The gas is circulated through each column by means of centrifugal compressors, which in the first stage develop 7000 hp per unit. Figure 12.19 shows an overall view

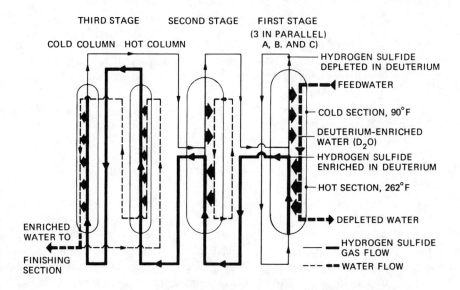

Fig. 12.17 Simplified diagram of the CGE/Lummus process.

Fig. 12.18 Construction of a sieve plate for the Bruce plant in Canada.

of the Port Hawkesbury plant. The construction material used was mainly fine-grain carbon steel (e.g., ASTM A-516, grade LI-70). The use of carbon steel is limited, however, to those parts of the plant in which the velocity of the gas does not exceed 2 m sec.$^{-1}$. Beyond this level the protective layer of sulfide might be worn away, and such stainless steels as 304 and 304L are used (for the sieve plates and valves) and even (for the heat-exchanger tubing) 316 and 316L.

The thermal insulation of the Bruce-plant columns consists of a layer of glass wool 10 cm thick. In addition, the plant is equipped with a dense system of steam tracing. The maximum amount of steam used for this purpose is 20 metric tons hr^{-1} for each of the two units.

At Glace Bay in Nova Scotia, another plant is being built to produce 415 metric tons D_2O year^{-1}, using some of the components of an earlier plant built on the same site. The old plant, which was never operated, had to be dismantled because of heavy corrosion in many of the parts, caused by inadequately treated feedwater and the use of seawater for both feed and cooling. The new Glace Bay plant, which is scheduled to go into operation in 1975 or 1976, will thus have a process design somewhat different from those of Port Hawkesbury and Bruce.

Fig. 12.19 Overall view of the Port Hawkesbury plant in Canada.

In all the Canadian plants, the primary enrichment with the dual-temperature process runs as high as 30 to 35%, and final enrichment is made by means of water distillation.

The investment required by the Savannah River plant, including the final enrichment installations, came to $145 million, distributed as follows:

	Millions of dollars
Enrichment plants	
H_2O/H_2S exchange units	110
Distillation plant	2.5
Electrolytic plant	1.5
Power plant (steam and electricity)	15
Feed and cooling-water systems	7
Miscellaneous	9
Total	145.0

In computing investments, allowance was made for the plant that generates the steam and electricity needed to operate the main plant. Hence the specific investment comes to $320 per kilogram of D_2O per year. Energy consumption per unit of product comes to 5600 kg steam (at 60 atm)/kg D_2O and 680 kWh electricity/kg D_2O. Operating costs in 1964 amounted to $30 per kilogram D_2O. In this figure, steam consumption accounted for 33% and electricity for 10%.

The improved design, suggested by Proctor and Thayer,[19] shows markedly lower estimated costs: specific investment, $148 per kilogram of D_2O per year; and operating costs, $17.50 per kilogram of D_2O per year in 1960 dollars, and for a plant producing 180 metric tons D_2O year^{-1}. A cost analysis for such a plant is shown in Table 12.6.

For a plant designed[21] in India (Bihar) in 1964, the following economic data were calculated: specific investment, $230 per kilogram of D_2O per year; and operating costs, $17.60 per kilogram of D_2O per year. For the Port Hawkesbury plant, completed in 1969, an investment cost of $65 million was cited,[25] which would work out to a specific investment of $170 per kilogram of D_2O per year.

Furthermore, in 1972 it was estimated that a plant to produce 400 metric tons D_2O year^{-1}, on which construction began in that same year, would have cost about $115 million, including the power plant and interest during construction. This figure works out to a specific investment of $290 per kilogram of D_2O per year. It has been maintained[26] that the price of Canadian-produced heavy water will not exceed $66 per kilogram for the rest of the current decade, even allowing for the steady decline in the value of the currency.*

---

*Nevertheless, further instructions led to a forecast cost of $80 to $100 per kg D_2O, the lower figure being applicable when nuclear steam is available.

Table 12.6

PLANT COSTS (1960) FOR A PLANT TO PRODUCE 180 TONS OF HEAVY WATER PER YEAR, ACCORDING TO PROCTOR AND THAYER

Columns	$ 4,700,000
Gas-fired heaters	2,000,000
Heat exchangers	2,900,000
Turbines and compressors	1,900,000
Pumps	300,000
Piping and structures	4,500,000
Instrumentation	1,300,000
Total chemical-exchange section	$17,600,000
Plant auxiliaries	4,900,000
Subtotal	$22,500,000
Contingencies + interest during construction	4,200,000
Total investment	$26,700,000

DUAL-TEMPERATURE H₂O/H₂ PROCESSES

Several dual-temperature water—hydrogen processes with exchange reactions in the gaseous phase have been explored. In all instances 100°C was used as the low temperature T_1, and 500 to 600°C was used as the high temperature T_2.

One of these processes, suggested by Cerrai et al.,[27] calls for running the exchange at 100°C in a Trail-type transfer column. The high-temperature exchange would be run in a single reaction chamber for each stage. Therefore the enrichment per stage is limited, and a large number of stages is required. Despite the fact that energy consumption for such a process is relatively modest (5000 to 6000 kWh/kg D_2O, most of it thermal), plant costs are too high. To our knowledge, not even a pilot plant has been built for this process.

It is possible to obtain separation-factor values per stage much higher than the K_1/K_2 ratio by running the water—hydrogen exchange in the liquid phase in a pair of columns, according to a design similar to that for the water—hydrogen sulfide process. Of course the high temperature must be held below the critical temperature of water, and the pressure must be kept rather high so as to increase the solubility of the hydrogen in water. In this way, given equal gas flow rates, we can greatly reduce the cross sections of the columns and hence, in the last analysis, the capital investment costs, which are the preponderant factors in building up total cost. Typical operating conditions are, for example, low temperature $T_1 = 30°C$, high temperature $T_2 = 200°C$, and the pressure p = 200 atm. At 200°C the vapor pressure of water is 15.3 atm.

In general, the catalysts used for the gaseous phase reaction do not lose their activity in the liquid phase. The speed of the process of deuterium transfer between the two components, however, is limited by the speed of diffusion through the liquid boundary layer around the catalyst and across the liquid–gas interface. For good efficiency in the transfer process, it is necessary in every case for the catalyst to be dispersed through the liquid in very finely subdivided form and for the liquid to be thoroughly stirred.

A contact system has been tested successfully by Becker et al.,[30] who used sieve plates. Becker et al. used as a catalyst a suspension of activated charcoal, upon which platinum is deposited. With plates having 1-mm holes, they found that a suspension of 10 g of activated charcoal per liter, containing about 5 wt.% platinum, was suitable.

Catalysts of other types were examined for these purposes, such as platinum on aluminum, colloidal platinum and palladium, and nickel on chromium oxide. Of these, colloidal platinum proved to be the most active, although it is quite sensitive to poisons. One problem all these liquid-phase catalysts present is that of separating the catalyst itself from the water that comes out of a separating element. This problem can be avoided if the water is circulated in closed circuit and the gas is circulated in open circuit. Of course, if this is done, the process will depend on industrial production of hydrogen. However, there is a certain advantage in the fact that—with the same flow rates—as between a water-fed element and a hydrogen-fed element at equal feed concentration, the latter element will give a larger yield. Further, we might consider recovering the deuterium directly from the H_2-N_2 mixture on its way to use in ammonia synthesis, provided it is free of poisons.

The Becker process was tested years ago in a pilot plant built at Dortmund, Germany, by the Uhde Company. The plant consisted of two cold columns (30°C) with sieve plates, 28 m high overall, and one hot column (200°C) 17.5 m high. The hydrogen flow (under 200 atm) was 600 STP m^3 hr^{-1}. They reached a separation factor of 1.29. So even this process requires many stages.

Energy consumption of the process is modest; it was estimated as 2100 kg steam/kg D_2O plus 200 kWh electricity/kg D_2O. Plant costs, however, are very high. In 1958 the specific investment was estimated at about $500 per kilogram of D_2O per year. The quantity of catalyst required was 16 g per kilogram of D_2O per year. The process might be more attractive if a catalyst could be found that would be more efficient, less costly, and less sensitive to poisoning.

DUAL-TEMPERATURE NH_3/H_2 AND AMINE/H_2 PROCESSES

The dual-temperature ammonia–hydrogen process is essentially based on a cycle of ammonia to extract the deuterium from a flow of hydrogen (or synthesis gas). In this process the cold column consists of a stripping section and an enrichment section, as is shown for the monothermal process described on pages 345 to 348. By comparison with the latter, the enrichment section is considerably larger because many more plates are needed and the gas/liquid mol-flow ratio is higher in the dual-temperature process. The hot column, too, calls for more plates. Finally, the volume of the transfer columns is greater in the dual-temperature process.

On the other hand, recycling of the liquid phase does not require any special equipment (evaporator and stripping column) for recovery of the catalyst (KNH$_2$). Neither does the dual-temperature process require conversion apparatus, i.e., a dissociation chamber and ancillary synthesis equipment for the liquid reflux. In the dual-temperature process, the heat-exchange surface is probably smaller besides.

Taken all together, a comparison between single- and dual-temperature processes comes down—according to some opinions—to greater plant volume for the latter, but also to a more advantageous energy balance. Dual-temperature processes such as these are now being studied, particularly in Canada and Germany. The Canadian process is based on the following parameters:

Pressure	200 atm
Cold columns (2)	$-20°C$ and $-40°C$ ($q_0 = 5.9$)
Hot column	$+70°C$ ($q_0 = 2.9$)

They are also contemplating circulating the H$_2$ in a closed cycle, with feed through hydrogen—water exchange at 200°C in the liquid phase.

The process being worked on in Germany centers on the following parameters:

Pressure	300 atm
Cold columns (2)	$-25°C$
Hot column	$+60°C$
H$_2$/NH$_3$ mol ratio	5.4
Deuterium yield	80%

For this process, the Germans are considering the adoption of sieve plates. An experimental column (2 m in diameter) for low-temperature exchange has been set up in an ammonia-synthesis plant at Dortmund. Of course the contact efficiency ratings are low, about 4 to 6%.

The German assessments show promising findings for the NH$_3$/H$_2$ dual-temperature process, which, at least from the angle of operating costs, is more attractive than the H$_2$O/H$_2$S process. In the German study[35] the following levels of energy consumption were calculated:

Steam (70 atm, superheated)	1000 kg/kg D$_2$O
Electricity	125 kWh/kg D$_2$O

In the same study the following economic data were found (1970):

Specific investment	$200 per kilogram of D$_2$O per year
Operating cost	$17.20 per kilogram of D$_2$O

These data refer to a plant producing 72.5 metric tons D_2O year^{-1} from 120,000 STP m^3 synthesis gas hr^{-1} (1000 metric tons NH_3 day^{-1}), containing 74.4% hydrogen with a deuterium content of 125 ppm D/H.

In the Canadian survey, however, the process is not found to be competitive with the H_2O/H_2S dual-temperature process, primarily because of the greater plant volume and consequent costs. Energy demands, too, are less attractive, as is shown in Table 12.7.

A variation of the above-discussed dual-temperature process substitutes an amine for the ammonia. The incentive for using amine in place of ammonia stems from the following considerations.

The kinetics of the ammonia—hydrogen exchange at the temperature of the cold column is very slow. This means that the cold column must be very large.

The vapor pressure of ammonia at the hot-column temperature is extremely high. This again means a very large volume for the hot column and an increase in energy consumption.

For hydrogen to dissolve into ammonia more readily, the plant must run at high pressures.

Some amines were found to have the following properties, by comparison with ammonia: (1) faster kinetics in the isotope exchange with hydrogen, (2) lower vapor pressure, and (3) greater hydrogen solubility.

According to the findings of preliminary research in Canada,[25] the likeliest of the various possible amines seems to be methylamine. Potassium amine can be used as a catalyst. Studies are under way on the process conditions shown in the first column of Table 12.7. The other two columns show the conditions pertaining to the dual-temperature NH_3/H_2 and H_2O/H_2S processes. It can be seen from the table that

Table 12.7

PROCESSING CONDITIONS FOR AN AMINE/H_2 PROCESS COMPARED WITH OTHER DUAL-TEMPERATURE PROCESSES

Process conditions	Amine/H_2	NH_3/H_2	H_2O/H_2S
Production D_2O, metric tons year^{-1}	64	100	180
Deuterium yield, %	85	80	20
T_1, °C	−40	−25	30
T_2, °C	+70	60	130
Pressure, atm	65	300	20
Column volume, m³	600	1,000	5,900
Equivalent volume at 20 atm, m³ metric ton^{-1} year^{-1}	31	150	33
Steam consumption, kg/kg D_2O	1,300	2,400	11,000
Electricity, kWh/kg D_2O	750	560	550

the prospects for the dual-temperature process with amines are fairly promising. A pilot plant was built at Chalk River in 1971 to develop this process.

REFERENCES

Monothermal H_2O/H_2 Processes

1. M. Benedict and T. H. Pigford, *Nuclear Chemical Engineering,* Chap. 11, McGraw-Hill Book Company, Inc., New York, 1957.
2. M. Benedict, Survey of Heavy-Water Production Processes, in *Progress in Nuclear Energy, Technology, Engineering, and Safety,* Series IV, Vol. 1, p. 3, Pergamon Press, Inc., New York, 1956.
3. S. Villani, Calculation Methods for Transfer Columns, *Energ. Nucl.,* **2**: 504 (1955).
4. E. Cerrai et al., Electrolytic Plants with Recovery Columns for Deuterium by Exchange Reaction, Italian Reports CISE-61, 62, and 63, 1954.
5. D. Dinelli, System for Graphic Calculation of the Number of Theoretical Plates in a Plant for Electrolytic Heavy-Water Production Using Exchange Towers, *Energ. Nucl.,* **2**: 426 (1955).
6. P. J. Selak and J. Finke, Heavy Water, *Chem. Eng. Progr.,* **50**: 221 (1954).

Monothermal NH_3/H_2 Processes

7. J. Bigeleisen and M. L. Perlman, The Concentration of Deuterium by Chemical Exchange Between Hydrogen and Ammonia, USAEC Report ANL-146, December 1961.
8. E. Roth et al., Heavy-Water Production in France, in *Proceedings of the Second United Nations International Conference on the Peaceful Uses of Atomic Energy, Geneva, 1958,* Vol. 4, p. 499, New York, 1958.
9. G. Dirian et al., Kinetics and Mechanics of Deuterium Exchange Between Liquid Ammonia and Hydrogen in the Presence of Potassium Amine, *J. Chim. Phys.,* **60**: 139 (1963).
10. B. Lefrancois, J. M. Lerat, and E. Roth, Study of Heavy-Water Production in France, in *Proceedings of the Third International Conference on the Peaceful Uses of Atomic Energy, Geneva, 1964,* Vol. 12, p. 382, United Nations, New York, 1965.
11. E. Roth et al., The Mazingarbe Heavy-Water Plant, *Energ. Nucl.,* **10**: 3 (1968).
12. E. Roth and M. Rostaign, Survey of Heavy-Water Production in France, in *Techniques and Economy of Production of Heavy Water,* Conference Proceedings, Turin, Italy, 1970, Comitato Nationale per l'Energia Nucleare, Rome, 1971.
13. B. Lefrancois, The Mazingarbe Heavy-Water Plant: Description and Operation, *ibid.,* p. 197.
14. E. Roth et al., Studies of Production Processes and Heavy-Water Using the French Process, in *Proceedings of the Fourth International Conference on the Peaceful Uses of Atomic Energy, Geneva, 1971,* Vol. 9, p. 69, United Nations, New York, 1962.

Dual-Temperature H_2O/H_2S Process

15. J. S. Spevack, Method of Isotope Concentration, U. S. Patent No. 2,787,526, Apr. 2, 1957.
16. J. S. Spevack, Isotope Concentration System, U. S. Patent No. 2,895,803, July 21, 1959.
17. W. P. Bebbington and V. R. Thayer, Production of Heavy Water, *Chem. Eng. Progr.,* **55**: 70 (September 1959).
18. F. T. Barr and W. P. Drews, The Future for Cheap Heavy Water, *Chem. Eng. Progr.,* **56**: 49 (March 1960).
19. J. F. Proctor and V. R. Thayer, Economics of Heavy-Water Production, *Chem. Eng. Progr.,* **58**: 53 (Apr. 1962).

20. W. P. Bebbington et al., Production of Heavy Water in the United States of America, in *Proceedings of the Third International Conference on the Peaceful Uses of Atomic Energy, Geneva, 1964,* Vol. 12, p. 334, New York, 1965.
21. P. G. Deshpande, D. C. Gami, and S. Nagaraja Rao, Technical and Economic Considerations for Producing 200 Tons Per Year of Heavy Water in India, *ibid.,* p. 415.
22. J. S. Spevack, Development of the Hydrogen Sulfide–Water Dual-Temperature Technology, in *Techniques and Economy of Production is Heavy Water,* Conference Proceedings, Turin, Italy, 1970, Comitato Nationale per l'Energia Nucleare, Rome, 1971.
23. P. H. G. Spray, Fabrication and Construction Experiences: Bruce and Port Hawkesbury Heavy-Water Plants, *ibid.,* p. 119.
24. R. K. Bhargava et al., Design Criteria for Heavy-Water Plant Based on H_2S-H_2O Exchange Process, *ibid.,* p. 209.
25. A. R. Bancroft, The Canadian Approach to Cheaper Heavy Water, Canadian Report-3044, February 1968.
26. L. R. Haywood, Heavy Water, paper 305 presented at the Canadian Nuclear Association Annual Conference, Ottawa, June 1972.

Dual-Temperature H_2O/H_2 Processes

27. E. Cerrai et al., A Thermal Method for Heavy-Water Production, *Chem. Eng. Progr., Symp. Ser.,* **50**: 271 (1954).
28. R. Montarnae, J. C. Balanceanu, and G. Dirian, Study of Isotopic Exchange Between Hydrogen and Water over a Catalyst in the Liquid Phase, in *Isotope Separation,* Symposium Proceedings, p. 247, North-Holland Publishing Company, Amsterdam, 1958.
29. K. Bier, *Chem.-Ing.-Tech.,* **28**: 625 (1955), and *ibid.,* **31**: 32 (1956).
30. E. W. Becker et al., Enrichment of Heavy Water by High-Pressure Exchange Between Hydrogen and an Aqueous Suspension of a Catalyst, in *Proceedings of the Second United Nations International Conference on the Peaceful Uses of Atomic Energy, Geneva, 1958,* Vol. 4, p. 543, New York, 1958.

Dual-Temperature NH_3/H_2 and Amine/H_2 Processes

31. H. K. Rae, A Review of Heavy-Water Production Processes, Canadian Report-2503, August 1969.
32. H. K. Rae, Chemical Exchange Processes for Heavy Water, Canadian Report-2555, May 1966.
33. A. R. Bancroft: See Ref. 25.
34. U. Schindewolf and G. Lang, Optimization of Heavy-Water Production Plant with the Ammonia–Hydrogen Dual-Temperature Exchange System, in *Techniques and Economy of Production in Heavy Water,* Conference Proceedings, Turin, Italy, 1970, Comitato Nationale per l'Energia Nucleare, Rome, 1971; see also *Chem. Eng. Tech.,* **43**: 804 (1971).
35. S. Walker and E. Nitschke, Problems of Design and Construction of a Plant for Heavy-Water Production Using the Dual-Temperature Ammonia–Hydrogen Exchange System, *ibid.,* p. 173.
36. L. Bracciforti et al., Problems Relating to the Design of a Plant for Production of Heavy Water, AGIP–Nucleare's Contribution, *ibid.,* p. 139.
37. A. R. Bancroft and H. K. Rae, Heavy-Water Production by Amine–Hydrogen Exchange, *ibid.,* p. 47.

3 ELECTROMAGNETIC SEPARATION

The major components of an electromagnetic isotope separator are: a magnetic field for ion-beam analysis, an ion source with its acceleration system, and a collection system for the separated ions.

MAGNETIC FIELD

If a beam of ions in which the forces deriving from the space charge are negligible is injected into a magnetic field B perpendicular to the direction of movement of the charged particles, the ions will follow circular paths whose radii will be

$$r = \frac{Mv}{eB} \tag{13.1}$$

in which M is the mass, v is the velocity, and e is the ion charge.

The magnetic field thus has the effect of causing ions with different amounts of momenta to follow different paths. If the ions have equal mass, there is scattering as a function of their speed. If the ions have equal speed, there is scattering as a function of mass. Hence the mere presence of a magnetic field is not enough to provide a focusing in velocity for ions of equal mass and different velocities. In mass spectrometers with high resolution power, for isotopic analysis or assignment of mass (like the Mattauch type, with powers of resolution as high as 100,000), focalization in velocity is

obtained by coupling the magnetic field with an electrostatic field as shown in
Fig. 13.1. This field will select only those ions for which

$$eV = \frac{Mv^2}{\rho} \tag{13.2}$$

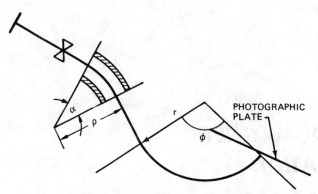

Fig. 13.1 Double-focus spectrometer.

This arrangement, however, leads to a considerable reduction of the instrument's
transmitting power. In isotope separators where the problems of yield are more
stringent than problems of resolution, it is generally preferable to use only one
magnetic stage and to limit the disadvantage of velocity scatter by using ion sources
that are almost monoenergetic and high acceleration voltages (up to 80 kV). As a
function of the acceleration voltage V, Eq. 13.1 can be rewritten as

$$r = \frac{1}{B}\left(\frac{2\,MV}{e}\right)^{\frac{1}{2}} \tag{13.3}$$

The dispersive power of a separator relative to given mass is defined as the
separation distance obtained for unit mass difference at the collector (Fig. 13.2). If the

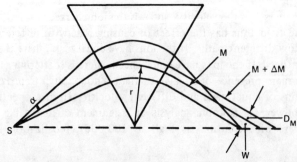

Fig. 13.2 Dispersion and image breadth at the collector in a sector magnetic spectrometer.

two monoenergetic ion beams of different mass M and M + ΔM are considered, we find from Eq. 13.3 that the variation in the radii of their paths is

$$\frac{\Delta r}{r} = \frac{\Delta M}{2M} \qquad (13.4)$$

Mass separation distance, which we have defined, measured along a line at right angles to the central radius of the beam for the ions of mass M and for a magnetic field of a symmetrical type is

$$D_M = 2 \, \Delta r = r \frac{\Delta M}{M} \qquad (13.5)$$

The efficient separative power of the instrument is defined as the highest obtainable $(M/\Delta M)$ ratio. This ratio is reached when the width W of the image of the source on the collector becomes equal to the separation D_M between two contiguous masses:

$$\left(\frac{M}{\Delta M} \right)_{max.} = \frac{r}{W} \qquad (13.6)$$

For a good separative power to be obtained, the image of the source on the collector must be small enough. However, the extraction slit in the beam must not be too small. Hence the need for using instruments with a large radius of curvature (up to 160 cm).

CAUSES OF ABERRATION

There are many causes of aberration, by which we mean broadening of the beam at the collector and distortion of the image.

The main causes, which must be eliminated or reduced in building an electromagnetic separator, are discussed here. The ion beam sent from the source slit generally has an angle of aperture of 2α. According to Herzog's law, which applies to a magnetic field of any shape, if the central radius of such an open beam of ions of equal momentum enters and exits normally to the edges of the field, the ions will be focused at a point lying on the straight line of conjunction between the source and the summit of the magnetic field (see Fig. 13.2). This focusing is of the first order in α, which is to say that the breadth of the image at the collector depends on the square of the angle of aperture. For a field with any sector of aperture whatever, of the symmetrical type, and for a rather small angle α of the beam, clearly the width of the image at the collector is

$$W = r\alpha^2 \qquad (13.7)$$

This equation of course applies to a slit of infinitesimal width. In practice, for a beam with $\alpha = 5°$ (approximately one-tenth of a radian), and for a magnetic field with $r = 50$ cm, we have $W = 5$ mm. For masses of about 200, the mass separation distance for two contiguous masses, given by Eq. 13.5, is $D_M = 2.5$ mm, about half the width of the image. To obtain separation under these conditions, we must narrow the beam's angle of aperture and hence the emission of current. It is a good idea, therefore, to try to improve the focusing conditions.

With suitable corrections to the limits of the magnetic field, it is possible to eliminate the second-order effects in α, or in other words to obtain, at the collector, images whose width depends on the cube of α. These corrections are usually done both in mass spectrometers and in isotope separators.

Hinterberger and Kerwin have shown that such aberrations can be eliminated by suitably shaping the boundaries of the magnetic field. The ideal profile is the one which is traversed normally by all the radii of a beam no matter how open and, in a Cartesian reference system, in which the axis of the abscissas is given by the line joining the source with the collector and the axis of the ordinates goes through the apex of the magnetic field:

$$y = \frac{x(a - x)}{(r^2 - x^2)^{1/2}} \tag{13.8}$$

The form described in Eq. 13.8 can be suitably approximated with straight-line or curved boundaries. If the approximation is an analytical curve of the first order, the focusing will be first order, and so on.

Instead of using a magnetic field with an adjusted profile to eliminate aberrations due to initial wandering of the beam, it is possible to correct the paths by varying the energy of the ions passing through a uniform magnetic field. To do this, we insert between the polar faces thin metallic strips, electrically coupled and given different potentials. This will provide in the air gap a proper distribution of potential to make up for the aberrations due to dispersal of the beam. The differences in the potential used are at most 1% of the total ion-acceleration voltage and are such as not to noticeably disturb the stability of the processes of neutralization of the space charge within the beam.

Divergence of the beam can give rise to a broadening of the image in a direction parallel with the dispersive magnetic field. This gives a reduction in transmission through ion loss on the walls of the vacuum chamber. The radial focusing conditions described earlier are, however, more limiting than those of axial focusing.

Under ideal focusing conditions, the image of the source on the collector has the same dimensions as the area corresponding to the smallest cross section of the ion beam. This area, which corresponds to the source of the focusing system, can be the slit through which the ions emerge from the source or a slit made in some other electrode or diaphragm, or a section external to both source and electrodes, if the potential distribution at the source is self-focusing.

Earlier we mentioned (page 375) the phenomenon of ion energy scattering and pointed out the necessity of working with monoenergetic ion beams since the magnetic field provides only a quantitative focusing of momentum. We said that it is better to use high acceleration voltages and ion sources that have low energy dispersal.

Here we will refer to only one application of the principle of double focusing to isotope separation in weighable quantities, as used in one of the Saclay separators. In this separator there are two mass-dispersing elements arranged in cascade: a magnetic field and an electrostatic field, separated by a diaphragm. The first separation is done conventionally in a magnetic stage. The image of the source slit for a particular isotope is shaped on the diaphragm that marks the entrance to the electrostatic field. The ion beam thus selected crosses the second electrostatic stage, is refocused on a second slit, and is then collected. The isotopic impurities that penetrate the diaphragm do not have the proper electrical and kinetic dimensions and hence are not focused on the second slit. In this way high enrichment factors are reached. The isotopic purity is of course obtained at the price of a decline in production and leads to the drawback that it is possible to collect only one isotope at a time.

The total length of the ion path in the separator can be as great as several meters. This means that there is a possibility of ions colliding with molecules of the residual gas, which helps to broaden the beam. Collisions may be of various kinds. There may be excitation or ionization of the residual gas, or there may be elastic or inelastic collisions. The kind of collision which is the most capable of upsetting the operation of a separator is that in which there is an exchange of charges; the fast ions are neutralized and give up their charge to slow atoms of the residual gas. If this process occurs before entry of the beam into the magnetic field or in the field itself, the ions are lost.

After bouncing off the walls of the vacuum chamber, the ions can enter the slit of the collector of another kind of ions and cause contamination. This problem can be reduced by means of suitable screens. Collisions between ions and residual-gas molecules could, theoretically, be cut down by using high vacuums in the separators. However, because of neutralization of the space charge, it is not advisable to go below 10^{-5} mm Hg.

The boundaries of the magnetic field are not really clear-cut, as postulated theoretically, because of the existence of the fringing field. The presence of the fringing field can give rise to three different problems: (1) shifting of the focal point, (2) variation in the intensity of the beam because of the effect of the field on axial focusing, and (3) deflection of the ions that do not happen to be on the plane midway between the polar faces, because of the transverse component of the scattered field.

Owing to the loss of flux, the magnetic field is invariably more intense on the polar faces than in the middle of the air gap. Consequently an ion moving along the central plane between the poles describes a circular trajectory slightly larger than that described by an ion that happens to be on the edges of the beam in proximity to a polar face. This fact gives rise to a slight curvature of the linear image obtained on the collector. Hence it is desirable to maintain the greatest possible distance between the ion beam and the polar faces.

Fluctuation in the level of the acceleration voltage V and in magnetic induction B in the air gap cause variations in the radii of the ion trajectories.

As can be seen, differentiating Eq. 13.3 gives

$$\frac{\Delta r}{r} = -\frac{\Delta B}{B} \qquad (13.9)$$

$$\frac{\Delta r}{r} = \frac{1}{2}\frac{\Delta V}{V} \qquad (13.10)$$

$$\frac{\Delta r}{r} = \frac{1}{2}\frac{\Delta M}{M} \qquad (13.11)$$

from which we find

$$\frac{\Delta B}{B} = -\frac{1}{2}\frac{\Delta M}{M} \qquad (13.12)$$

$$\frac{\Delta V}{V} = \frac{\Delta M}{M} \qquad (13.13)$$

If we separate two close isotopes having masses near M = 250, allowing a fluctuation of the image no greater than 10% of the separation distance at the collector, we must make very sure that fluctuations in voltage and magnetic field correspond at most to a mass fluctuation corresponding to $\Delta M = 0.1$. From Eqs. 13.12 and 13.13, we then find

$$\frac{\Delta V}{V} = \frac{1}{2500} \quad \text{and} \quad \frac{\Delta B}{B} = \frac{1}{5000} \qquad (13.14)$$

It is necessary, therefore, that the stability of the feed voltages be at least of the order given by Eq. 13.14.

Two charged particles having the same sign and moving along parallel paths set up two types of forces between them, electrostatic repulsion and attraction of a magnetic nature. This is because the two particles are equivalent to two parallel currents having the same direction. Given the velocities usually involved in spectrometers, the magnetic attraction is negligible. The electrostatic repulsion, however, becomes evident for currents on the order of 10^{-6} A.

In electromagnetic separators it is best to work with currents of a few milliamperes. The paths of the ions are then not determined solely by the characteristics of the source and by the magnetic and electrical fields applied. Hence it is impossible to obtain an ideal focusing with suitable fields since the electrostatic interaction between the ions in the beam sets up strong aberrations at the collector, and the different isotopes are completely mixed.

The broadening of the image at the collector was easily calculated for a 180° separator, and it was found that

$$\Delta W = \frac{8\pi c^2 \; eir^2}{Mv^3} \qquad (13.15)$$

in which i is the intensity of the current per centimeter of height of the beam. For a separator having a source slit of 100 × 2 mm^2 and a radius of curvature of 100 cm, we have an image width of 2 mm for mass 100, an acceleration voltage of 25 kV, and a total emitted current of 10 μA.

Thus we see the impossibility of high production in the absence of a system for neutralizing the space charge. Various methods have been suggested for neutralizing the positive space charge of the beam. In all separators the most effective method has proved to be that of allowing a residual pressure, about 5 × 10^{-5} mm Hg, in the separator's vacuum chamber. The ions in the beam then ionize the residual gas and create electrons that accumulate within the beam and thus neutralize the positive space charge. The processes by which these negative charges are set up are manifold. There may be (1) interaction of ions with molecules of the residual gas so as to produce negative charges, (2) interaction with the walls of the vacuum chamber, or (3) processes that involve the capture of free electrons by molecules of O_2 or Cl_2 in the residual gas so as to form negative ions. The basic processes are ionization and charge exchanges. There may also be elastic collisions that cause only the deflection of the fast ions from their initial path. Such deflections can give rise to scattering and consequent broadening of the image at the collector if the fraction of the ions involved in this process is fairly high. However, these deflections for fast ions are small-angle deflections, and their total effect is not very great. Naturally, in these neutralization processes there is an optimum operating pressure, above which phenomena of scattering and particle loss from the beam become unacceptable.

The process of neutralizing the space charge takes place in the following way. Initially the fast ions within the beam, through the processes we have seen, form slow ions and electrons. The slow positive ions are pushed out of the beam area and are lost on the walls. But the electrons accumulate in the positive potential gap formed by the fast ions of the beam. As the density of negative particles within the beam builds up, the potential gap is gradually nullified, while the slow ions and more highly energetic electrons are continually escaping from the beam. At the conclusion of the process, we have in the beam a gas made up of electrons with almost thermal-energy levels, and the positive-potential gap has been reduced to a level determined by the balance between the production and the loss of charged particles.

The effect of compensation for the space charge by electrons is enhanced by the presence of the analyzing magnetic field. There is, in fact, a component of the radial electric field, due to the ionic space charge in the beam, perpendicular to the principal magnetic field. This determines for the electrons a drift velocity perpendicular to the two fields and hence in the direction of the beam. The paths of the electrons then become cycloids moving in the direction of the beam, and the stay of the electrons in the potential gap is prolonged. For this reason the big separators that operate at high currents should preferably be built with magnetic fields with 180° sectors. Fields with sectors of 60 or 90° are selected for reasons of cost, in those separators which operate with lower current levels, on the order of a few milliamperes. Formation of a beam with a compensated space charge requires a certain time, generally much longer than the time it takes the ions to pass through the separator.

This formation time is easily estimated. The number of secondary electrons produced by a beam of ions having a current density of J is, per unit of time,

$$\frac{dN^-}{dt} = \frac{J\sigma_i N_0}{e} \tag{13.16}$$

with σ_i being the ionization cross section and N_0 the number of residual-gas molecules present per unit of volume. When the beam is completely neutralized, the density of the negative charges produced must be equal to the density of positive charges in the beam

$$N^- = N^+ = \frac{J}{ev} \tag{13.17}$$

if v is the velocity of the ions.

As a first approximation, then, the time τ of formation of the neutralized beam is

$$\tau = \frac{N^-}{dN^-/dt} = \frac{1}{N_0 \sigma_i v} \tag{13.18}$$

Assuming the values $\sigma_i = 10^{-16}$ cm^2, $N_0 = 10^{12}$ atoms cm^{-3} (corresponding to pressures in the residual gas of about 3×10^{-5} mm Hg), and $v = 2 \times 10^7$ cm sec^{-1}, we have $\tau \sim 5 \times 10^{-4}$ sec. The calculation is purely indicative since it neglects the loss of electrons during the period of formation of the neutralized beam, owing primarily to recombination processes. Hence the experimental values of τ are a little higher than those calculated. Fluctuations in the ion current can disturb the process of compensating for the space charge.

In fact, we assume that the compensated ion current suddenly drops in intensity. The excessive negative charge is then pushed out toward the walls of the chamber. If the energy of the electrons is on the order of 1 eV, they will leave the region of the beam in a fraction of a microsecond. When the ionic current increases, the beam is no longer compensated and the time required to achieve the compensated stage again will depend on the speed with which negative charges are produced. About 8% of the fast ions produce negative charges in the beam; hence the time required to produce a number of negative charges equal to the number of fast positive charges is about 12 times longer than the transit time of the ions and hence on the order of 2×10^{-4} sec.

This indicative finding is close to that found from Eq. 13.18 for the time τ of neutralization. In fact, the time can be considerably longer because only those electrons with energy less than 1 eV are effective in reducing the beam's potential to a low enough level.

We can then predict that fluctuations in current intensity with a frequency less than 1 kHz will not damage the beam, because the process of neutralization of the space charge is capable of following these fluctuations. Fluctuations with frequencies greater than a few megahertz will not damage the beam, because the negative charges do not have time to escape. Fluctuations at intermediate levels will give rise to a temporary decompensation of the beam and to fluctuating positive potentials. These variations in potential deflect the ions from their proper path. The beam is no longer focused, and the current at the collector is gathered over a broad area fluctuating in time.

It has been ascertained that fluctuations in the current or discharge voltage, with principal frequencies in the neighborhood of 8 kHz, produce violent fluctuations in the beam. These frequencies are typical of a drop in the vapor pressure within the chamber to a level below a critical minimum value. The frequencies of fluctuations in the beam are independent of the frequencies of the corresponding fluctuations in the source.

There are other causes of fluctuation independent of disturbances in the source. Apparently the presence of charged surfaces in the region of the beam is quite critical. Slight variations in either the potential of these surfaces or in their position in relation to the beam have very marked effects on the appearance and disappearance of fluctuations, but these effects are not usually reproducible. Particularly frequent, therefore, is the appearance of such fluctuations in the region of ion acceleration where the introduction of electrodes is inevitable. These fluctuations are affected by the value of the acceleration potential and by very slight variations in the position of the acceleration slit and of the focusing electrode.

In practice, by adjusting the geometrical configuration of the source and the conditions of operation, we can improve the stabilization of the beam. Since the speed at which space-charge neutralization can follow fluctuation in the beam intensity depends on the electron production rate, it might be expected that at higher pressures in the vacuum chamber the beam would be less affected by source disturbances. In fact, increasing that pressure can eliminate fluctuations in the beam. This remedy of course has its limits since the scattering of ions at high pressures tends to spread the image at the collector. Various methods have been devised to improve the process of beam neutralization. Some of the methods were based on attempts to achieve greater effectiveness in the use of the electrons produced by ionization. Other methods were based on artificial production of new negative charges to inject into the beam.

The first method was chosen by Bernas,[5] who introduced into the vacuum chamber of the Saclay (France) separator a system of grids, giving them a negative potential with respect to ground, which prevents the extraction of electrons from the beam by the ion-accelerating voltage and limits their movement along the axis of the beam.

Artificial production of electrons has been studied at Oak Ridge, where various experimental methods have been used.

Thermionic emission processes have been studied by the introduction of sufficiently heated electrodes into the beam. Although electron production is very high, cathodes coated with oxide cannot be used, because the emitting surface is quickly destroyed by the action of chlorine and fluorine which are frequently contained in the feed material. Furthermore, surfaces that emit at high temperatures, such as tungsten or tantalum, require excessive consumption of energy. Good results have been reported with graphite grids. In every case, methods of this kind can be helpful only when the direct ionization process is not efficient, as happens in separators with low accelerating voltage.

Another possibility that has received some attention is the release of electrons from the walls by the photoelectric effect. Used in this method is a direct current discharge between carbon electrodes in the direction of the magnetic field. From the surfaces irradiated with ultraviolet light from the arc, surprisingly high currents of electrons are obtained. The neutralization effect, however, is not too efficient because the photoelectrons emitted have fairly high energy levels, about 10 eV.

Still another method used is the production of electrons by means of subsidiary discharges in the region of the beam as a result of introducing a positive-potential grid between the beam and the wall of the vacuum chamber. In this way electrons are produced by a process that is similar to what occurs in Penning vacuum gauges. The usefulness of the method is limited, however, by the nonnegligible effect of the grid potential on the beam, by the efficiency of the electron production process that requires excessively high pressure in the chamber, and by the fluctuations induced in the beam by Penning-type discharges.

Some experimenters have even tried to exploit the Malter effect, which consists in the production of electrons by field emission on surfaces of slightly oxidized aluminum in the presence of positive ions.

ION SOURCES

One of the basic problems in the construction of an isotope separator is that of designing an adequate ion source. Such a source must have high ion-emission levels, low pressure under operating conditions, almost monoenergetic ions produced, and no fluctuation in the current emitted. The first two features govern the yield and economy of the source, whereas the last two are essential conditions for facilitating the focusing of the beam.

Various types of sources that meet these requirements have been developed; some sources use arcs, some use high frequencies, and others use oscillating electrons. In high-frequency sources, the electrons present in the gas take on energy from a high-frequency alternating electromagnetic field and produce intense ionization. The field may be applied with a system of electrodes inside or outside the discharge chamber or with a coil wrapped around the discharge tube. Filaments emitting electrons are not needed, because the discharge is maintained by the secondary electrons. These sources are particularly effective in proton production and are widely used in accelerators.

For use in separators, however, there has been a tendency to design sources using arcs of the magnetic type with axial or radial ion extraction, sometimes equipped with electron-reflecting electrodes (see Fig. 13.3). Theoretically these sources consist of stainless-steel or graphite discharge chambers in which ion production takes place. The materials used in construction of the sources are chosen from among those which are resistant to high temperatures, are easy to clean, and are not excessively impregnated with gas.

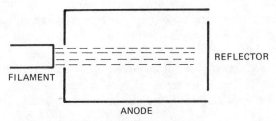

Fig. 13.3   Hot-filament ion source.

The ion-production process takes place in an atmosphere of the vapors of the substances to be separated, at a pressure of about 10^{-3} mm Hg, held constant by means of controlling the temperature of a crucible attached to the chamber and into which the substance is introduced in the solid state, or by setting an intake valve if the substance is in the gaseous state. The discharge is triggered and maintained by a beam of electrons given off by a hot tungsten or tantalum filament. The electrons are accelerated by an electrical field set up by maintaining a difference in potential of a few hundred volts* between the filament and the chamber, and are focused by an axial magnetic field. Sometimes an electrode facing the filament, and raised to the same potential, sets up a counterfield that induces the electrons to swing inside the chamber and thus augment the efficiency of ionization.

The discharge process inside the source takes place via the following mechanism. The electrons given off by the filament and accelerated by the electric field oscillate between the filament and the reflecting electrode. However, the electrons can hardly reach the anode, since the magnetic field B hinders their diffusion in the direction perpendicular to the lines of force. When the electrons lose energy through ionization processes, the radius of the orbit they follow decreases, making it harder for them to reach the anode. With strong magnetic fields and low pressures, the anode current is therefore weak.

However, when the vapor of the substance to be ionized has reached sufficient pressure ($\sim 10^{-3}$ mm Hg) inside the chamber, a discharge is triggered with a high

---

*Oak Ridge uses 50 to 200 volts.

production of ions and an electrically neutral zone known as a "plasma" is formed, in which the density of positive and negative charges is just about equal. This plasma is confined to a region of the chamber around the beam of primary electrons, outside of which the density of charges present declines exponentially with a typical relaxation length that varies inversely as the magnetic induction B. Under these working conditions, there is a strong gain in the anode current and the possibility of extracting ion currents on the order of several tens of milliamperes. The axial condition is the most favorable one for extracting the ions in the same direction as the magnetic field of the source (Finkestein sources). Ion emission can occur within a few hundred milliamperes. In separator design, most emphasis has gone, for reasons of convenience, to radial extraction sources, those in which extraction is perpendicular to the magnetic field of the source (Heil sources). Here the currents extracted are nevertheless smaller since extraction takes place perpendicular to the lines of force of the magnetic field, and the diffusion of the ions is thereby countered.

As we mentioned earlier, the isotopes to be separated must be introduced into the source in the form of vapor. In case we are dealing with solid-state compounds, they must be evaporated in a crucible. With a maximum temperature of 800°C, almost any element can be evaporated at vapor pressures high enough to allow the source to operate. Sources have recently been designed to separate such low-vapor-pressure elements as ruthenium, palladium, and iridium. In these sources the sample is heated by means of an accelerated beam of electrons, using a potential difference of tens of thousands of volts and aimed directly at the graphite container. In this way temperatures of 2800°C are achieved with dissipated powers of 10 to 20 kW.

Generally it is helpful to use solid samples for evaporation. In fact, for many separation processes, the material to be used consists of several grams, and so a very large volume of gas must be used. Furthermore, the un-ionized gas leaves the source and increases the residual pressure in the separator. In the case of a solid load, however, the pressure inside the separator is not markedly affected by the pressure in the source because most of the material evaporated condenses on the cold walls in the immediate vicinity of the source.

By reason of the very nature of the ionization process, the above-described sources have a rather low yield. The yield, defined as the ratio between the quantity of ionized gas and the quantity of gas that leaves the source as neutral vapor, is on the order of only 10 to 20%. As has been said, there is a pressure threshold in the operation of the source below which discharge is not maintained at all or displays phenomena of fluctuation and instability which are not compatible with steady operation. If a good yield is to be obtained, this threshold must be the lowest possible, partly because under these conditions we can work with wide extraction slits without markedly increasing the residual pressure in the separator.

To encourage neutralization of the space charge, we must make sure that there are no rapid fluctuations in ion emission.

There can be several forms of instability in an arc. There can be fluctuations at very low frequencies in which discharge is triggered and spent every few seconds because of an excessively low pressure or because of an extremely low cathode temperature. Fluctuations of higher frequency can be due to extraction slits that are too narrow or too deep, chambers that are too small, arcing currents or voltages that are too high or too low, or chamber pressures that are too low.

The way ions are carried inside the source toward the slit is governed primarily by the distribution of source potential, by which we mean the conditions of triggering and extraction. For discharges that are not too intense, penetration of the extraction electric field in the source gives rise to a distribution of potential like that shown in Fig. 13.4. Distribution of this kind is self-focusing, which means that it encourages the flow of ions toward the exit.

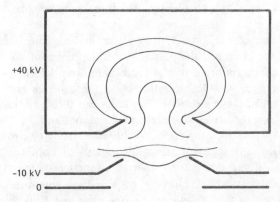

Fig. 13.4 Ion-extraction system and pattern of the equipotential curves.

If ionization in discharge is low, all the ions produced will be extracted. Often, however, the current extracted is limited by effects of the space charge, and its value will depend on the geometry of the electrodes and on the extraction voltage. For an infinite emitting plane located at a distance d from a flat electrode with a potential of V, we find that the density of the extracted current J is

$$J = 5.462 \times 10^{-8} \left(\frac{V^3}{M}\right)^{\frac{1}{2}} \times d^{-2} \qquad (A\ cm^{-2}) \qquad (13.19)$$

For other configurations we must remember a geometrical correction factor. In every case a saturation current is reached which can be increased only by increasing the extraction voltage.

The extraction system must be properly designed so as to obtain a beam as collimated as possible. The usual arrangement is the same as the one shown in Fig. 13.4. Between the source slit and the ground electrode, we often have insertion of an extraction electrode with a potential that is negative with respect to ground. The advantages of such a system by comparison with acceleration with a single electrode are many. The negative electrode forms a reflector for the electrons in the beam so that they cannot reach the source. In this way the neutralizing effect of the space charge is boosted. Furthermore, since the electrons cannot reach the source, there is a decrease in the high-voltage load and a reduction of discharges between the live parts and ground. These bursts are very frequent, and they hamper the proper operation of the equipment by causing instability and fluctuations in the high voltage. The bursts can be reduced by improved shaping and spacing of the electrodes. We should keep in mind that here we are working with pressures that put us to the left of Paschen's minimum. Consequently it is best to cut to a minimum the distance between the electrodes, at least to the point where the effects of surface roughness or other processes such as field emission do not become evident. Furthermore, the zone between electrodes is saturated with free charges produced by ionization of the residual gas or by ion impact on surfaces, which make the discharge conditions even more critical.

Other advantages of the extraction arrangement being discussed here are weak axial focusing of the beam and the possibility of fine tuning of the focal position of the beam. In fact, the position of the focal plane from which the ions appear to emerge and the image of which is gathered on the collector also depends on the potential of the intermediate electrode. The focus can then be adjusted by means of this potential, holding the overall accelerating voltage constant.

A calculation of the focusing effect of the accelerating electrodes was made by Pierce[9] for fairly simple geometrical configurations of both beams and emitting surfaces. His calculation allows us to find, as a function of the distance from the emitting surface and of the beam intensity, the shape and potentials of the electrodes. The theory has been further developed by Wakerling and Guthrie[6] for beams with hyperbolic boundaries and suitable forms of the meniscus of the source plasma, with partially satisfactory results. The actual form of the meniscus of the plasma is hard to determine and depends to a large extent on the discharge conditions. The presence of local discharges and secondary electrons is also important in effecting the distribution of potential in the region of the electrodes. All these effects cannot of course be brought into the calculations. A further difficulty stems from the fact that the calculations do not provide for the effect of bombardment of the electrodes by the ions, which release gas and electrons.

ISOTOPE COLLECTION

On emerging from the magnetic field, the separated isotopes are gathered on a collector. For each element a suitable collection system must be built since the separation distance per unit of mass at the collector declines as the mass of the separated isotopes increases. The shape of the collector, as is the material chosen to make it, and the cooling system are important. One of the major drawbacks in isotope collection is in fact the heating of the collector under the impact of the ions that bombard it. It is not unusual in working with separators to deal with currents of 100 mA at the collector and extraction voltages of 30 kV, values that represent a dissipation of a good 3 kW on a surface of just a few square centimeters. If the cooling system is not well designed, we may find that the isotopes already deposited evaporate. Equally harmful is the effect of direct impact of ions which displaces the material already gathered, along with the material of which the collector is made (a phenomenon called "sputtering").

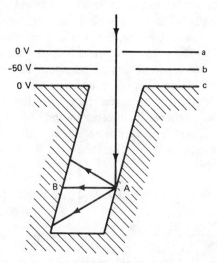

Fig. 13.5   Diagram of a collector.

All these phenomena cause a drop in the collection yield, as well as severe contamination of the samples collected. And so an adequate design for a collector must allow for many factors and requirements, among them maximum efficiency in the collection of the separated isotopes, very great stability of the collection surfaces with respect to the sputtering phenomenon so that collection can be continued for a great many days, efficient carry-off of the heat generated, and relatively easy fabrication.

It is difficult to comply with all these requirements at the same time since, in the choice of dimensions, we are almost always limited by insufficient dispersion. Unlike other methods, in electromagnetic separation as a rule, all the isotopes of a given element are collected simultaneously, and therefore the number of collector pockets may be large.

Collectors are generally built as shown in Fig. 13.5 to avoid the effect of direct impact by the ions on the gathering surfaces. The isotope strikes the collector at A and bounces off to B, where it is collected without being struck by the incident beam. The position of the ion beams entering the individual pockets can be determined visually, taking advantage of the excitation of the molecules of residual gas by the fast ions. The mass spectrum can also be continuously monitored and displayed on an oscillograph.

As previously mentioned, the fundamental factors opposing a good yield of ions at the collector are evaporation of the material at the receiver and sputtering due to the high-energy ions. In separator design hitherto, there has not been a single attempt to slow down the ions so that they would arrive at the pockets with too little energy to erode or vaporize the surfaces they find there. Preliminary tests have shown that this slowing down produces a marked reduction both of focus and of collection.

Collectors are generally made of graphite or copper, according to the lesser or greater volatility of the element collected. For volatile elements the temperature of the surfaces must be held down to avoid loss of the material by evaporation, contamination of the gathered isotope through passage of material from one pocket to those nearby, or, in the extreme case, actual melting of the collector. In the case of a metallic collector, it is fairly easy to assess the temperature and thus to design the collector accordingly and to choose its dimensions and cooling system on the basis of available space. As a practical criterion for determining allowable temperature levels for a collector, the following will do. Calculate as a first approximation the loss of material by evaporation by:

$$Q_e = 5.8 \times 10^{-2} \ Ap(TM)^{-\frac{1}{2}} \tag{13.20}$$

where A = area of the collector slit, cm^2
  p = vapor pressure, mm Hg
  M = mass number of the isotope collected
  T = absolute temperature of the collector, °K

If i is the total current at the collector (mA) and a is the abundance (%) of the isotope gathered, the quantity of material incoming is

$$Q_i = 1.04 \times 10^{-10} \ ai \tag{13.21}$$

If we want to hold material losses below 1%, the following equation must be satisfied:

$$p < \frac{1.8 \times 10^{-11} \ ai(TM)^{\frac{1}{2}}}{A} \quad (mm \ Hg) \tag{13.22}$$

The effects of sputtering are also very harmful both to yield and in contamination. It is estimated that about 30% of the material can be reextracted by the incident beam. Of course the phenomenon can be reduced by the use of the arrangement shown in Fig. 13.5 and the use of very deep pockets.

Collection techniques vary according to the different elements. The not so volatile metals like the platinum group require no special precautions, whereas the common metals require only adequate cooling and, for the more volatile metals, the use of graphite or copper collectors. In particular, iron requires the use of special, purified graphite since iron is a common impurity in that material. In the case of mercury, cooled screens are needed to avoid contamination from the material evaporating from the source. Mercury is gathered in silver collectors so as to form an amalgam. Collecting a gas is naturally far less efficient. In the case of chemically active gases, compounds of low vapor pressure may be formed at the collector if a suitable material is chosen for the collector. With oxygen and nitrogen, oxides and nitrates, respectively, are formed, preferably with the use of tungsten or copper for oxygen and molybdenum for nitrogen. The problem of collecting the inert gases is more complex. Fairly good results are obtained by exploiting the effect by which highly charged ions can penetrate to a depth of several hundred atomic layers of a metallic surface and be held there. However, if we are to avoid a rapid saturation of the surface itself, collectors with large surfaces or moving strips must be used. An interesting technique for collecting inert gases has been tested at Oak Ridge. It consists in causing magnesium vapor to condense continually and at regular intervals on a collector that is bombarded by the inert-gas ions; this action forms a kind of sandwich that permits retention of about 50% of the ionized gas.

A problem sometimes arises in measurement of the ion currents at the collector. An absolute measurement of the ion beam is of some importance since it enables us to obtain data as to the efficiency of the source, to find the precise weight of the material coming into the pockets, and thus to find the yield of collection and of recovery of the material through chemical processes. Measurement of ion current is complicated by the emission of secondary electrons when the beam strikes the collector. In some cases we also have thermic emission of ions or electrons. There are two ways of getting around this difficulty. We can apply to the collector a magnetic field on the order of several hundred gauss, normal to the direction of movement of the ion beam, in such a way as to keep the electrons at the collector. This arrangement is always present in 180° separators. The second method consists in inserting between the pocket and the slit in the screen (usually placed there to cut down contamination) another electrode that has been given a slightly negative potential. Sufficient in this case are retarding potentials of about 100 V; such potentials represent the maximum energy in the spectrum of electrons emitted by ion impact.

CHEMICAL ASPECTS OF SEPARATION

The chemical aspects of electromagnetic separation have to do both with the preparation of the feed material for the source and with the processes of recovering the material gathered at the collector.

The choice of feed material for the source must be considered separately for each type of element; however, a few general criteria can be laid down. First we must keep in mind that the ion source must operate at pressures of a few tens of microns of mercury. If the element in question is not very volatile, a suitable compound must be chosen. A simple molecular structure is preferable, and there should be good thermal stability for the substance. As a general rule the element is preferable if it is easy to ionize, whereas such compounds as nitrates or sulfates should be avoided because they will corrode the tantalum or tungsten filaments in the source. The material must be anhydrous and completely volatile, without residue. Chlorides or fluorides can damage the oil in the vacuum pump, and thus suitable precautions are required.

Particular care must be taken in removal of the isotopes gathered by the collector to avoid loss of material or contamination during the various chemical processes used.

Since the deposit in the collectors is intimately mixed with the material of which the pockets are made and is contaminated with many other elements, the isotope cannot ordinarily be used directly but must be refined so as to obtain a chemically stable sample whose mass is well determined. The chemical impurities present may be isobars emitted as ions by the source, but they may also be produced by evaporation, by scattering effects, or by the presence of different molecular compounds. It can easily happen that the elements making up the stainless steel, of which the separator is largely built, are present in every collection in considerable amounts.

The first operation to be performed in any purification process is the removal of collector materials from the deposited isotope. To avoid the risk of isotopic contamination, we would be wise to use very pure materials for the collector. One of the difficulties that may arise during the purification treatment is that the product gathered is not easily dissolved by ordinary chemical reagents because the deposit was formed at high temperature and may combine with oxygen, nitrogen, or carbon in the surfaces of the collector. Of course the reagents must be of suitable purity, and proper vessels must be selected for the treatment. The purity of the separated products must be high. As a rule, the percentage of impurities allowable must be between 0.001 and 0.01%.

Another chemical aspect of separation is the recovery of the unseparated substance, which is extracted from the separator and again transformed into the starting-feed material. Of course this recovery operation is not always necessary. The material is usually recovered in the case of separation of a product that has already been enriched or of particularly rare or precious substances, such as in the separation of rare earths or elements of the platinum—palladium group. In these cases the overall loss of material is held to about 10%.

ELECTROMAGNETIC-SEPARATION PLANTS

Many isotope separators are in operation today all over the world. According to what they are used for, it is helpful to divide them into two categories: (1) laboratory separators, used to produce small quantities of isotopically pure samples needed for special experiments in nuclear physics, and (2) the big separators, used for regular commercial production of all isotopes.

For purposes of orientation, the diagram in Fig. 13.6 shows the amount m (microgram atoms) of isotope separated as a function of the current i (microamperes) and of the separation time t (hours). The weight of the sample is found if the value thus obtained is multiplied by the mass number of the separated isotope. Normal mass

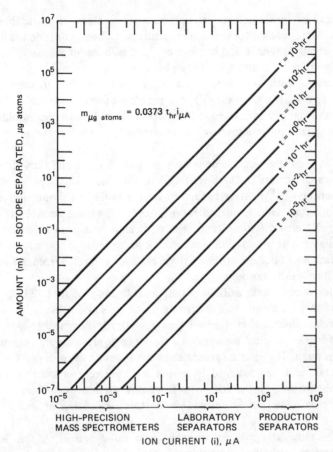

Fig. 13.6 Diagram showing the quantity of isotope separated as a function of the ion current and the separation time.

spectrometers for isotopic analysis operate in the interval between 10^{-5} and 1 μA; laboratory separators use currents on the order of several milliamperes whereas higher currents are utilized only in the big production separators.

Laboratory separators, in general, are found in nuclear physics laboratories. Isotopes are produced only when needed by research teams and in the form most suitable to the particular experiment in which they are to be used. In nuclear physics today, separated isotopes are widely used as targets for particle accelerators and thus provide easier interpretation of the results of nuclear reactions. In such cases the isotope gathered on the collector by direct impact in very small quantities is not treated chemically because the surface of the collector itself makes a suitable target.

Over the past few years, several laboratory separators have been built expressly for the preparation of artificially produced samples of radioactive isotopes. In this way it is possible to get isotopically pure samples in suitable form for the study of radiation of active nuclei by means of beta and gamma spectrometers. Of course the separation of radioactive isotopes calls for special techniques, both because of the small quantities of material usually available and because of the possibility of radioactive contamination of the instrument. To this type belong the separators used by the Swedish–Danish group that works with low currents (up to a few hundred microamperes) at high acceleration potentials (40 to 80 kV); the problem of extraction and collimation of the beam is thus greatly facilitated, and it is possible to achieve high resolution levels. Under these conditions radioactive contamination of the separator is extremely limited.

Separation on a large scale is done only in the Oak Ridge and Harwell centers and in a few research centers in the Soviet Union. The Oak Ridge separators were used initially to separate ^{235}U. After 1945 they were modified for production of enriched isotopes of other elements in quantities on the order of a gram. Between 1945 and the present time, 57 elements have been separated, and there is an abundant supply of isotopes available. The production work at Oak Ridge today is concentrated primarily on the separation of large quantities of those nuclides needed to maintain an adequate inventory of high-purity isotopes.

After a few years' work, workers in the Soviet Union produced 222 isotopes of 50 elements, and they have built up a reserve supply of stable isotopes.

The Hermes separator at Harwell was specifically designed to produce small quantities of highly enriched isotopes of active or toxic elements and, in particular, to produce plutonium. The Hermes generates an ion beam on the order of 1 mA, is quite efficient overall, and was designed to permit easy recovery of material used in the source but not focused on the collector. The entire machine is enclosed in an airtight chamber so that it can safely be used for isotopic separation of the transuranium elements.

Table 13.1 shows the principal features of several separators. At Oak Ridge there are two separators of the first type shown in the table and dozens of the second type. The Russians report data for more than a dozen big production separators of various types; one is a separator with a rotationally symmetrical magnetic field at an aperture of 225°, designed mainly to separate the isotopes of heavy elements. Separators with similar fields have high dispersion and can focus, without aberration, ion beams with an angle of aperture as high as 15°.

The Saclay separator may be considered a prototype of laboratory separators for stable isotopes with medium mass. There have been many of this type built; among them is the one in Belgrade (see Table 13.1) and the one at the Politecnico in Milan.

The Copenhagen separator is the prototype of the separators built by the research group of Denmark and Sweden. This group of separators provides isotopes chiefly for nuclear physics work. Most American and Soviet separators operate with multiple sources, meaning that in a single separating element there are several sources working simultaneously; under these conditions high production levels per unit can be obtained.

The data shown in the last column of Table 13.1 are merely indicative, in that the values of the currents received at the collector vary in quite marked degree according

Table 13.1

ELECTROMAGNETIC SEPARATORS

Location	Magnetic-field sector, deg	Mean radius of curvature, cm	Maximum magnetic induction, gauss	Acceleration voltage, kV	Collector current, mA
Oak Ridge	180	122	3,500	35	100
Oak Ridge	180	61	6,000	35	100
USSR	180	162	5,500	35	100
USSR	180	90	8,000	35	100
Harwell	180	61	6,000	30	100
Amsterdam	180	102	3,750	50	10
Saclay	60	50	12,000	50	5
Harwell (Hermes)	90	61	6,000	40	1
Belgrade	60	50	12,000	50	5
Copenhagen	90	80	8,000	80	0.1
Marburg	90	100	6,000	20	0.1

to the elements separated. The values shown in the table, on the order of 100 mA, should be considered feasible, in general, for elements with low atomic weights and high ionization yields. In the case of lithium, currents as high as 700 mA have been obtained.

REFERENCES

1. J. Koch, R. H. Dawton, M. L. Smith, and W. Walcher (Eds.), *Electromagnetic Isotope Separators and Applications of Electromagnetically Enriched Isotopes,* North-Holland Publishing Company, Amsterdam, 1958.
2. M. L. Smith (Ed.), in *Electromagnetically Enriched Isotopes and Mass Spectrometry,* Conference Proceedings, Harwell, 1955, Butterworth Scientific Publications, London, 1956.
3. G. F. Barnard, *Modern Mass Spectrometry,* Institute of Physics, London, 1953.
4. C. J. Zilverschoon, *An Electromagnetic Isotope Separator,* Uitgeverij Excelsior, 's Gravenhage, 1954.
5. R. Bernas, Electromagnetic Separator for Isotopes of Light and Medium Elements (French), *J. Phys. Radium,* 8: 453 (1953).
6. R. K. Wakerling and A. Guthrie (Eds.), Electromagnetic Separation of Isotopes in Commercial Quantities, USAEC Report TID-5217, June 1949.
7. V. S. Zolotarev, A. I. Iljin, and E. G. Komar, Isotope Separation by Electromagnetic Separators in the Soviet Union, in *Proceedings of the Second United Nations International Conference on the Peaceful Uses of Atomic Energy, Geneva, 1958,* Vol. 4, p. 471, United Nations, New York, 1958.
8. M. L. Cartan, On the Focusing of Beams of Charged Particles by Circular Deviation in a Transverse Magnetic Field (French), *J. Phys. Radium,* 8: 453 (1937).
9. J. R. Pierce, Rectilinear Electron Flow in Beams, *J. Appl. Phys.,* II: 548 (1940).

10. A. H. Barnes, S. M. MacNeille, and C. Starr, Problems of Physics in the Ion Source, H. W. Savage (Ed.), USAEC Report TID-5219, 1951.

11. J. Kistemaker and H. L. Douwes Dekker, Investigations on a Magnetic Ion Source, *Physica*, **16**: 209 (1950).

12. P. S. Baker et al., Production and Distribution of Electromagnetically Enriched Isotopes, in *Proceedings of the Second United Nations International Conference on the Peaceful Uses of Atomic Energy, Geneva, 1958,* Vol. 20, p. 245, United Nations, New York, 1958.

13. M. Benedict et al., Report of Uranium Isotope Separation Review Ad Hoc Committee, USAEC Report ORO-694, June 1972.

APPENDIX A: PHYSICAL CONSTANTS AND DATA IN COMMON USE

Constants

Planck's constant	$h = 6.624 \times 10^{-27}$ erg sec
Boltzmann's constant	$k = 1.380 \times 10^{-16}$ erg $^{\circ}K^{-1}$
Avogadro's number	$N_{Av.} = 6.023 \times 10^{-23}$ mol^{-1}
Constant for perfect gases	$R = 8.314 \times 10^{7}$ ergs $^{\circ}K^{-1}$ mol^{-1}
Mechanical equivalent of a calorie	1 cal = 4.1855 J
Electron volt in centimeter gram seconds	$1 eV = 1.60 \times 10^{-12}$ erg
Faraday's constant	$F = 96,500$ coulombs gram-equivalent^{-1}
Electronic charge	$e = 1.60 \times 10^{-19}$ coulomb
Electron rest mass	$m = 9.11 \times 10^{-28}$ g
Proton mass	$m_p = 1.67 \times 10^{-24}$ g
Atomic mass unit (amu)	1 amu = 1.657×10^{-24} g $(^1/_{16} \times M_O{}^{16})$
Energy equivalent of the amu	1 amu = 931 MeV = 1.49×10^{-3} erg
Proton mass expressed as amu	$m_p = 1.00759$ amu
Neutron mass expressed as amu	$m_n = 1.00898$ amu

Some Physicochemical Data

	He	H_2	N_2	O_2	Ar	H_2O	CO_2
Melting point, $^{\circ}K$	1.2	14	63.1	54.4	83.2	$0^{\circ}C$	
Boiling point, $^{\circ}K$	4.4	20.4	77.4	90.2	87.4	$100^{\circ}C$	$-78.5^{\circ}C$ (subl.)
Critical temperature, $^{\circ}K$	5.3	33.3	126.1	154.4	150.8	$374^{\circ}C$	$31.1^{\circ}C$
Critical pressure, atm	2.26	12.8	33.5	49.7	48	217.7	73

Vapor Pressure of Water at Various Temperatures

Temperature, $^{\circ}C$	0	15	30	50	80	100	110	200
Pressure, torrs	4.6	12.8	31.8	92.5	355	760	1,075	15.3, atm

Periodic System of the Natural Elements

Group (period)		0	I	II	III	IV	V	VI	VII	VIII
	1		1 H 1.008							
First short period	2	2 He 4.003	3 Li 6.94	4 Be 9.02	5 B 10.82	6 C 12.01	7 N 14.008	8 O 16.00	9 F 19.0	
Second short period	3	10 Ne 20.183	11 Na 22.997	12 Mg 24.32	13 Al 26.97	14 Si 28.06	15 P 30.98	16 S 32.06	17 Cl 35.457	
First long period	4	18 Ar 39.944	19 K 39.096	20 Ca 40.08	21 Sc 45.1	22 Ti 47.90	23 V 50.95	24 Cr 52.01	25 Mn 54.93	26 Fe 27 Co 28 Ni 55.85 58.94 58.69
	5		29 Cu 63.57	30 Zn 65.38	31 Ga 69.72	32 Ge 72.6	33 As 74.91	34 Se 78.96	35 Br 79.916	
Second long period	6	36 Kr 83.7	37 Rb 85.48	38 Sr 87.63	39 Y 88.92	40 Zr 91.22	41 Nb 92.91	42 Mo 95.95	43 Tc 98.3	44 Ru 45 Rh 46 Pd 101.7 102.91 106.7
	7		47 Ag 107.88	48 Cd 112.41	49 In 114.76	50 Sn 118.7	51 Sb 121.76	52 Te 127.6	53 I 126.92	
Third long period	8	54 Xe 131.3	55 Cs 132.91	56 Ba 137.36	57 La 138.92	58 Ce 140.13	59 Pr 140.92	60 Nd 144.27	61 Pm	
	9		62 Sm 150.43	63 Eu 152.0	64 Gd 156.9	65 Tb 159.2	66 Dy 162.46	67 Ho 164.935	68 Er 167.2	
			69 Tm 169.4	70 Yb 173.04	71 Lu 174.99	72 Hf 178.6	73 Ta 180.88	74 W 183.92	75 Re 186.31	76 Os 77 Ir 78 Pt 190.2 193.1 195.23
			79 Au 197.2	80 Hg 200.61	81 Tl 204.39	82 Pb 207.21	83 Bi 209.0	84 Po 210.0	85 At	
Fourth long period	10	86 Rn 220.0	87 –	88 Ra 226.97	89 Ac 227	90 Th 232.12	91 Pa 231	92 U 238.07		

APPENDIX B: NATURAL ISOTOPIC CONCENTRATIONS

(The Atomic Numbers A of Unstable Nuclei Are in Italics)

Z	Element	Symbol	N	A	Mol fraction, %
1	Hydrogen	H	0	1	99.9844
	Deuterium	D	1	2	0.0156
	Tritium	T	2	*3*	
2	Helium	He	1	3	1.3×10^{-4}
			2	4	99.9999
3	Lithium	Li	3	6	7.52
			4	7	92.48
4	Beryllium	Be	5	9	100.0
5	Boron	B	5	10	18.98
			6	11	81.02
6	Carbon	C	6	12	98.892
			7	13	1.108
			8	*14*	
7	Nitrogen	N	7	14	99.635
			8	15	0.365
8	Oxygen	O	8	16	99.759
			9	17	0.0374
			10	18	0.2039
9	Fluorine	F	10	19	100.0
10	Neon	Ne	10	20	90.92
			11	21	0.257
			12	22	8.82

Z	Element	Symbol	N	A	Mol fraction, %
11	Sodium	Na	12	23	100.0
12	Magnesium	Mg	12	24	78.60
			13	25	10.11
			14	26	11.29
13	Aluminum	Al	14	27	100.0
14	Silicon	Si	14	28	92.27
			15	29	4.68
			16	30	3.05
15	Phosphorus	P	16	31	100.0
16	Sulfur	S	16	32	95.1
			17	33	0.74
			18	34	4.2
			20	36	0.016
17	Chlorine	Cl	18	35	75.4
			20	37	24.6
18	Argon	Ar	18	36	0.337
			20	38	0.063
			22	40	99.600
19	Potassium	K	20	39	93.08
			21	*40*	0.0119
			22	41	6.91
20	Calcium	Ca	20	40	96.97
			22	42	0.64
			23	43	0.145
			24	44	2.06
			26	46	0.0033
			28	48	0.185
21	Scandium	Sc	24	45	100.0
22	Titanium	Ti	24	46	7.95
			25	47	7.75
			26	48	73.45
			27	49	5.51
			28	50	5.34
23	Vanadium	V	27	*50*	0.24
			28	51	99.76
24	Chromium	Cr	26	50	4.31
			28	52	83.76
			29	53	9.55
			30	54	2.38
25	Manganese	Mn	30	55	100.0
26	Iron	Fe	28	54	5.84
			30	56	91.68

Z	Element	Symbol	N	A	Mol fraction, %
Iron (Continued)			31	57	2.17
			32	58	0.31
27	Cobalt	Co	32	59	100.0
28	Nickel	Ni	30	58	67.76
			32	60	26.16
			33	61	1.25
			34	62	3.66
			36	64	1.16
29	Copper	Cu	34	63	69.1
			36	65	30.9
30	Zinc	Zn	34	64	48.89
			36	66	27.81
			37	67	4.11
			38	68	18.56
			40	70	0.62
31	Gallium	Ga	38	69	60.2
			40	71	39.8
32	Germanium	Ge	38	70	20.55
			40	72	27.37
			41	73	7.61
			42	74	36.74
			44	76	7.67
33	Arsenic	As	42	75	100.0
34	Selenium	Se	40	74	0.87
			42	76	9.02
			43	77	7.58
			44	78	23.52
			46	80	49.82
			48	82	9.19
35	Bromine	Br	44	79	50.52
			46	81	49.48
36	Krypton	Kr	42	78	0.354
			44	80	2.27
			46	82	11.56
			47	83	11.55
			48	84	56.90
			50	86	17.37
37	Rubidium	Rb	48	85	72.15
			50	*87*	27.85
38	Strontium	Sr	46	84	0.56
			48	86	9.86
			49	87	7.02
			50	88	82.56

Z	Element	Symbol	N	A	Mol fraction, %
39	Yttrium	Y	50	89	100.0
40	Zirconium	Zr	50	90	51.46
			51	91	11.23
			52	92	17.11
			54	94	17.40
			56	96	2.80
41	Niobium	Nb	52	93	100.0
42	Molybdenum	Mo	50	92	15.86
			52	94	9.12
			53	95	15.70
			54	96	16.50
			55	97	9.45
			56	98	23.75
			58	100	9.62
43	Technetium	Tc	56	99	
44	Ruthenium	Ru	52	96	5.68
			54	98	2.22
			55	99	12.81
			56	100	12.70
			57	101	16.98
			58	102	31.34
			60	104	18.27
45	Rhodium	Rh	58	103	100.0
46	Palladium	Pd	56	102	0.8
			58	104	9.3
			59	105	22.6
			60	106	27.2
			62	108	26.8
			64	110	13.5
47	Silver	Ag	60	107	51.35
			62	109	48.65
48	Cadmium	Cd	58	106	1.215
			60	108	0.875
			62	110	12.39
			63	111	12.75
			64	112	24.07
			65	113	12.26
			66	114	28.86
			68	116	7.58
49	Indium	In	64	113	4.23
			66	*115*	95.77
50	Tin	Sn	62	112	0.95
			64	114	0.65
			65	115	0.34

Z	Element	Symbol	N	A	Mol fraction, %
Tin (Continued)			66	116	14.24
			67	117	7.57
			68	118	24.01
			69	119	8.58
			70	120	32.97
			72	122	4.71
			74	124	5.98
51	Antimony	Sb	70	121	57.25
			72	123	42.75
52	Tellurium	Te	68	120	0.089
			70	122	2.46
			71	123	0.87
			72	124	4.61
			73	125	6.99
			74	126	18.71
			76	128	31.79
			78	*130*	34.49
53	Iodine	I	74	127	100.0
54	Xenon	Xe	70	124	0.096
			72	126	0.090
			74	128	1.919
			75	129	26.44
			76	130	4.08
			77	131	21.18
			78	132	26.89
			80	134	10.44
			82	136	8.87
55	Cesium	Cs	78	133	100.0
56	Barium	Ba	74	130	0.101
			76	132	0.097
			78	134	2.42
			79	135	6.59
			80	136	7.81
			81	137	11.32
			82	138	71.66
57	Lanthanum	La	81	*138*	0.089
			82	139	99.911
58	Cerium	Ce	78	136	0.193
			80	138	0.250
			82	140	88.48
			84	142	11.07
59	Praseodymium	Pr	82	141	100.0
60	Neodymium	Nd	82	142	27.13
			83	143	12.20

Z	Element	Symbol	N	A	Mol fraction, %
Neodymium (Continued)			84	144	23.87
			85	145	8.30
			86	146	17.18
			88	148	5.72
			90	150	5.60
61	Promethium	Pm	84	*145*	–
62	Samarium	Sm	82	144	3.16
			85	*147*	15.07
			86	148	11.27
			87	149	13.84
			88	150	7.47
			90	152	26.63
			92	154	22.53
63	Europium	Eu	88	151	47.77
			90	153	52.23
64	Gadolinium	Gd	88	152	0.20
			90	154	2.15
			91	155	14.73
			92	156	20.47
			93	157	15.68
			94	158	24.87
			96	160	21.90
65	Terbium	Tb	94	159	100.0
66	Dysprosium	Dy	90	156	0.0524
			92	158	0.0902
			94	160	2.294
			95	161	18.88
			96	162	25.53
			97	163	24.97
			98	164	28.18
67	Holmium	Ho	98	165	100.0
68	Erbium	Er	94	162	0.136
			96	164	1.56
			98	166	33.41
			99	167	22.94
			100	168	27.07
			102	170	14.88
69	Thulium	Tm	100	169	100.0
70	Ytterbium	Yb	98	168	0.140
			100	170	3.03
			101	171	14.31
			102	172	21.82
			103	173	16.13
			104	174	31.84
			106	176	12.73

Z	Element	Symbol	N	A	Mol fraction, %
71	Lutetium	Lu	104	175	97.40
			105	*176*	2.60
72	Hafnium	Hf	102	174	0.18
			104	176	5.15
			105	177	18.39
			106	178	27.08
			107	179	13.78
			108	180	35.44
73	Tantalum	Ta	108	181	100.0
74	Tungsten	W	106	180	0.135
			108	182	26.4
			109	183	14.4
			110	184	30.6
			112	186	28.4
75	Rhenium	Re	110	185	37.07
			112	*187*	62.93
76	Osmium	Os	108	184	0.018
			110	186	1.59
			111	187	1.64
			112	188	13.3
			113	189	16.1
			114	190	26.4
			116	192	41.0
77	Iridium	Ir	114	191	38.5
			116	193	61.5
78	Platinum	Pt	112	190	0.012
			114	192	0.78
			116	194	32.8
			117	195	33.7
			118	196	25.4
			120	198	7.23
79	Gold	Au	118	197	100.0
80	Mercury	Hg	116	196	0.146
			118	198	10.02
			119	199	16.84
			120	200	23.13
			121	201	13.22
			122	202	29.80
			124	204	6.85
81	Thallium	Tl	122	203	29.50
			124	205	70.50
			125	*206*	
			126	*207*	
			127	*208*	
			129	*210*	

Z	Element	Symbol	N	A	Mol fraction, %
82	Lead	Pb	122	204	1.55
			124	206	22.51
			125	207	22.60
			126	208	53.34
			128	*210*	
			129	*211*	
			130	*212*	
			132	*214*	
83	Bismuth	Bi	126	*209*	100.0
			127	*210*	
			128	*211*	
			129	*212*	
			131	*214*	
84	Polonium	Po	126	*210*	
			127	*211*	
			128	*212*	
			130	*214*	
			131	*215*	
			132	*216*	
			134	*218*	
85	Astatine	At	131	*215*	
			132	*216*	
			134	*218*	
86	Radon	Rn	133	*219*	
			134	*220*	
			136	*222*	
87	Francium	Fr	136	*223*	
88	Radium	Ra	135	*223*	
			136	*224*	
			138	*226*	
			140	*228*	
89	Actinium	Ac	138	*227*	
			139	*228*	
90	Thorium	Th	137	*227*	
			138	*228*	
			140	*230*	
			141	*231*	
			142	*232*	100.0
			144	*234*	
91	Protactinium	Pa	140	*231*	
			143	*234*	
92	Uranium	U	142	*234*	0.0058
			143	*235*	0.71
			146	*238*	99.28

Z	Element	Symbol	N	A	Mol fraction, %
93	Neptunium	Np	144	*237*	
94	Plutonium	Pu	148	*242*	
95	Americium	Am	148	*243*	
96	Curium	Cm	147	*243*	
97	Berkelium	Bk	148	*245*	
98	Californium	Cf	148	*246*	

APPENDIX C: FINITE-DIFFERENCE EQUATIONS

Various problems relating to separation processes will sometimes make it necessary to solve finite-difference equations of the type

$$Af(x + 2) + Bf(x + 1) + Cf(x) = \varphi \tag{C.1}$$

This is a second-order equation in x (the order is given by the highest multiple of the variation, which in this case is 2). It is linear, with constant coefficients (A, B, C), and not homogeneous. Let the term φ, for example, be a known function of x.

The solution to Eq. C.1, like that for linear differential equations with constant coefficients, is found by combining linearly a particular integral of the complete equation with the general integral of the corresponding homogeneous equation

$$Af(x + 2) + Bf(x + 1) + Cf(x) = 0 \tag{C.2}$$

The particular integral is found, when possible, by trial and error. A very simple case is the one in which φ is a constant, and hence a particular integral is represented by the expression $\varphi/(A + B + C)$. The general integral $f_0(x)$ for the homogeneous equation C.2 is found by writing the corresponding characteristic algebraic equation

$$A\alpha^2 + B\alpha + C = 0 \tag{C.3}$$

extracting the roots, which we shall call α_1 and α_2, respectively, and linearly compounding the exponential functions α_1^x and α_2^x:

$$f_0(x) = C_1\alpha_1^x + C_2\alpha_2^x \tag{C.4}$$

The constants C_1 and C_2 are determined by means of two suitable conditions on the boundary. What has just been said about a second-order equation can be applied to any order.

APPENDIX D:
TABLE OF SEPARATION POTENTIAL V'*

$$[V' = (2N - 1) \ln R]$$

N	0	1	2	3	4	5	6	7	8	9
0.0010	6.89294	6.88286	6.87288	6.86300	6.85321	6.84351	6.83391	6.82439	6.81496	6.80562
0.0011	6.79636	6.78718	6.77809	6.76907	6.76014	6.75128	6.74250	6.73379	6.72515	6.71659
0.0012	6.70809	6.69967	6.69132	6.68303	6.67481	6.66665	6.65856	6.65053	6.64257	6.63466
0.0013	6.62682	6.61903	6.61130	6.60363	6.59602	6.58846	6.58096	6.57351	6.56612	6.55878
0.0014	6.55149	6.54425	6.53706	6.52992	6.52283	6.51579	6.50880	6.50185	6.49495	6.48810
0.0015	6.48129	6.47452	6.46780	6.46112	6.45449	6.44790	6.44135	6.43484	6.42837	6.42194
0.0016	6.41555	6.40921	6.40290	6.39662	6.39039	6.38419	6.37803	6.37191	6.36582	6.35977
0.0017	6.35375	6.34777	6.34182	6.33590	6.33002	6.32418	6.31836	6.31258	6.30683	6.30111
0.0018	6.29542	6.28977	6.28414	6.27854	6.27298	6.26744	6.26194	6.25646	6.25101	6.24559
0.0019	6.24020	6.23483	6.22949	6.22418	6.21890	6.21365	6.20842	6.20321	6.19803	6.19288
0.0020	6.18776	6.18265	6.17758	6.17252	6.16750	6.16249	6.15751	6.15256	6.14762	6.14271
0.0021	6.13783	6.13296	6.12812	6.12330	6.11851	6.11373	6.10898	6.10425	6.09954	6.09485
0.0022	6.09018	6.08553	6.08091	6.07630	6.07171	6.06715	6.06260	6.05807	6.05357	6.04908
0.0023	6.04461	6.04016	6.03573	6.03132	6.02692	6.02255	6.01819	6.01385	6.00953	6.00523
0.0024	6.00094	5.99667	5.99242	5.98819	5.98397	5.97977	5.97559	5.97142	5.96727	5.96313
0.0025	5.95902	5.95491	5.95083	5.94676	5.94270	5.93867	5.93464	5.93064	5.92664	5.92266
0.0026	5.91870	5.91475	5.91082	5.90690	5.90300	5.89911	5.89524	5.89137	5.88753	5.88369
0.0027	5.87988	5.87607	5.87228	5.86850	5.86474	5.86099	5.85725	5.85352	5.84981	5.84612
0.0028	5.84243	5.83876	5.83510	5.83145	5.82782	5.82419	5.82058	5.81699	5.81340	5.80983
0.0029	5.80627	5.80272	5.79918	5.79566	5.79214	5.78864	5.78515	5.78167	5.77820	5.77475
0.0030	5.77130	5.76787	5.76445	5.76103	5.75763	5.75424	5.75086	5.74750	5.74414	5.74079
0.0031	5.73745	5.73413	5.73081	5.72751	5.72421	5.72093	5.71765	5.71439	5.71113	5.70789
0.0032	5.70465	5.70143	5.69821	5.69501	5.69181	5.68863	5.68545	5.68228	5.67913	5.67598
0.0033	5.67284	5.66971	5.66659	5.66348	5.66037	5.65728	5.65420	5.65112	5.64805	5.64500
0.0034	5.64195	5.63891	5.63587	5.63285	5.62984	5.62683	5.62383	5.62084	5.61786	5.61489
0.0035	5.61193	5.60897	5.60602	5.60308	5.60015	5.59723	5.59431	5.59140	5.58850	5.58561
0.0036	5.58273	5.57985	5.57698	5.57412	5.57127	5.56842	5.56558	5.56275	5.55993	5.55712

*For values of N greater than 0.5, note that $V'(N) = V'(1 - N)$.

N	0	1	2	3	4	5	6	7	8	9
0.0037	5.55431	5.55151	5.54871	5.54593	5.54315	5.54038	5.53761	5.53485	5.53210	5.52936
0.0038	5.52662	5.52389	5.52117	5.51846	5.51575	5.51304	5.51035	5.50766	5.50498	5.50230
0.0039	5.49964	5.49698	5.49432	5.49167	5.48903	5.48639	5.48377	5.48114	5.47853	5.47592
0.0040	5.47331	5.47072	5.46813	5.46554	5.46296	4.46039	5.45782	5.45526	5.45271	5.45016
0.0041	5.44762	5.44508	5.44255	5.44003	5.43751	5.43500	5.43249	5.42999	5.42750	5.42501
0.0042	5.42253	5.42005	5.41758	5.41511	5.41265	5.41020	5.40775	5.40530	5.40287	5.40043
0.0043	5.39801	5.39558	5.39317	5.39076	5.38835	5.38595	5.38356	5.38117	5.37878	5.37640
0.0044	5.37403	5.37166	5.36930	5.36694	5.36459	5.36224	5.35990	5.35756	5.35523	5.35290
0.0045	5.35058	5.34826	5.34594	5.34364	5.34133	5.33904	5.33674	5.33445	5.33217	5.32989
0.0046	5.32762	5.32535	5.32309	5.32083	5.31857	5.31632	5.31408	5.31183	5.30960	5.30737
0.0047	5.30514	5.30292	5.30070	5.29849	5.29628	5.29407	5.29187	5.28968	5.28749	5.28530
0.0048	5.28312	5.28094	5.27877	5.27660	5.27443	5.27227	5.27012	5.26796	5.26582	5.26367
0.0049	5.26153	5.25940	5.25727	5.25514	5.25302	5.25090	5.24879	5.24668	5.24457	5.24247
0.0050	5.24037	5.23828	5.23619	5.23410	5.23202	5.22994	5.22787	5.22580	5.22373	5.22167
0.0051	5.21961	5.21756	5.21551	5.21346	5.21142	5.20938	5.20735	5.20531	5.20329	5.20126
0.0052	5.19924	5.19723	5.19521	5.19321	5.19120	5.18920	5.18720	5.18521	5.18322	5.18123
0.0053	5.17925	5.17727	5.17529	5.17332	5.17135	5.16938	5.16742	5.16546	5.16351	5.16156
0.0054	5.15961	5.15767	5.15572	5.15379	5.15185	5.14992	5.14799	5.14607	5.14415	5.14223
0.0055	5.14032	5.13841	5.13650	5.13460	5.13270	5.13080	5.12891	5.12702	5.12513	5.12324
0.0056	5.12136	5.11949	5.11761	5.11574	5.11387	5.11201	5.11015	5.10829	5.10643	5.10458
0.0057	5.10273	5.10088	5.09904	5.09720	5.09537	5.09353	5.09170	5.08987	5.08805	5.08623
0.0058	5.08441	5.08259	5.08078	5.07897	5.07717	5.07536	5.07356	5.07176	5.06997	5.06818
0.0059	5.06639	5.06460	5.06282	5.06104	5.05926	5.05749	5.05572	5.05395	5.05218	5.05042
0.0060	5.04866	5.04690	5.04515	5.04339	5.04165	5.03990	5.03816	5.03641	5.03468	5.03294
0.0061	5.03121	5.02948	5.02775	5.02603	5.02431	5.02259	5.02087	5.01916	5.01745	5.01574
0.0062	5.01403	5.01233	5.01063	5.00893	5.00724	5.00554	5.00385	5.00217	5.00048	4.99880
0.0063	4.99712	4.99544	4.99377	4.99209	4.99043	4.98876	4.98709	4.98543	4.98377	4.98211
0.0064	4.98046	4.97881	4.97716	4.97551	4.97387	4.97222	4.97058	4.96895	4.96731	4.96568
0.0065	4.96405	4.96242	4.96080	4.95917	4.95755	4.95593	4.95432	4.95270	4.95109	4.94948
0.0066	4.94788	4.94627	4.94467	4.94307	4.94148	4.93988	4.93829	4.93670	4.93511	4.93352
0.0067	4.93194	4.93036	4.92878	4.92720	4.92563	4.92406	4.92249	4.92092	4.91935	4.91779
0.0068	4.91623	4.91467	4.91311	4.91156	4.91000	4.90845	4.90690	4.90536	4.90381	4.90227
0.0069	4.90073	4.89920	4.89766	4.89613	4.89460	4.89307	4.89154	4.89002	4.88849	4.88697
0.0070	4.88545	4.88394	4.88242	4.88091	4.87940	4.87789	4.87638	4.87488	4.87338	4.87188
0.0071	4.87038	4.86888	4.86739	4.86590	4.86441	4.86292	4.86143	4.85995	4.85847	4.85699
0.0072	4.85551	4.85403	4.85256	4.85108	4.84961	4.84814	4.84668	4.84521	4.84375	4.84229
0.0073	4.84083	4.83937	4.83792	4.83647	4.83501	4.83356	4.83212	4.83067	4.82923	4.82778
0.0074	4.82634	4.82491	4.82347	4.82204	4.82060	4.81917	4.81774	4.81632	4.81489	4.81347
0.0075	4.81204	4.81062	4.80921	4.80779	4.80637	4.80496	4.80355	4.80214	4.80073	4.79933
0.0076	4.79792	4.79652	4.79512	4.79372	4.79233	4.79093	4.78954	4.78814	4.78675	4.78537
0.0077	4.78398	4.78259	4.78121	4.77983	4.77845	4.77707	4.77570	4.77432	4.77295	4.77158
0.0078	4.77021	4.76884	4.76747	4.76611	4.76474	4.76338	4.76202	4.76066	4.75931	4.75795
0.0079	4.75660	4.75525	4.75390	4.75255	4.75120	4.74986	4.74852	4.74717	4.74583	4.74449
0.0080	4.74316	4.74182	4.74049	4.73916	4.73782	4.73650	4.73517	4.73384	4.73252	4.73119
0.0081	4.72987	4.72855	4.72723	4.72592	4.72460	4.72329	4.72198	4.72067	4.71936	4.71805
0.0082	4.71674	4.71544	4.71414	4.71283	4.71153	4.71024	4.70894	4.70764	4.70635	4.70506
0.0083	4.70376	4.70247	4.70119	4.69990	4.69861	4.69733	4.69605	4.69477	4.69349	4.69221
0.0084	4.69093	4.68966	4.68839	4.68711	4.68584	4.68457	4.68330	4.68204	4.68077	4.67951
0.0085	4.67825	4.67699	4.67573	4.67447	4.67321	4.67196	4.67070	4.66945	4.66820	4.66695
0.0086	4.66570	4.66445	4.66321	4.66196	4.66072	4.65948	4.65824	4.65700	4.65576	4.65453
0.0087	4.65329	4.65206	4.65083	4.64960	4.64837	4.64714	4.64591	4.64469	4.64346	4.64224
0.0088	4.64102	4.63980	4.63858	4.63736	4.63615	4.63493	4.63372	4.63251	4.63130	4.63009
0.0089	4.62888	4.62767	4.62646	4.62526	4.62406	4.62285	4.62165	4.62045	4.61926	4.61806

N	0	1	2	3	4	5	6	7	8	9
0.0090	4.61686	4.61567	4.61448	4.61328	4.61209	4.61090	4.60972	4.60853	4.60734	4.60616
0.0091	4.60498	4.60379	4.60261	4.60143	4.60025	4.59908	4.59790	4.59673	4.59555	4.59438
0.0092	4.59321	4.59204	4.59087	4.58970	4.58854	4.58737	4.58621	4.58505	4.58388	4.58272
0.0093	4.58157	4.58041	4.57925	4.57809	4.57694	4.57579	4.57464	4.57348	4.57233	4.57119
0.0094	4.57004	4.56889	4.56775	4.56660	4.56546	4.56432	4.56318	4.56204	4.56090	4.55976
0.0095	4.55863	4.55749	4.55636	4.55523	4.55409	4.55296	4.55183	4.55071	4.54958	4.54845
0.0096	4.54733	5.54620	4.54508	4.54396	4.54284	4.54172	4.54060	4.53948	4.53837	4.53725
0.0097	4.53614	4.53503	4.53392	4.53280	4.53170	4.53059	4.52948	4.52837	4.52727	4.52616
0.0098	4.52506	4.52396	4.52286	4.52176	4.52066	4.51956	4.51846	4.51737	4.51627	4.51518
0.0099	4.51409	4.51300	4.51190	4.51082	4.50973	4.50864	4.50755	4.50647	4.50538	4.50430
0.01	4.50322	4.39983	4.30492	4.21715	4.13547	4.05905	3.98723	3.91944	3.85525	3.79426
0.020	3.73615	3.73048	3.72485	3.71923	3.71365	3.70809	3.70255	3.69704	3.69155	3.68608
0.021	3.68064	3.67523	3.66984	3.66447	3.65912	3.65380	3.64845	3.64322	3.63796	3.63272
0.022	3.62751	3.62232	3.61715	3.61200	3.60787	3.60177	3.59668	3.59162	3.58657	3.58155
0.023	3.57654	3.57156	3.56659	3.56164	3.55672	3.55181	3.54692	3.54205	3.53720	3.53237
0.024	3.52755	3.52276	3.51798	3.51322	3.50848	3.50375	3.49904	3.49435	3.48968	3.48403
0.025	3.48039	3.47577	3.47116	3.46657	3.46200	3.45744	3.45290	3.44838	3.44387	3.43938
0.026	3.43491	3.43045	3.42600	3.42157	3.41716	3.41276	3.40838	3.40441	3.39965	3.39531
0.027	3.39099	3.38668	3.38238	3.37810	3.37383	3.36958	3.36534	3.36111	3.35690	3.35270
0.028	3.34852	3.34435	3.34019	3.33604	3.33191	3.32779	3.32369	3.31960	3.31552	3.31145
0.029	3.30740	3.30336	3.29933	3.29531	3.29131	3.28732	3.28334	3.27937	3.27541	3.27147
0.030	3.26754	3.26362	3.25971	3.25582	3.25193	3.24806	3.24420	3.24035	3.23651	3.23268
0.031	3.22886	3.22506	3.22126	3.21748	3.21371	3.20995	3.20619	3.20245	3.19873	3.19501
0.032	3.19130	3.18760	3.18391	3.18023	3.17657	3.17291	3.16926	3.16563	3.16200	3.15838
0.033	3.15477	3.15118	3.14759	3.14401	3.14044	3.13688	3.13337	3.12980	3.12627	3.12274
0.034	3.11923	3.11573	3.11224	3.10875	3.10528	3.10181	3.09836	3.09491	3.09147	3.08804
0.035	3.08462	3.08121	3.07780	3.07441	3.07102	3.06764	3.06428	3.06091	3.05756	3.05422
0.036	3.05088	3.04756	3.04424	3.04093	3.03762	3.03433	3.03104	3.02776	3.02449	3.02123
0.037	3.01798	3.01473	3.01149	3.00826	3.00504	3.00182	2.99861	2.99541	2.99222	2.98904
0.038	2.98586	2.98269	2.97953	2.97637	2.97322	2.97008	2.96695	2.96382	2.96070	2.95759
0.039	2.95449	2.95139	2.94830	2.94522	2.94214	2.93907	2.93601	2.93295	2.92991	2.92687
0.04	2.92381	2.89383	2.86450	2.83578	2.80765	2.78009	2.75308	2.72658	2.70058	2.67506
0.05	2.65000	2.62538	2.60119	2.57741	2.55403	2.53103	2.50840	2.48613	2.46421	2.44262
0.06	2.42135	2.40040	2.37976	2.35941	2.33934	2.31956	2.30005	2.28080	2.26180	2.24306
0.07	2.22455	2.20629	2.18825	2.17044	2.15284	2.13546	2.11829	2.10131	2.08454	2.06796
0.08	2.05157	2.03537	2.01934	2.00349	1.98781	1.97231	1.95696	1.94178	1.92676	1.91190
0.09	1.89718	1.88262	1.86820	1.85392	1.83978	1.82579	1.81192	1.79820	1.78460	1.77113
0.10	1.75778	1.74456	1.73146	1.71848	1.70561	1.69286	1.68023	1.66770	1.65529	1.64298
0.11	1.63078	1.61868	1.60669	1.59479	1.58300	1.57130	1.55971	1.54820	1.53679	1.52547
0.12	1.51425	1.50311	1.49206	1.48110	1.47022	1.45943	1.44873	1.43810	1.42756	1.41709
0.13	1.40671	1.39640	1.38617	1.37602	1.36595	1.35594	1.34601	1.33615	1.32637	1.31665
0.14	1.30701	1.29743	1.28792	1.27848	1.26911	1.25980	1.25056	1.24138	1.23226	1.22321
0.15	1.21422	1.20529	1.19642	1.18762	1.17887	1.17018	1.16155	1.15297	1.14446	1.13600
0.16	1.12760	1.11925	1.11095	1.10271	1.09453	1.08640	1.07832	1.07029	1.06231	1.05439
0.17	1.04651	1.03869	1.03092	1.02319	1.01552	1.00789	1.00031	0.99278	0.98529	0.97785
0.18	0.97046	0.96312	0.95582	0.94856	0.94135	0.93418	0.92706	0.91998	0.91295	0.90596
0.19	0.89901	0.89210	0.88523	0.87841	0.87163	0.86488	0.85818	0.85152	0.84490	0.83832
0.20	0.83178	0.82527	0.81881	0.81238	0.80600	0.79965	0.79333	0.78706	0.78082	0.77462
0.21	0.76846	0.76233	0.75624	0.75018	0.74416	0.73818	0.73223	0.72631	0.72043	0.71458
0.22	0.70877	0.70300	0.69725	0.69154	0.68586	0.68022	0.67461	0.66903	0.66348	0.65797
0.23	0.65249	0.64704	0.64162	0.63623	0.63088	0.62555	0.62026	0.61500	0.60977	0.60456
0.24	0.59939	0.59425	0.58914	0.58406	0.57901	0.57398	0.56899	0.56403	0.55909	0.55418

N	0	1	2	3	4	5	6	7	8	9
0.25	0.54931	0.54446	0.53964	0.53484	0.53008	0.52534	0.52063	0.51595	0.51129	0.50667
0.26	0.50206	0.49749	0.49295	0.48843	0.48393	0.47947	0.47503	0.47061	0.46622	0.46186
0.27	0.45753	0.45322	0.44893	0.44467	0.44044	0.43623	0.43205	0.42789	0.42376	0.41965
0.28	0.41556	0.41150	0.40747	0.40346	0.39947	0.39551	0.39157	0.38766	0.38377	0.37990
0.29	0.37606	0.37224	0.36845	0.36468	0.36093	0.35720	0.35350	0.34982	0.34616	0.34253
0.30	0.33892	0.33533	0.33177	0.32822	0.32470	0.32120	0.31773	0.31427	0.31084	0.30743
0.31	0.30405	0.30068	0.29734	0.29401	0.29071	0.28743	0.28418	0.28094	0.27772	0.27453
0.32	0.27136	0.26821	0.26508	0.26197	0.25888	0.25581	0.25276	0.24974	0.24673	0.24375
0.33	0.24078	0.23784	0.23492	0.23201	0.22913	0.22627	0.22342	0.22060	0.21780	0.21502
0.34	0.21225	0.20951	0.20679	0.20409	0.20140	0.19874	0.19609	0.19347	0.19086	0.18828
0.35	0.18571	0.18316	0.18064	0.17813	0.17564	0.17317	0.17072	0.16828	0.16587	0.16348
0.36	0.16116	0.15875	0.15641	0.15409	0.15179	0.14951	0.14724	0.14500	0.14277	0.14057
0.37	0.13838	0.13621	0.13405	0.13192	0.12980	0.12771	0.12563	0.12357	0.12152	0.11950
0.38	0.11749	0.11550	0.11353	0.11158	0.10964	0.10773	0.10583	0.10395	0.10208	0.10024
0.39	0.09841	0.09660	0.09481	0.09303	0.09127	0.08953	0.08781	0.08610	0.08442	0.08275
0.40	0.08109	0.07946	0.07784	0.07624	0.07465	0.07309	0.07154	0.07001	0.06849	0.06699
0.41	0.06551	0.06405	0.06260	0.06117	0.05976	0.05837	0.05699	0.05563	0.05428	0.05295
0.42	0.05164	0.05035	0.04907	0.04781	0.04657	0.04534	0.04413	0.04294	0.04176	0.04060
0.43	0.03946	0.03833	0.03722	0.03613	0.03505	0.03399	0.03295	0.03192	0.03091	0.02992
0.44	0.02894	0.02798	0.02703	0.02611	0.02519	0.02430	0.02342	0.02256	0.02171	0.02088
0.45	0.02007	0.01927	0.01849	0.01772	0.01698	0.01624	0.01553	0.01483	0.01415	0.01348
0.46	0.01283	0.01219	0.01157	0.01097	0.01039	0.00982	0.00926	0.00872	0.00820	0.00770
0.47	0.00721	0.00674	0.00628	0.00584	0.00541	0.00500	0.00461	0.00423	0.00387	0.00353
0.48	0.00320	0.00289	0.00259	0.00231	0.00205	0.00180	0.00157	0.00135	0.00115	0.00097
0.49	0.00080	0.00065	0.00051	0.00039	0.00029	0.00020	0.00013	0.00007	0.00003	0.00001
0.50	0.00000									

INDEX

Aberrations, in electromagnetic separators
  effect of space charge, 381
  finite aperture of the ion beam, 377
  fringing field, 379
  instability of the acceleration voltage
    and of the magnetic field, 380
  interaction of the ions, 379
  velocity scatter of ions, 375
Abundance
  of the elements in nature, 8
  of nuclides (rule of), 6
  relative, 36
Analysis of deuterium
  by absorption in the infrared, 27
  by densimetric methods, 29
  by mass spectrometry, 23
  by thermal conductivity, 30
Analysis of ^{235}U
  by mass spectrometry, 21
  by neutron activation, 22
  by optical spectrometry, 22
^{36}Ar$-^{40}$Ar, separation, 40, 77, 245, 262
Astatine, 3

Barriers for gaseous diffusion
  characteristics, 181

efficiency, 155
permeability, 172, 181
Batch processes, 98, 151
Benedict column, 245
Bethe–Weizsäcker cycle, 11
Boron-10
  separation, 40, 53
  uses, 15

Calutrons, 89
Carbon, cycle, 11
Carbon-13, separation, 40, 53, 70, 75, 245, 260, 262-263
Carbon-14, 3
Cascades, 99
  asymmetric, 101
  countercurrent, 100
  ideal with enrichment factor close
    to one, 112
  ideal and nonideal, comparison
    between, 139
  schemes of designs, 100
  square, 116, 126, 140
  squared-off or step, 127, 145
  with stripping section, 101, 106
  symmetric, 100, 105
  symmetric ideal, 110

413

Centrifuge
  materials for, 210
  types of, 207
Characteristic pressure (gaseous
  diffusion), 157
Chemical isotopic exchange, 49, 336
Cichelli columns, 247-248
$^{35}Cl-^{37}Cl$, separation, 78, 86
Clausius–Clapeyron law, 38
Collection of isotopes, in electromagnetic
  separators, 388
Columns
  bubble-cap trays, 277
  distillation (calculation principles),
    277, 282, 284
  mass diffusion, 257
  packed, 282
  sieve trays, 281
  trail, 338
  transfer (calculation), 350
Compressors (for diffusion plants), 182
Countercurrent centrifuge, 207
  of Beyerle and Groth, 214
  demonstration installations, 239
  theory of, 221
  of Zippe, 218
Cut, 103
Cycle, of Bethe–Weizsäcker, 11

Deuterium, analysis of
  by float method, 29
  by infrared absorption, 27
  by mass spectrometry, 23
  by thermal conductivity, 30
Deuterium, separation of, 40, 53, 64, 77,
  84, 274, 299, 322, 335
Diffusers
  characteristics of, 177
  with cross flow, 162
Dispersive power of an electromagnetic
  separator, 376
Distillation, 37
Distillation of hydrogen
  closed-cycle processes, 318
  energy consumption, 302
  plants, 309
  purification problems, 305
  thermal insulation, 308
Distillation plate
  bubble-cap, 44, 277
  scheme, 277

Distillation of water
  characteristics of the process, 274, 286
  economic considerations, 292
  energy consumption, 287
  packed columns, 282
  plants for, 293
  plate column, 277
  separation factors, 276
  for upgrading, 294
Dixon rings, 284
Double focusing, 379
Driving force in mass transfer, 283
Dual-temperature exchange
  amine–hydrogen process, 372
  ammonia–hydrogen process, 370
  generalities, 348
  water–hydrogen process, 369
  water–hydrogen sulfide process, 353

Effective resolving power (electromagnetic
  separation), 337
Efficiency
  in distillation, 280, 284
  in gaseous diffusion, 155, 160
  of Murphree, 279-280
Efficiency factors, 283
Electrolysis, 84, 322
Electromigration, 86
Electromagnetic separation, 88, 375
Electromagnetic separators, 375
Electrolytic plants
  with exchange reactions, 335
  for final enrichment, 330
  for preliminary enrichment, 322
  for substantial enrichment, 325
Elementary separation factors, 36
  in centrifugation, 79
  in distillation, 38
  in electrolysis, 85
  in exchange reactions, 51
  in gaseous diffusion, 67
  in mass diffusion, 73
  in molecular distillation, 47
  in thermal diffusion, 78
Elements
  abundance in nature, 8, 10
  hypotheses on genesis of, 10
  isotopic composition of, 1
  natural radioactivities with $Z < 84$, 2
  regularity in the isotopic composition of, 7
Energy consumption in isotopic separation, 92

Enrichment factors, 102
Enrichment sections, 43, 101
Equilibrium constants
  calculation of, 52
  of some isotopic reactions, 52-53, 58
Equilibrium time, 134
Equivalent to the theoretical plate, 280
Evaporation centrifuge, 207
Exchange reactions, 49
  between hydrogenated compounds, 52-53, 335

Fermi—Dirac gas, 5
Field emission, 384, 388
Finkelstein source, 386
Flooding flow rate, 286
Fractionation, 43
Francium, 3

Gain
  in enrichment, 102
  in separation, 102
Gaseous diffusion, 66, 155
Gaseous diffusion plants
  construction characteristics, 177
  existing, 195

^{3}He$-^4$He, separation, 40
Head, 99
Height equivalent to a theoretical plate
  (HETP), 281
Height of the transfer unit (HTU), 283
Heil source, 386
Helipack (packing), 284
Hermes (Harwell), 394
Hertz diffusion stage, 287
Herzog principle, 377
HETP, 281
Holdup factors, 283
H_2S-H_2O systems, phase diagram, 355
HTU, 283

Ion-exchange resins, 61
Ion extraction in electromagnetic
  separation, 386
Ion sources for electromagnetic
  separation, 384
Isotopes
  radioactive, 1
  stable, 1
  uses, 15

^{39}K$-^{41}$K, 86, 87
Knudsen law, 68
Kuhn column, 284

Laws
  of Mattauch, 7
  of nuclide abundance, 6
  Oddo—Harkins empirical, 6
  of the square root, 144
^{6}Li$-^7$Li, separation, 48, 63, 86, 88
Liquid hydrogen
  fractionation, 300
  properties, 299
  purification, 305

McCabe—Thiele graphic method, 278
Magic numbers, 4
Maier diffusion stage, 242
Mass diffusion, 71
Mass spectrometer
  for the analysis of deuterium, 23
  double focusing, 376
Mass spectrometry, 18
Mass of the stable atom, 6
Mattauch rule, 7
Mercury, isotopic separation, 48, 91
Molecular constants
  hydrochloric acid, 57
  hydrogen, 57
Molecular distillation, 45
Murphree efficiency, 279-280

^{20}Ne$-^{22}$Ne, separation, 40, 77, 89
Neptunium, family, 2
Nitrogen-15, separation, 40, 53, 61, 77, 86, 245
Nuclei
  parity, 6
  stability, 4
Nucleus
  drop model, 4
  radius, 5
  shell, 4

Oddo—Harkins empirical rule, 6
Operating line (distillation), 278
Ortho-hydrogen, 299
Oxygen-18, separation, 40, 53, 86, 245

Para-hydrogen, 299
Partition functions, 54
Penning vacuometers, 384
Permeability of barriers (gaseous diffusion), 172, 190
Plants for the H_2O-H_2S process, 360
Polpack (packing), 287
Porous barriers for mass diffusion, 250
Promethium, 3
Proton—proton chain, 11

Raschig (rings), 44, 283-284
Rayleigh distillation, 151
Reaction rate, 64
Reduced pressure (gaseous diffusion), 159

Separating agent, 71
Separating element, 99
Separating nozzle, 81, 265
Separating power
  in batch processes, 153
  case of any α, 133
  case of infinitesimal ϵ, 122, 129
  in countercurrent centrifuges, 230
  total, 131
Separation factors, 36, 102
Separation potential, 130
Separation work, 121, 131
Shell nucleus, 4
SMOW (Standard Mean Ocean Water), 32
Spraypak, 283-284
Sputtering, 389
Stability of the nucleus, 4
Stages
  definition of, 99
  equations for, 102
  Hertz diffusion, 244
  Maier diffusion, 242
  with two or more diffusers, 165
Standard ^{235}U samples, 23
Stripping section, 43, 101, 125
  optimization, 148
Sulfur isotopic separation, 53, 63

Tail, 99
Technetium, 3
Thermal diffusion, 75
Thorium family, 1
Total flow, 128
Trail plant, 338, 341
Transfer parameter, 352
Transfer unit, 283
Transient of a cascade, 134
Transport, 120
Tritium
  formation, 4
  uses, 16

Uranium—actinium family, 1
Uranium hexafluoride
  production, 183
  properties, 168
Uranium isotopic separation, 40, 53, 62, 70, 75, 80, 81, 91-92, 261
Uranium—radium family, 1

Value functions
  case of any α, 133
  case of infinitesimal ϵ, 130
Vapor pressures
  ratios, 39-40
Volatility
  definition, 37
  relative, 38

Water, deuterium content in, 12
Withdrawal of the first and second species, 127

Xenon isotopic separation, 40

Yield
  definition of, 123
  of ideal cascade, 123
  relative, 127
  of square cascade, 126